Edmond Halley

Edmond Halley

GENIUS IN ECLIPSE

by Colin A. Ronan

1969

DOUBLEDAY & COMPANY, INC.

GARDEN CITY, NEW YORK

BH185R

To the Memory of
My Mother

Contents

PREFACE   ix

CHAPTER 1   *Early Years*   1

CHAPTER 2   *The Astronomical Background*   10

CHAPTER 3   *Oxford and St. Helena*   24

CHAPTER 4   *The Visit to Hevelius*   43

CHAPTER 5   *The Grand Tour, Marriage, and Domestic Crises*   57

CHAPTER 6   *The Royal Society and the* Principia   69

CHAPTER 7   *Science and Sea-Diving*   89

CHAPTER 8   *The Distance of the Sun*   106

CHAPTER 9   *Flamsteed and Halley*   118

CHAPTER 10   *Comets and Other Subjects*   133

CHAPTER 11   *The Mint and Visit of the Czar*   152

CHAPTER 12   *Voyages*   161

CHAPTER 13   *Recognition*   183

CHAPTER 14 *Astronomer Royal*   196

CHAPTER 15 *Halley—An Assessment*   215

TEXT REFERENCES   223

BIBLIOGRAPHICAL SOURCES   232

APPENDIX I *Chronological Résumé of Halley's Life*   235

APPENDIX II *Appearances of Halley's Comet*   240

APPENDIX III *Sources of Original Material and Other Information*   241

APPENDIX IV *Biographical Publications*   242

INDEX   243

Preface

Any biographer of Halley faces great difficulties because of the paucity of personal material that has survived. Halley kept no diary, as
did some of his contemporaries, and such letters as exist are almost
entirely concerned with his science. A few personal details were
supplied by his son-in-law Henry Price to the compilers of a biographical article that appeared in 1757, and a few odd references
are to be found among the reminiscences of contemporary gossips
like Aubrey and Hearne, but in general the only way to re-create
something of his personality is to take what papers there are and
read between the lines. It is, of course, impossible to divorce the
man from his science, since his work was the central pivot of his
life. In order to build up a picture of the man, it has seemed best
to deal with his science in sequence, just as it occurred, and see
from it how his mind worked and his enthusiasms changed. I have
also included a somewhat full description of his voyages since these
were the first of their kind, are little known, and provide a useful
insight into Halley's character.

In collecting material and for advice and assistance, I am much
indebted to Dr. Angus Armitage, Sir Edward Bullard, Dr. Michael
Hoskin, Lieutenant Commander Derek Howse, Dr. Harrison Matthews, Mr. G. P. B. Naish, the late Mr. Henry Robinson, and the late
Professor Turnbull. To Professor E. N. da C. Andrade I am grateful
for permission to use the Royal Society Library, and to Mr. I. Kaye
and Mr. Norman Robinson, the librarian and assistant librarian, for
their cooperation; to Dr. R. E. W. Maddison, librarian of the Royal
Astronomical Society, and Mr. John Hopkins, librarian of the Society
of Antiquaries, for their ready assistance. I am also grateful to Miss

Andrea Balchan and her colleagues at Doubleday for their kindness and care with the manuscript. To my wife I owe an especial debt not only for typing a very heavily corrected manuscript, but also for many useful discussions and for supplying much of the illustrative material.

23 May 1968   *Colin A. Ronan,*
                                                          Cowlinge,
                                                          Suffolk.

Edmond Halley

CHAPTER 1

Early Years

Some three miles to the northeast of St. Paul's Cathedral, in the borough of Hackney, lies Haggerston Road. Today it is a rather dreary part of the sprawling, noisy, never-ending forest of buildings that is London. But three hundred years ago it was nothing more than a quiet hamlet, with a large house and a few cottages, surrounded by farmland and perhaps market gardens. It was here that Edmond Halley, Sr., citizen and soapboiler of Winchester Street, had his country house, well away from the grime of London.

His father, Humphrey Halley, had been a haberdasher and later a vintner, but the early history of the family is obscure. The gossip and antiquary John Aubrey (1626–97) claimed that they came from "the Halleys, of Derbyshire, a good family," and this seems also to have been the opinion of John Flamsteed (1646–1719), the first Astronomer Royal, who was at first to befriend but later turn against Edmond's elder son. Flamsteed himself was a Derbyshire man and employed as one of his computers a certain Luke Leigh, "a poor kinsman of Mr. Halley's, of the same clan." At all events, whatever his forebears, Edmond the elder had prospered; he is described variously as a soapboiler and a salter, while he also had a considerable amount of property within the City that brought him in rents to the value of one thousand pounds a year.* When it is appreciated that there was no income tax and that this sum ought now to be

---

* Today one thousand pounds is equivalent to about $2400. Here and elsewhere in this book I have given dollar equivalents, but to gauge the value of money in Halley's time, it may be noted that when Samuel Pepys began to work at the "Court of the Exchequer" in 1658, his salary was fifty pounds ($120) per annum, and yet this enabled him to have his own house where he lived with his wife and one servant.

multiplied by a factor of eight or nine, it becomes clear that Edmond Halley, Sr., was a rich man. Besides his country house at Haggerston he also owned his town house in Winchester Street within the City boundary, a street now buried beneath the railway lines that lead to Broad Street Station.

Edmond Halley had at least three children, Edmond, Humphrey, and Katherine, but the records of the time yield little more information. Katherine was born in 1658 and seems to have died in infancy; Humphrey was born at some date unknown, but died in 1684, leaving his brother Edmond as sole executor. Edmond appears to have been the eldest of the three, and since he began to show his scientific abilities while still in his teens it is worth trying to attempt to come to some conclusion about his age and background. Searches have revealed no evidence of an entry of birth in a baptismal register, but many City churches and their records were destroyed in the Great Fire of 1666. The only direct information we have is his own word that he was born on October 29, 1656; doubtless this ought to be sufficient but for the fact that his father and mother were married at St. Margaret's, Westminster only seven weeks earlier. A search through such contemporary accounts of his life as exist corroborate his own date for his birth when we take into account that Halley gave the date in terms of the Julian calendar in use in England in his day but already replaced by the newer Gregorian calendar in Europe. Additional confirmation comes from university records of Edmond's entry into Queen's College, Oxford, in 1673.

In view of this his parents could have been married in haste and for obvious reasons, but there are two other possibilities. In 1649 Charles I was executed at Westminster and the Commonwealth established, and during the ensuing decade the country came under Puritan rule which to a great extent was anticlerical in outlook, so that by 1653 the climate of thought enabled an act of parliament to be promulgated permitting civil marriages to be contracted before a magistrate; and there were many who took advantage of this, some going through a religious ceremony later. It is conceivable that this may have been so in the case of Edmond Halley and his bride, Anne Robinson. A third, and perhaps more remote possibility, is that the register at St. Margaret's was wrong. This is not as wild a suggestion as it might seem, for it appears to have happened about the same time to Samuel Pepys (1632–1703). His marriage there is registered on December 1, 1655, yet both he and his bride—"a pretty girl of fifteen"—were always under the impression that they had been married almost two months earlier, and impressions of this kind are not likely to be wrong.

The difficulty of knowing precisely when Halley was born is typical of most of the private life of this surprising man whose career was of a variety matched by few if any of his contemporaries. Unfortunately he kept no diary like Pepys, John Evelyn (1620–1706), or even that brilliant if irascible physicist Robert Hooke (1635–1702). Such letters of his as have survived relate almost entirely to his work, and where he comes into the correspondence of others it is only here and there that one gets a glimpse of his personality. What his wife was like, how he spent his leisure, what his opinions were on the issues of the day we cannot know for certain; but by carefully combing contemporary sources it is possible to construct a picture of an amiable and dynamic personality.

Edmond Halley was born at the country house in Haggerston and divided his earliest years between there and Winchester Street. Before he was four years old the monarchy was restored, and this was later to prove an advantage to him as to all who took part in the new scientific movement in England. But except, perhaps, for some celebrations at home and in the City, this event must have passed unnoticed by him. According to Aubrey, "At 9 years old, his father's apprentice taught him to write, and arithmetique," and in the following year there came some reverse in the family fortunes, for 1666 saw the Great Fire of London. One imagines that Halley was then in Haggerston, since the bubonic plague had been raging in London itself for the previous eighteen months and anyone of substance who did not need to be in a densely populated area moved away. The financial losses came, of course, from his father's property that was burned and from which rents were no longer available to swell his income, but the reverse does not seem to have been very severe to begin with, although later on Edmond's father was not able to renew the leases on other property when these fell due. The soap-boiling and salting businesses were flourishing concerns: Indeed, the plague may well have made those who could afford it become a little more concerned with cleanliness, for there was considerable fear of personal contamination. In the markets, for instance, when anyone bought meat, they would not take it from the butcher's hands, but took it off the hooks themselves, while the butcher would not touch the money directly but had it put into a pot full of vinegar; also, the gradual regrowth of the navy that followed the return of Charles II would have kept the saltery profitably busy, as salted meat formed a substantial part of naval provisions.

How much young Edmond learned from the apprentice, if this is how he was taught, one cannot tell, but as Henry Price, his son-in-law, put it many years later when he was supplying details to the author† of the entry on Edmond Halley in the *Biographia Britannica,* Edmond's father "resolved to give his son, an only child, and a youth of the most promising genius, an education suitable to it." Presumably Price, recollecting more than sixty years after the event, forgot that his father-in-law once had an infant sister, and a brother who died in his twenties; but there is no doubt that Halley, Sr. did the best for his son, for he sent him to St. Paul's School, which was great in both reputation and scholarship.

St. Paul's School had been founded by Dean Colet (1456–1519) in 1509. Colet, who was a friend of the Renaissance scholar Erasmus (1467–1536) and the only surviving member of a family of twenty-two children, had been appointed dean of St. Paul's in 1505. His aim in founding the school in the City of London, where his father was a mercer and twice Lord Mayor, was to provide an education for poor boys, and it is said that he originally designed it to receive 153 pupils, a number equivalent to the number of fishes taken by St. Peter in his miraculous draft on the Sea of Galilee. Erasmus drew up a grammar for the use of the boys, none of whom were to be admitted unless they could read and write and say the catechism,

---

† The author of the article seems likely to have been either Thomas Birch (1705–66), the historian, or John Machin (?–1751), mathematician and astronomer.

and the staff was planned to number three: a chaplain, an under master, and a high master. Colet died in 1519 and left the school in trust to the Mercers' Company in which "body of citizens" Colet said he would find "less corruption . . . than in any other body of mankind."

In the Great Fire the school suffered the same fate as the cathedral, and was razed to the ground, but the Mercers' Company started rebuilding the school in 1670. When Edmond Halley entered it we do not know, but it was likely to have been before the rebuilding, and this means that unless his parents boarded him out, he would have had to travel a considerable distance each day since the then high master, Samuel Cromelholme, had opened a school in Wandsworth, a village about six miles southwest of the cathedral. By then the school seems to have departed from Colet's original intention, for Halley was certainly not poor.

He could read, write, and do some arithmetic before he went to St. Paul's, but it is likely that his attainments may well have been greater. In the preface to his *Catalogue of the Southern Stars* he mentions that "from my tenderest youth I gave myself over to the consideration of Astronomy," and admits that he studied it intensely; ten or earlier is not too young to become intrigued with the science which Halley says gave him "so great pleasure as is impossible to explain to anyone who has not experienced it," and it seems probable that he had as wide if not wider interests and knowledge than any new entrant of his day. This does not mean that he was a bookworm or overwhelmingly precocious. His "promising genius" was recognized by his father, but this is no more than a rather flowery indication that he was highly intelligent. We can assume that he was a normal boy in every way, for he grew up with a sense of humor and a great charm of manner; these qualities probably made themselves obvious from the start, as they do in many children.

There is another fact that points in this direction, and that is Halley's appointment as captain of St. Paul's in 1671. No boy becomes school captain if he is a prig or a pedant, and this, perhaps above all, gives the clue to Halley's character, even at the age of fifteen. He was captain, then, just before or just after the new building was ready in April of 1671 and Cromelholme was still high master, at least if we are to believe Henry Price.‡

The next year an important change took place, for in August 1672 Cromelholme's position was taken by Thomas Gale (1636–1702), and it is with his name that Halley's had been linked by the authors of Halley's obituary notices and biographical notes. Gale was a Yorkshireman and had been appointed regius professor of Greek at Cambridge when he was thirty. Nevertheless he gladly moved as high master to St. Paul's, where he was to remain for the next twenty-five years before moving on to become dean of York. Gale was a cleric, a distinguished scholar, and a man of wide interests, which included the "new philosophy" of science, which was then the intellectual pursuit of many of the ablest minds. Under him Halley must have had his ability for classics nourished and encouraged, for, since Gale was no stranger to mathematics which in those days included the science of astronomy and the art of navigation, this side of the boy's character would also have been stimulated. Indeed, it was at St. Paul's that Halley made his first recorded scientific observation: In 1672 he observed and measured the variation between the geographical north and the magnetic north, to which a magnetic compass points.

In general Halley did extremely well at school, and when in 1673, at the age of seventeen, he went to Queen's College, Oxford as a commoner, the antiquary Anthony à Wood (1632–95) could write of him, "He not only excelled in every branch of classical learning, but was particularly taken notice of for the extraordinary advances he made at the same time in the Mathematicks. In so much, that he seems not only to have acquired almost a masterly skill in both plain and spherical Trigonometry, but to be well acquainted with the science of Navigation, and to have made great progress in Astronomy before he was removed to Oxford." Again, he had ". . . at this time perfectly learned the use of the celestial globe, and could make a compleat dial." In other words Halley knew

‡ Sir Michael McDonnell, in *A History of St Paul's School*, London, 1909, claims that it was in 1673 that Halley became captain, "the first of whom there is any record as having attained that position." Possibly Price was mistaken or wrongly informed, but the date is not very significant.

the basic facts and computations not only of navigation but also
those with which the practical astronomer is concerned when he
sets about the delicate task of measuring the positions of celestial
bodies in the sky. And Halley had also acquired "good skill in the
Latin, Greek and Hebrew tongues" before he went up to Oxford.

In his introduction to the *Catalogue of Southern Stars* Halley
himself refers to his early interest and ability in astronomy, and he
goes on to claim, "my study was so intense that I read through and
found out in a short time every hidden fact in that Science [astron-
omy] that is unknown to the general public." Interestingly enough,
some youthful notes appear in a folio-size commonplace book now
in the library of the Earl of Macclesfield at Shirburn Castle. The
book contains a miscellany of material, some of it in Halley's handwriting and some not. It is undated, but from its contents would
appear to have been made in his early years. Some of his notes are
called "Observations and Maximes," and these include various astronomical phenomena ranging from "a Blazing starr" (or nova, as
it would now be termed) to eclipses of the sun, a host of general
scientific facts about sponges and lodestones, here and there some
general maxims, and even a simple but illuminating statement that
one should take a different attitude over religious and scientific subjects, religion being based on divine revelation but science on "logical discourse." The source of this quotation (for quotation it seems
to be) is not given, but all the same the fact that it was inserted is
interesting, since later in Halley's career his different attitudes toward religion and science became a bone of contention between
him and the orthodox clergy, leading to charges against him of religious infidelity (see Chapter 9). Other items in the book concern
"Exposition of Certain Termes of Geometry," "Definitions of Termes
in ye Art of Navigation and Astronomy," some notes on Galileo and
his work, and a great deal more on astronomy, mainly in the form
of definitions or statements of fact. The book contains many blank
pages, but of the forty-six that have been used, the majority seem
to be in Halley's hand.

All the evidence, then, goes to show that as a youth Halley was
full of intellectual promise, had thought out what he wanted to do,
and already, while still at school, had decided to lay the foundations

of his knowledge. In his love of astronomy he was helped by his father, who bought him appropriate scientific instruments. Halley tells us in his *Catalogue of the Southern Stars,* "I soon realized that it is not from books one should try to advance this Art, but that one ought to have recourse to instruments for measuring celestial Arcs and spend many nights making observations, for by this means one can learn from the Skies the true and natural paths of the Planets," and it seems obvious that as soon as he had acquired the basic theory necessary, he set about observing.

The planets took his fancy since there was still some argument about precisely how they moved; it would clearly be an interesting adventure to see what he himself could discover about them. The general method of observation was simple enough in principle—one measured the angle or "celestial Arc" between a planet and neighboring stars—and for this he needed a sighting tube or small telescope mounted on a metal frame. This instrument usually took the form of a sextant with two arms set at an angle of sixty degrees and a curved scale between. Besides a sextant a young and enthusiastic observer would not be content before he also possessed at least one telescope of considerable length for viewing the planets themselves, and fitted with movable wires in the eyepiece—a micrometer—for careful checking of planetary positions when a planet appeared very close to a star in the sky.

We do not know exactly what instruments Halley's father purchased for him since there is no complete inventory. The author of the *Biographia Britannica* article refers to his taking to Oxford "a curious apparatus of instruments" which were "purchased by his father, who spared no expense to encourage his son's genius," and whatever the "curious apparatus" may have contained we do know from Price in that article that two of the items were a telescope twenty-four feet long and a sextant two feet in diameter. These were scientific instruments of which any astronomer of the day might be proud, and the others must have been of equally high standing and good quality, as is shown by the work that Halley did with them later. This was no hodgepodge of pseudoscientific devices, but a collection that must have been the envy of many of the other Oxford commoners.

Before Halley went to Oxford there had been one great tragedy at home: the death of his mother. We do not know the actual date of her death but she was buried at Barking in Essex, on the east side of London, on October 24, 1672. This sad blow was later to have unpleasant repercussions for Halley's father, for by all accounts, his second marriage was nothing short of disastrous.

With the move to Oxford Halley's life entered a new phase that was to prove as surprising as it was successful. To appreciate what Halley achieved and why he left Oxford before he had graduated, we must spend a moment glancing at the state of astronomy and the concepts of the universe with which he came in contact there.

CHAPTER 2

The Astronomical Background

As Edmond Halley entered Queen's College, the ancient science of astronomy was undergoing a revolution, of immense proportions which lasted for more than a century. Halley played his own vital part in the upheaval from as early as 1676 until his death, but the first disturbance on any scale came many years earlier. The view of the universe proposed by Aristotle in the fourth century B.C., and worked out in some detail by Ptolemy in the second century A.D., had been under attack spasmodically from the thirteenth century onward, but matters came to a head in 1543 with the publication of a book by the Polish cleric Nicolas Copernicus (1473–1543). This book, *De Revolutionibus Orbium Coelestium* (*On the Revolutions of the Celestial Spheres*), had a great importance for the future, as it put forward the idea that the sun and not the earth was the center of the universe. Such a view had been proposed as far back as 350 B.C. by some bolder spirits among the Greek astronomers,* but there were difficulties against its acceptance, not the least of which was the general climate of thought, which was opposed to such an idea. Moreover, Aristotle argued fully and, in the light of his knowledge, logically, that the earth stood still in the center of the entire universe; holding such a view, he was able also to provide an explanation of many physical matters such as why bodies fall to the ground, flames always burn upward, and water forever "seeks its own level."

In other words, Aristotle provided a broad physical analysis of the universe, which covered both the observed behavior of the

---

* Notably after hints from a few Pythagorean philosophers and by men such as Apollonios and, perhaps, Aristarchos of Samos, but ancient records are not complete enough to make a full and detailed compilation certain.

earth, moon, planets, and stars, and that of terrestrial things. Aristotle's work was a synthesis of previous ideas welded to his own views and these, together with later observations such as those of Hipparchos in the second century B.C., were joined together in a magnificent synthesis by Ptolemy about A.D. 150. Ptolemy put forward his system of planetary motion in a large treatise which has become known as the *Almagest*. It enshrined all the Greek teachings on astronomy and contained not only the firmly argued idea that the earth lay at the center of all things, but also that the sun, moon, and planets moved around it in circular paths with a steady, regular motion.

The concept of uniform circular motion had been an axiom of Greek astronomy since the days of Pythagoras in the sixth century B.C., but it led to certain difficulties, since most of the planets are seen not only to weave their way in and out among the "fixed" stars but also to stop at times, and sometimes to reverse direction. Consequently it was not sufficient, as even Pythagoras had appreciated, to consider a planet moving uniformly in a circle around the earth. It was necessary to imagine that the planet also carried out other uniform circular motions at the same time, and the main problem of Greek and medieval astronomy was to discover what kind of additional motions were needed to account satisfactorily for the observed behavior of each of the planets. Many explanations were put forward but, after many centuries, the idea known as the deferent and epicycle was generally adopted, and it is this which was given by Ptolemy in his *Almagest*. Briefly, the basis of the idea was to consider that a planet moved uniformly around a small circle (the epicycle), the center of which not only lay on the circumference of another circle (the deferent) but also moved around it in uniform motion. The deferent had its center near the center of the earth. Such an explanation did account for the apparently capricious behavior of the planets, at least in principle, and as new observations were made over the succeeding centuries refinements consisted merely of adding extra epicycles and considering the deferent and epicycles as oscillating in a particular way.†

† For a fuller explanation of Greek ideas of planetary motion see, for example, J. L. E. Dreyer, *History of Astronomy*, Dover Publications, New York, 1953 or,

Copernicus, stimulated partly by a desire to improve the calendar and partly by a wish to simplify planetary theory itself, did not move from the old Greek idea of the deferent and epicycle, but made the whole matter much simpler by proposing that the sun lay at the center of the deferent of each planet. From the point of view of the mathematician who had to compute future planetary positions this was a considerable advantage. Having read the Greek case for a geocentric (earth-centered) system, Copernicus realized that in order to make his case he had to produce arguments in favor of a moving earth, and this he did using some of Aristotle's arguments and turning them about; he claimed that Aristotle had been wrong and that if properly handled they really proved that the earth moves in space. He does not seem to have appreciated that, in view of this new approach, all the laws of physics would have to be changed, nor does he seem to have fully realized the revolutionary nature of his proposals. Nevertheless, Copernicus knew that what he proposed was a new outlook in the astronomy of the sixteenth century, and he was also equally well aware that the general teaching of Christianity was by then tied in with the theories of Aristotle and Ptolemy. He therefore delayed publishing his book, and was only persuaded to do so at the end of his life—one of the first copies, we are told, was brought to him on his deathbed.

When the book finally appeared it contained not only Copernicus's own dedication of the volume to Pope Paul III, but also a preface by Andreas Osiander (1498–1552), a Lutheran divine, who had checked the manuscript at the press in Nuremberg. Osiander pointed out that the reader should not take too seriously the idea of the physical motion of the earth, and emphasized that the real purpose of Copernicus's scheme was to make simpler and quicker the calculation of the future positions of the planets, the moon, and the sun. Some accepted Osiander's preface, some did not and, in due course, many arguments arose about whether the earth really *did* move in space. Observations were made to try to decide the issue, but neither instruments nor techniques were developed enough for a definite answer to be found. And there was an addi-

for a general picture of their astronomical thought, the present author's *Changing Views of the Universe,* Macmillan, New York, 1962.

tional complication. Some of the Greek philosophers had taught that the celestial bodies were fixed to perfectly transparent spheres, and the concept of "crystalline spheres" was taken up vigorously in medieval times, becoming an integral part of the geocentric universe. A moving earth conflicted with this idea, and it has been suggested that the desire to preserve belief in the crystal spheres was the motivating force behind Osiander's preface; certainly it appears that he changed the original title of the book, inserting the word "spheres" and that Copernicus himself meant it to be *De Revolutionibus Coelestium.*

To begin with, opposition to the Copernican theory came from the Protestant church, especially from Luther himself and Philip Melancthon, as well as from astronomers who felt that the new heliocentric (sun-centered) theory ran counter to observation. Their main argument was that if the earth orbited around the sun as Copernicus suggested, then at different times of the year we should be closer to some of the stars on their particular crystal sphere than at others; in consequence, their apparent positions in the sky should alter. Such an apparent movement of the stars due to the annual motion of the earth—stellar parallax—had been sought since the days of Pythagoras, and since it could not be observed, was one of the scientific factors that weighed heavily against the hypothesis of a moving earth. Copernicus was well aware of this point and supposed that there was an immense distance between the sphere of the stars and the farthermost known planet, Saturn, but his supposition was not looked on favorably since a vast, empty space was thought to display a pointless aspect of divine design.

The opposition on religious grounds did not remain the prerogative of the Protestants. Copernicus's own Roman Catholic Church began to relegate the heliocentric view to the twilight position of being suitable for calculation but beyond belief, looking on it as a useful mathematical fiction but denying the reality of a moving earth. The theory was used as a basis for new calculations that resulted in the promulgation of the Gregorian calendar in 1582, but gradually became anathema largely due to the support given it by Giordano Bruno (c.1548–1600), a Neapolitan who was a member of the Dominican order during his youth.

Bruno had rebeled and left the Dominicans, becoming as has been aptly said "an indiscreet intellectual vagabond," who traveled over western Europe until, in 1600, he was burned at the stake in Rome. He warmly supported the Copernican concept of a moving earth and advocated it in his writings, which were numerous and received wide circulation, but a study of his arguments shows that it was for reasons of magical anthropomorphism that he accepted the theory, not for its scientific appeal. Bruno was a hermetist,‡ advocating with great pungency a hermetic religious reformation, and it was for this heresy that he was burned and not, as is sometimes romantically suggested, for his support of the heliocentric theory. The very fact that the Copernican views had been favorably mentioned in his books, however, whatever his reasons for supporting them, brought heliocentricity into disrepute. The Copernican theory was placed on the *Index librorum prohibitorum* soon after Bruno had been put to death. Thus the idea of the sun being the center of the physical universe received the disapprobation of the most powerful of all Christian bodies, and in consequence new thoughts along these lines had to be discussed in secret, if at all.

In England no religious objections of any substance were made against Copernicus's views. His book was known, and many openly supported heliocentricity, even publishing popular descriptions of it written not only in Latin for the information of the learned, but also in the vernacular, bringing it within the reach of a much wider audience. In 1556, exactly one hundred years before Halley's birth, two books were published in London setting forth Copernican ideas. The first was *Castle of Knowledge* by Robert Recorde, (c.1500–50) which contained a description of the new theory, while the second was an *Almanack* published by John Feild (1525?–87), in which the famous Dr. Dee (1527–1608), physician to Elizabeth I and a man of immense reputation and learning, wrote a preface which was notably pro-Copernican. Although in Latin, Dee's preface had considerable influence, and at a time when the spread of new knowledge was so much slower than it is today, it is remarkable

‡ For a thorough and valuable discussion of Bruno's outlook see Frances A. Yates, *Giordano Bruno and the Hermetic Tradition,* Routledge and Kegan Paul, London, 1964.

that the heliocentric theory was being widely promoted in England only thirteen years after it had first appeared in Europe.

Yet this was not all. In 1576 Thomas Digges (1546–95), a pupil of Dee, published a new edition of *A Prognostication Everlasting,* a "perpetual calendar" which had originally been published by his father Leonard (?–c.1571). Here the Copernican theory was given in an appendix, but this time with another new and important idea added. The ideas of Copernicus really demanded the removal of the crystal spheres and, in particular, an alteration of the concept of a comparatively close sphere of fixed stars. Thomas Digges appears to have appreciated this, and in the appendix proposed that the universe of stars was infinite in extent. This was a radical departure, for before this the stars were invariably thought of as fixed to an immense sphere or spread over a sphere which was of limited thickness. But Digges' idea was adopted, for in England after 1576 the Copernican theory was inextricably linked with the concept of an infinite universe of stars (a concept which Halley later ingeniously defended).

The limitations of sixteenth-century observing techniques still prevented support of the Copernican revolution by means of observation, and new methods were needed. The first significant changes arrived through the tenacity of a Dane, Tycho Brahe (1545–1601), who, on the island of Hveen in Öre Sound off the southwestern coast of Sweden, set up an observatory which he called "Uraniborg"—his "City of Urania." Brahe used large quadrants and sextants which were made with the greatest accuracy then possible, but he had the sagacity to realize a fundamental factor which has been generally accepted in all scientific observational and experimental work ever since: namely, that every instrument, however beautifully and carefully fashioned, must have its own inherent errors. No matter how one tries, it is impossible either to design or to construct a "perfect" observing instrument. As Brahe realized, the only solution is to measure these errors and then take them into account in every observation. It was this that enabled him to make far more accurate observations than any before.

Brahe also made a practice of observing the planets whenever they were visible. This may seem an obvious thing to do, but it was actually an innovation, since previous observers had been in the habit of watching carefully only at times of special interest, such as at opposition§ or at those times when various planets were in conjunction.¶ Brahe made his observations day in and day out and, with his increased accuracy, provided information which soon led to the second stage in the astronomical revolution which preceded Halley's own efforts and discoveries.

Meanwhile Brahe's careful observing techniques allowed him to discover that a large comet, which appeared in 1557, lay farther from the earth than does the moon. This was significant because such a path made it a truly celestial phenomenon; comets had usually been looked on as existing only in the upper reaches of the earth's atmosphere. Brahe's discovery also hit hard at the idea of crystal spheres, for if they existed the comet clearly must have penetrated a number of them. Soon the almost universally held belief in the real existence of the spheres had of necessity to be thrown aside.

Brahe not only observed carefully, but he also attempted to tackle the theory of planetary motion. Here he made a retrograde step, suggesting that the planets Mercury and Venus went around the sun but that the remainder, together with the moon and the sun, went around the earth. Brahe put forward this idea not because he was led to it solely by observation, but because he took the Bible literally and believed that when, in Psalms, it said that the earth stood still, then it did so and there could be no argument about it. For a time his theory had wide currency, yet ironically it was by means of his own observations that the hypothesis was to be demolished. The man to do this was Johannes Kepler (1571–1630), who joined Brahe in Prague, where he had settled after being forced to leave Hveen.

Kepler, primarily a mathematician, worked with Brahe for only a short time, as Brahe died the year after his arrival. Although the two men were together so briefly, Brahe liked and trusted Kepler, and he passed on to him all his meticulous observations. Among

§ This occurs when the planet, in its orbit, lies directly on the opposite side of the sun as the earth.

¶ Planets are in conjunction when they appear close together in the sky.

the observations that Kepler inherited was an extensive set for the planet Mars. Mars has the most elliptical orbit of all the planets except Mercury and Pluto, and although this ellipticity is small— the planets have orbits which are very nearly circular—it is large enough to be detectable with really accurate observations, and Brahe's work was of sufficient standard.

Kepler worked hard, at first in an attempt to substantiate Brahe's concept of the planetary system, for he had left his observations in the express hope that this was the course Kepler would follow. But Kepler found that the hypothesis would not fit the facts, and moved on to consider other possibilities. In doing so he was one of the pioneers of the new philosophy, where one is led by the observational or experimental evidence alone and not by the hypotheses, teachings, or ideas of previous authorities, however brilliant they may have been. Kepler therefore tried computing an orbit on the basis of the Copernican theory that all planets travel around the sun. He found the observations fitted more nearly to this theory than to Brahe's. Yet even so they did not fit exactly enough considering Brahe's precision and Kepler plodded on, trying this and then that kind of orbit.

At last, after eight years' work, he found that the uniform circular motions beloved of the Greeks and all who had followed their planetary theories could no longer give a satisfactory answer, and was forced to conclude that Mars moves around the sun in an elliptical path. Ten years later he was able to prove that all the planets move in ellipses around the sun, and also to enunciate his three laws of planetary motion, which state that 1. all planets move in ellipses with the sun occupying one of the two foci;* 2. the ratio between the time taken to complete an orbit and its distance from the sun is the same for all planets;† and 3. the velocity of a planet

* A focus of a curve is a point from which the distance to any place on the curve is given by a simple proportional formula. In a circle there is one focus which lies at the center, and the distance to any point on the circumference is constant; it is given by the radius. In an ellipse there are two foci, and the distance to points on the curve measured from them is not constant but a constantly varying quantity. The foci are farther apart the more oval or eccentric an ellipse is.

† The actual ratio Kepler discovered involved a "power" relationship: the second power or square of the time, and the third power or cube of the distance.

varies as it travels along its elliptical orbit, being greater the closer it is to the sun. The laws fitted in with observation, since they were derived from observational evidence, but Kepler could give no physical reason why a planet moves in this kind of path rather than a circular one.

The next step forward was taken during the time Kepler was at work on planetary orbits, and concerned methods of observation. In about 1609 the telescope came into use; exactly when and precisely where it was invented no one can be certain, but telescopes were then being manufactured in Holland, and news of them reached Galileo Galilei (1564–1642) in Venice during May 1609. Galileo immediately worked out the optical principle of the instrument, built his own telescope and then, in the true spirit of an inquiring scientist, turned the instrument to the heavens. What he saw astonished him, astounded others, and engendered a religious storm.

Galileo looked at the moon and was amazed to see that it was like the earth itself, having mountains, valleys and, he thought, seas. This was a surprising enough observation, primarily because it was universally believed in Greek times, and still in 1609, that the heavenly bodies were entirely different in nature from the earth or anything found on it. They seemed to be eternal and were made of an eternal substance. By observation, Galileo showed that the moon was akin to the earth and—equally significant—provided evidence that could be confirmed by any other scientist with a telescope.

Next he turned his telescope to the planets. The first in a convenient place for observation was Jupiter, and here other surprises awaited him, for Jupiter was seen as a disk, not as a dot like the stars, although four small bright "stars" appeared near it. Observing a few nights later, Galileo was puzzled to see only three stars, and a few nights later still to observe four stars once again. This time one at least was in a different position. Further observations made it clear to Galileo that the four stars were bodies connected with Jupiter and rotating around it—in other words, Jupiter possessed four natural satellites. In the twentieth century this is accepted as a matter of course, but when we recollect that one of the arguments against the heliocentric theory was that if the earth moved, then a natural consequence would be that the moon would be left behind, we see that Galileo had adduced observational proof that such an argument was fallacious. The moon would no more be left behind than the satellites of Jupiter which even the most conservative of philosophers must recognize moved in an orbit, even though there might be disagreement about the nature of the orbit itself. Thus Galileo's observations broke down the arguments against the Copernican theory and against the belief that all celestial bodies were composed of immutable, unchanging, eternal material —clearly they were of like substance to the earth.

The next logical step was then to argue that the motions of the heavenly bodies were amenable to the kind of laws operating on earth. Rigid mathematical proof of this did not come until Halley's day, but theories and suggestions were not long in making their appearance, and one idea in particular must be mentioned—the vortex theory of the French philosopher René Descartes (1596–1650)—for it was this theory which for a time was widely accepted and was the view of the universe taught when Halley was at Oxford.

René Descartes gradually formulated a complete and novel cosmology based on a physical theory. His views were set out in his *Principia Philosophiae,* published at Amsterdam in 1644 which, as might be expected from the title, began with a discussion of the general principles of his own philosophical outlook. Descartes progressed from one basic premise, namely that he himself existed, and from this he built up a divinely created universe, first discussing evidence of the material world and then propounding his cosmology. Descartes divided the universe into two main kinds of substance which we may conveniently refer to as "extended" or material and "thinking" or rational, of which the human mind is an example. He followed Digges in assuming the universe to be infinite and, further, he believed it to be a plenum, physically filled with extended substance. This substance took the form of minute particles, although he rejected any idea of the existence of indivisible material atoms. (He argued that since one could think of the infinite division of all material, finite bodies which could be subdivided no more—that is, atoms—could not therefore exist.) The extended substance which filled space was subtler in kind than any atoms and could in theory be divided ad infinitum. Descartes held that there were different sized particles of the extended substance: The heaviest and largest were "earthy," and it was these that composed material things; the lightest and smallest were "fiery" particles. The fiery particles were supposed to circulate more quickly and the earthy ones more slowly. This, whether Descartes realized it or not, was really a partial return to the ideas of Aristotle, who had postulated the existence of four substances—"earth," "air," "fire," and "water"—from which the whole earth and its surroundings were made. The crucial difference between the materials of Descartes and those of Aristotle was that Descartes considered his particles to exist throughout the universe, while Aristotle had confined his to the earth where everything underwent change, teaching that all celestial bodies were composed of a fifth, eternal substance. In filling the whole cosmos with his "extended" substance Descartes laid foundations for later application of the laws of physics, established on earth, to the behavior of celestial bodies as well.

In the third part of Descartes' *Principia* all these philosophical ideas were welded together into his famous vortex theory. Here he suggested that the cosmos was filled with circulating, extended matter which collected into whirlpools or vortices. The life cycle of a vortex was believed to commence with fire (fiery particles) accumulated at the center. As time progressed, this fiery substance condensed into stars. Next, the rotation of the vortex caused the rotation of the central star, which gradually became covered with a skin of coarser particles; an idea which was doubtless due to the telescopic discovery of the existence of dark spots on the surface of the sun. Descartes, always keen to take observation into account, synthesized these facts into his general hypothesis. When the skinning over of the star was complete, its light could no longer escape and the outward pressure which it was supposed to exert in its unskinned state also ceased. As a result the vortex collapsed and the star became a planet which then wandered to another vortex and orbited around the central star there, an ingenious if wildly incorrect suggestion for the creation of our solar system.

Such was the general idea, but there were other aspects of the vortex theory. First, the transformation of the planets into satellites; these were created by the stars which were now planets continuing to skin over still further. Second, there was the question of the formation of comets. Descartes suggested comets were formed in a similar way to planets, by stars becoming skinned over, a comet being created when the star was too massive to become a planet and so unable to attach itself to the vortex system of another star. So, after a fashion, he was able to explain why comets appeared for only a short time and at apparently irregular and unpredictable intervals.

Whatever one may now think of Descartes' strange cosmology, it must be emphasized that within its own bounds it was a self-consistent system based upon some kind of physical laws or, at least, an interpretation of them. It stimulated thought and was the general cosmological outlook to which Halley was exposed while at the university; only by realizing this can we appreciate the great strides which he made in astronomy.

Moreover, it must be stressed that Descartes was no crank. A brilliant mathematician, he initiated a marriage between geometry and algebra which has been of incalculable use to succeeding generations and even now is used by scientists and engineers. Known as coordinate geometry, it provides a means whereby the positions of bodies can be expressed in terms of a reference point or reference framework, and allows precise description of their relative positions. Still more important, it permits the relationships of bodies in space to be worked out without elaborate geometrical theorems, using instead the mathematical shorthand of algebra. Thus it becomes possible to undertake the solution of problems which, using pure geometry, might be too involved and difficult to work out. The use of a reference framework for points or bodies in space was not unknown. It had been applied by astronomers ever since Hipparchos who, in the second century B.C., made a catalogue of the positions of the stars. What Descartes did was to develop it into a rigid mathematical system.

Catalogues of stars were made by others as well as Hipparchos. The plotting of star positions has always been considered an important matter; Ptolemy, three hundred years after Hipparchos, continued his work and made a more extensive catalogue. The great fifteenth-century Arab astronomer Ulu-Begh (1394–1449)‡ again recatalogued the stars, and the work was extended by the indefatigable Tycho Brahe, with his customary degree of accuracy. Although astronomy had never been noted for its directly practical applications, this work was to be of singular importance in the sixteenth and seventeenth centuries when the maritime countries of western Europe were competing with one another for supremacy in sea power and the need for really accurate star catalogues became predominant. The reason was that in order to win the battle for supremacy it was necessary to be able to sail safely across oceans and far out of sight of land, yet know the ship's position at any moment. This entailed the observation of celestial bodies.

Determining the latitude of a ship was not too difficult as it could be obtained directly by observing the apparent altitude of a star, or of the sun or moon, and mariners were practiced at this. It was the determination of longitude that presented serious problems, for here it was necessary to find the local time at sea; since existing clocks were not sufficiently accurate for this purpose, it appeared that celestial observations provided the only conceivably practical method. Observation of the movements of the planets was no use as they move too slowly across the background of the stars for navigational purposes. The sun is of no help since its position cannot be compared directly with those of the stars.

By the mid-seventeenth century the conclusion reached was that the only practicable solution was to observe the moon, whose motion is far faster than that of the planets, measuring its position with respect to the background stars; in effect, to use the moon as the hand of a clock and the stars as the dial across which it moves. Another suggestion had been made once the telescope was invented, and this was to observe the moments at which Jupiter's satellites crossed behind or in front of the planet, or when they became eclipsed by moving into its shadow. But while such observa-

‡ Ulu-Begh's name is variously transliterated. He was the grandson of the Tartar, Tamerlaine, but he is referred to here as an Arab since his work was part of the Arab culture and written in Arabic.

tions are admirable theoretically, they would be impossible to rely on at sea where it is seldom calm enough to train a telescope on the planet, let alone keep it there long enough to time the behavior of its satellites. It seemed the moon presented the only real solution.

After the Restoration, the problem was brought to the notice of Charles II by the Duchess of Portsmouth, who had been approached by a Frenchman, Le Sieur de Saint-Pierre. Saint-Pierre claimed that lunar observations were the only way to overcome the difficulty; the methods he proposed had been worked out some forty years earlier by one of his compatriots. The King sought expert advice and appointed a committee to report on Saint-Pierre's proposals. After consideration they were found to be impractical since the positions of the stars and of the moon were not known with sufficient accuracy. The outcome was a decision to make new observations, and in 1675 Charles II established ". . . a small observatory within our park at Greenwich, upon the highest ground, at or near the place where the Castle stood, with lodging rooms for our astronomical observatory and assistant, . . ." The observatory was designed by ". . . our trusty and well-beloved Sir Christopher Wren . . ." (1632–1723), mathematician, astronomer, and architect of St. Paul's, and it was here that the Rev. John Flamsteed (1646–1719), the first Astronomer Royal, in due course set up telescopic instruments and began his work, cataloguing the stars, and the motions of the planets and the moon.

In Paris Louis XIV also had founded an observatory which was completed in 1672 and placed under the direction of Giovanni Domenico (Jacques Dominique) Cassini (1625–1712), while in Danzig the outstanding observer Johannes Hevelius (1611–87) was at work, too, cataloguing the northern stars.

The labors of Cassini, Flamsteed, and Hevelius, and the great move to bring the problem of longitude to a solution, clearly must have influenced the outlook and ideas of the youthful Edmond Halley.

CHAPTER 3

Oxford and St. Helena

On July 24, 1673, Edmond Halley, aged almost seventeen, entered Queen's College, Oxford, as a commoner, that is, as an undergraduate not dependent upon any bursary or foundation grant for his upkeep. He did not go up to Oxford to "read science"—no such specialized course existed in the seventeenth century. Certainly he continued his school subjects of Latin and Greek and, most probably, Hebrew. He also studied mathematics, which meant he carried on working at geometry, algebra, navigation, and astronomy, because these were then part of the mathematics syllabus, forming a useful exercise in spherical trigonometry. In addition to these subjects there is evidence that Halley pursued his beloved observational astronomy with more than normal avidity. He made considerable use of his twenty-four-foot telescope and large quadrant, observing not only during the term at Oxford but also during vacations at his family's home on Winchester Street.

We know of these efforts in practical astronomy from Halley's preface to the *Catalogue of Southern Stars* and from his correspondence with the Astronomer Royal, John Flamsteed. On March 10, 1675, while only eighteen, Halley wrote to Flamsteed from Oxford. He had been making some of his observations at home and at Oxford with an undergraduate friend, Charles Bouchar. Bouchar had written to Flamsteed on some astronomical matters and received a courteous reply, but as soon after he left for Jamaica, Halley decided to write to Flamsteed on his own account. After mentioning the kindness extended to his friend Bouchar, general courtesies, and an expression of his intense love for and interest in astronomy, Halley explains the degree of precision with which his observations

were made, ". . . whensoever the heavens favour us with seren-
ity . . ." He used a small telescope fitted to his quadrant, and with
this was able to claim that ". . . I can confide to one minute* without error by means of the telescopicall sights and skrew for the
subdivision of my Quadrant . . ." This was no idle boast, for Halley
then goes on to inform Flamsteed that his observations of the positions of the planets Jupiter and Saturn clearly show that the main
published tables of the planetary positions (which contained computed, not observed values) were in error. The truly scientific approach to these questions comes out well in this letter, for Halley
then asks, "If you have observed anything of the like nature in
Saturn† I beg you would communicate it." In other words, he
wanted independent confirmation of his results, primarily because
his own observations had led him to find errors in the professional tables.

Flamsteed is next told of observations made of a lunar eclipse
on the first of January 1675. These observations Halley made from
Winchester Street with the assistance of another friend, a Mr. Street.
They did not see the beginning of the eclipse because they had not
made their instruments ready in time, "trusting too much to calculation," as Halley put it. However, they watched the remainder, timing by simultaneous observations of the position of the bright star
Pollux, the exact moment when the whole disk of the moon was
immersed in the earth's shadow, as well as the moments when the
moon began to emerge from its eclipse, and when the eclipse
ended. These observations also showed the published tables to be
wrong, and again Halley requests confirmation from Flamsteed. Halley also "thinks fit to signifie" that he has even found errors in the
star catalogue of the famous Tycho Brahe, and mentions his intention to observe a conjunction of Mars and the moon twelve days
later which he hopes Flamsteed will watch too. The results given
in this letter show clearly Halley's observational competence. Also
apparent is a characteristic self-confidence, even at this age, in not
fearing to put forward his own ideas when they opposed those of

* That is, to one minute of arc or one-sixtieth part of a degree.
† In this sentence, as elsewhere in the letter, Halley actually refers to the
planets and constellations by astrological signs—a convenient form of shorthand.

other and better-known astronomers, exemplified in his criticism of the work of a figure such as Brahe.

Halley did not confine his letter to his own observations. He inquires about details Cassini had published about the refraction of starlight by the earth's atmosphere and some resultant conclusions about the atmosphere's extent. He goes so far as to discuss important points of his own, and it is obvious that Halley feels that Flamsteed should consider these as seriously as Cassini's. One is tempted to think that the young man had rather too great an opinion of himself, but it must be remembered that his criticisms were based on observational evidence, the value and accuracy of which he had no doubt. The truth would seem to be that as well as his abundant self-confidence he had an overwhelming zeal to make known his prowess as an astronomer. He was ambitious and wanted to cooperate with professional astronomers—indeed, he writes of the observations he is to make of Mars and the moon, "I desire you would send me those observations made with you, whereto I shall subjoin my own if the heavens favour us;" and goes on, referring to the observations already reported earlier in the letter, "these Sr. as a specimen of my Astronomical endeavours I send you, being ambitious of the honour of being known to you, of which if you shall deem me worthy I shall account my self exceedingly happy in the enjoyment of the acquaintance of so illustrious and deserving person as your self." He was not only anxious for recognition but was also impatient to make a reputation for himself in the subject by which he was so fascinated, and his desire for patronage, in an intellectual, not a monetary sense, is again apparent when he signs himself, "I am Sr. Your and Urania's most humble servant thô unknown, Edm. Halley."

Flamsteed's reply does not seem to have survived, but it is clear from what followed that Halley's letter began a close collaboration between them. Flamsteed was the elder by ten years, yet there is no doubt that he was impressed by the details sent to him and probably encouraged Halley to persevere with his careful observing. Halley certainly continued enthusiastically: He made planetary observations, carefully noted sunspots, and expended considerable time and effort on the moon and the stars. He sent the results to Flamsteed, who published Halley's sunspot observations side by side with others in the Royal Society's scientific journal *Philosophical Transactions* under the title, "Observations on the Spots in the Sun appearing July and August, 1676"; and his work on the occultation‡ of Mars by the moon was published in the same volume of *Philosophical Transactions*. Such occultation observations had considerable significance for they were, and still are, the most satisfactory way of determining accurately the moon's real position in the sky.

From these scientific papers it is obvious that Flamsteed considered the practical astronomy of a youth still in his teens worthy to stand by the side of work of others with more years and more experience behind them. But Halley's interests and talents were not confined to the purely observational aspects of astronomy, even at this early stage in his career. He also explored the theoretical side, and in 1675, with Flamsteed's support, began to write his first scientific paper, which was accepted for publication in *Philosophical Transactions*. Its impressive title,§ "A Direct and Geometrical Method of finding the Aphelia, Eccentricities, and Proportions of the Primary Planets, without supposing the equality in angular motion," is matched by its content.

Kepler, as mentioned in Chapter 2, working on Tycho Brahe's observations, had discovered that the orbits of the planets were not circular with the sun at the center, but were ellipses with the sun lying at one focus. One of Kepler's three laws of planetary motion states that the line drawn from the sun focus to the planet moves at a rate that causes it to sweep out equal areas inside the ellipse in equal times. The essential point of this law is that a planet moves more quickly near the sun than when farther away, and these changes of velocity can be calculated. The idea that planets move at a single, steady pace in a circle around the sun, however, was still lingering in the minds of many astronomers, and it had been tacitly assumed that there was, somewhere within the ellipse, a point about which a planet's motion would be found to be uniform.

‡ An occultation occurs when the disk of the moon appears to pass in front of some other celestial body.

§ The original title was in Latin, as was the paper.

With this as a basis, geometrical methods for determining Kepler's form of planetary orbits had been developed. But Halley ignored this old concept and developed a method to determine the elements of Kepler's orbits from observations. Thus, without recourse to any old-fashioned ideas of uniform circular motion, Kepler's elliptical orbits were shown to be logical consequences of the observed paths of the planets. Halley's paper was primarily geometrical, ending with an algebraic analysis, and as the original work of a youth of nineteen it was a brilliant mathematical feat.

The paper was redrafted a number of times at the instigation of Henry Oldenburg (c.1626–78), one of the Royal Society's honorary Secretaries, but this is hardly surprising as Halley had no experience in preparing such a communication for the press. Part of the problem was his lack of practice in expressing his ideas clearly. We find Oldenburg taking him to task on this very point, and also remarking that some parts of the paper should be modified lest they give offense to the Bishop of Salisbury. The bishop, Seth Ward (1617–89), once professor of astronomy at Oxford, had written on the same subject, but using a point of uniform motion—the very idea that Halley was casting out. Halley took Oldenburg's criticism and advice into consideration and softened the wording, avoiding unnecessary ill-feeling.

As soon as the paper appeared in 1676 its value was recognized, for it had some relevance to earlier papers on the subject by Cassini and Nicholas Mercator (c.1630–87 and not to be confused with the famous cartographer of the previous century). Our interest in this first paper is in the fact that besides confirming Halley as a first-rate mathematician, it shows an independence of thought and a live imagination—factors that were apparent throughout his career.

Stimulated by his success, he went on to work out an improvement of the geometrical methods then in use for determining where on the earth's surface a total eclipse of the sun would be visible. Because the shadow of the moon cast on the earth during an eclipse is small, covering only a few square miles at a time and moving quickly over the ground, detailed calculations are needed to determine precisely where the shadow will be at a given moment. He communicated his results, but not his method of arriving at them, to Flamsteed, who published them several years later (1681) in the preface of his book, *Doctrine of the Sphere*. Why Halley showed reticence we shall discuss later together with his relationships with Flamsteed. At the time of his first paper in *Philosophical Transactions*, however, all was well between them, and in letters to his friend the mathematician and astronomer Richard Towneley (fl. 1660–1705), Flamsteed refers to Halley as "an ingenious young man from Oxford" and "an ingenious youth well versed in calculations and almost all parts of mathematics, tho' yet scarce 19 years of age."

There is no doubt that Halley was outstanding among the undergraduates of his day, and he was fortunate enough to be studying under two professors whose direction was soon to bring his talents to maturity. The professor of geometry, the Rev. John Wallis (1616–1703), was one of the greatest mathematicians of his time, a brilliant expositor of his art, and a man who contributed much new knowledge, especially in the field of mechanics. Equally important to Halley was the professor of astronomy, Edward Bernard (1638–96). Bernard had himself been a pupil of Wallis, and although astronomy is not especially indebted to him, the history of mathematics certainly is, for he made exceptional contributions to our knowledge of Greek mathematics. This meant that he had to read Arabic, for the original Greek texts had come into western Christendom by way of Islam. He was therefore not only a mathematician and astronomer, but also an Arabic scholar. His excursions into Arabic must have intrigued Halley for, from what followed many years later, it is clear that he learned at least enough under Bernard to emulate his teacher and himself tackle Arabic versions of Greek mathematical texts. It is reasonable to assume that Halley enjoyed his work at the university and was at one with his teachers. Yet if this is true it makes it more difficult to understand why, at the age of twenty and before he had taken his degree, he voluntarily left Oxford to embark on an expedition to the island of St. Helena.

What made him leave before he had graduated? Probably it was a combination of two factors: on the one hand the obvious success which had accompanied the publication of his paper and, on the other, his observing ability, of which he had ample confirmation from the Astronomer Royal. To these must be added the impetuosity of youth; his early correspondence with Flamsteed shows his impatience to start work on his own account. But above all he had a thorough grasp of the essential problems of observational astronomy as they existed in the 1670s, and was well aware not only of what was being done but, more to the point, of what still needed doing.

While Halley was at Oxford, Flamsteed was busily engaged in making a careful catalogue of star positions using every recently developed observational technique to ensure the greatest possible accuracy. Flamsteed was able to give star positions correct to within ten seconds of arc, a degree of precision forty times greater than that achieved by Tycho Brahe. This improvement was due primarily to the fact that Flamsteed's measuring instruments, like Halley's, were fitted with small telescopes as sighting tubes instead of the open sights which Brahe had had to use. But Flamsteed's observations were made from Greenwich, and consequently there were parts of the southern skies which he was unable to observe. Similar work to Flamsteed's was being pursued by Cassini and Hevelius, and it was apparent that the stars of the Northern Hemisphere were being well covered. Halley therefore conceived the idea of observing the southern stars invisible to Cassini, Flamsteed, and Hevelius and so himself contribute to this great work. Already in his letter of 1675 to Flamsteed he had claimed an accuracy four times greater than that of Brahe, and the only thing for him to do now seemed to be to obtain permission and official support for an expedition somewhere in the Southern Hemisphere. By now he felt no hesitation in writing to those in authority if it suited his purpose and, once he had conceived the plan—probably very early in 1676 —he began to put it into operation.

The first question to be decided was the place from which the observations should be made. He discussed the matter with friends, and no doubt wrote to Flamsteed seeking his advice. Rio de Janeiro was suggested, but the idea was rejected because this would mean going to a foreign settlement and learning a foreign language. As

Halley put it, "this would render useless time that could better be spent on the work I had set out to do." The general consensus preferred a British territory for work of this kind. For similar reasons the Cape of Good Hope, then in Dutch hands, was rejected, and it was finally resolved that the island of St. Helena, which lies a little to the west of the African continent and at a latitude of 16° South, would be the most suitable station of all; it was the most southerly province then under British control, and from it the south celestial pole would appear sufficiently elevated above the horizon for satisfactory observations. In addition, the weather was reported as generally favorable. In July 1676 Halley wrote to Oldenburg informing him of his intention to observe the southern stars and to do so from St. Helena, no doubt hoping to elicit the help of the Royal Society which, even then, was consulted on scientific matters by the King and members of the Government.

Edmond Halley, Sr. agreed to his son's proposed expedition and, wishing to support him by every means at his disposal, agreed to make him an annual allowance of three hundred pounds ($720) —three times as much as the Astronomer Royal's salary and six times more than Samuel Pepys received in his early days as a government employee. Halley's father probably made the project known to influential connections that he must have had in the City, but there is no clue as to who these men might have been.

Deciding on such an expedition is a very different matter from getting arrangements under way. The island of St. Helena then came under the jurisdiction of the East India Company, which had been formed at the end of the previous century and provided with a royal charter by Elizabeth I giving it sole rights to trade in those parts of the world where English merchant shipping was used, with, as its name implies, special preference for India. Such a measure was not unusual in those days, and in this instance had been made necessary by economic competition with other maritime nations of western Europe. The Dutch had for long been England's greatest rivals in overseas trade, but at the time of Halley's trip France and Portugal were also strong competitors. In consequence the company had to take energetic action to protect its property; it needed good merchant vessels, and in 1609 had constructed large shipyards at Deptford, southeast of the City of London and close to Greenwich.

The yards were enormously successful, and it was their establishment that led to the construction of really large merchant ships in England; here the famous sailing ships known as "East Indiamen" were built and launched, ships which earned respect in the mercantile world until the nineteenth century. But the construction of ships, and offices to administer a mercantile shipping business, were not enough to ensure success. Voyaging on the high seas was beset by many dangers, not the least of which were attacks either by the ships of other nations or, more likely, by pirates. It is no wonder that the East India Company, which in its more distant trading posts could not hope for the support of the British Navy, had its own armed forces. On his restoration Charles II consolidated the company's position by providing it with five new charters; these gave royal permission for the company to acquire territory, form alliances, command fortresses and troops, and exercise criminal and civil jurisdiction in its territories where, in addition, it coined its own money. The East India Company was a great power in those distant places where it operated, and St. Helena was one of these. Halley therefore had to obtain permission at the highest level if the plan for his astronomical expedition was to be approved by and receive support from the company.

An approach to the Government was required and, even more, the King's sympathy was needed. Halley began by enlisting the aid of his friends and acquaintances, including Flamsteed and Oldenburg, and in September 1676 he prevailed upon them to draw up a statement highly commending the purpose of the visit and the scientific results which they believed it likely to produce. This statement was sent to the Secretary of State, Sir Joseph Williamson (d. 1701) who, it so happened, had himself been an undergraduate at Queen's. Williamson lost little time in placing the matter before the King and by the beginning of October, one month after the supporting statement had been prepared, Charles II sent a letter to the East India Company by the hand of Sir Jonas Moore (1617–79), his Surveyor of Ordnance, who had been instrumental in establishing the Royal Observatory at Greenwich. He recommended that Halley, together with a friend of his, a Mr. Clerke, should be given free passages to St. Helena.

There seems no doubt that Moore and Williamson had discussed the proposals together and had each told the King about the astronomical expedition, for both men were known to be "great promoters of these studies," while Moore was himself a mathematician of considerable ability. Another sponsor may have been Hon. Robert Boyle (1627–92), famous as a physicist and chemist and for whom Hooke had worked for a number of years. Boyle was a Director of the East India Company from 1662 to 1677 and, as a Fellow of the Royal Society, would have been only too glad to further such an exploit.

The directors of the East India Company, who must have appreciated the navigational advantages such an expedition might bring, did not refuse the King's request. At a meeting of their court of committees held on October 4, 1676, they minuted their approval and agreement to the suggestion "that Mr Edmond Hally a Student of Queen's College in Oxford, with a friend of his might have their passage in the first ship for St Helen' whether they are desirous to go & remayn for some time to make observation of the planets & starrs, for rectifying and finishing the celestial globe, being a place (he conceives) very fit and proper for that design;" going on to order that "Mr Hally with his friend doe take their passage for St Helena on the Unity with their necessary provisions free of charge."

Two days later written instructions were sent to the "Committee for shipping," and the orders contained a strict injunction that Halley and his friend ". . . be treated in their passage with all civilitie," this being followed by a letter dated October 27 to the "Governor and Council at St Helena" in which instructions were given ". . . that you accomodate them with convenient lodging in the house of the Governor or his Deputy or in some other fitt & convenient habitation dureing their stay, & to afford them such assistance and countenance as may be for their encouragement to proceed in so usefull an undertaking, They being to provide diet at their own charge, Wee also recommend it to our Commandrs. to assist Mr Halley upon his request in what they can for his furtherance in making his observations, And wee doe order That when

Mr Halley and his freind shall desire to return back for England; That you recommend him to some of our Commanders that are bound from our Island homewards, and in the mean time, while he shall inhabit with you to use him with all respect and kindness."

Things had moved extraordinarily quickly, for the general statement had only been prepared in September, and yet Halley and Clerke were able to sail in November. This speedy negotiation would be remarkable today, and it is the more surprising for the seventeenth century when the pace of living was so much slower. That Halley was anxious to get to work on his new project is obvious, and even he cannot have had any cause for complaint at the speed with which the expedition came to fruition.

The ship in which the two friends sailed, the *Unity*, was owned by a Mr. Lethiouler and under the command of a Captain William Cruft. Although the log of the voyage is now lost, we know the fifty-six-hundred-mile journey was made without mishap and took three months, so that sometime in February 1677 they landed and were able to set up their observatory. By this time Halley was practiced enough to know exactly what he wanted to do and how to do it. His observations were aimed at finding the apparent positions of the southern stars, and this meant that he had to measure the angle between one star and another on the celestial sphere.¶ In order that his observations might be useful to all astronomers, however, and correlated with the work of Cassini, Flamsteed, and Hevelius, he had also to observe some stars visible in both the northern and southern skies: Using these as a key, he could then profitably measure the distance of those farther south. In this way he was able to compile his catalogue so that it was valuable to astronomers as well as to navigators. What made Halley's catalogue even more worthwhile was that he included his measurements of the distances between individual stars, so that when a key star was later more accurately plotted his values of the southern stars could be adjusted rather than becoming obsolete.

Halley was sufficiently practical to realize that the instruments he took to St. Helena needed not only to be accurate but also

¶ The celestial sphere is the apparent sphere of the sky on which the stars seem to be fixed.

readily disassembled for transportation by ship. With his father's backing he had special instruments constructed for his expedition. The largest of these items was a great metal sextant of 5½-foot radius, the arms and arc of which were of brass but all fixed to an underlying steel framework. The movable arm of this sextant possessed a small telescope which was specially mounted so that it was adjustable by two long screws, enabling it to be exactly aligned with the arm. This was an innovation which allowed greater observational accuracy. Besides this large sextant he took the two-foot radius quadrant which he had been using in Oxford and London; with this he observed the altitude of the sun so that he could keep his clock continually in adjustment, since accurate time measurement is a necessary adjunct to determination of star positions.

The quadrant he used was the then ubiquitous backstaff or "Davis' quadrant" that had been designed by John Davis (d. 1605), a Welsh sea captain, and with it the sun's altitude was determined (see Figure 1) by observing the horizon through a wooden slit and moving a wooden arm and block until the shadow of the block coincided with the horizon slit. This was an admirable method if the sun was shining strongly but a poor one in cloudy weather since the shadow was often too faint. Halley, no doubt stimulated by the poor observing conditions he encountered, improved the instrument by fitting a lens in place of the wooden block and so concentrating the sun's light into a bright spot on the horizon slit, an improvement that was later to be developed, especially by the mathematician John Hadley (1682–1744). For measuring time at night Halley used a pendulum clock which he took with him in pieces and reassembled on the island. Finally, he provided himself with a number of telescopes, the largest of which was twenty-four feet long and fitted with two micrometers.

St. Helena is a small island, covering no more than forty-seven square miles. It was discovered by the Portuguese in 1502 but had belonged to the East India Company since 1651. It was once actively volcanic and its country is rough and rugged, its coastline precipitous. Halley and Clerke set up their observatory on the northern slopes of Diana Peak, the largest and most central moun-

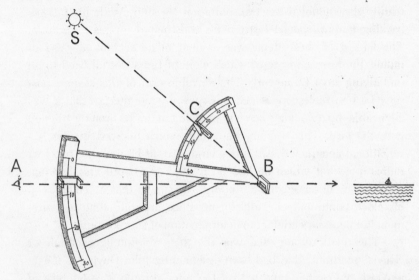

FIGURE 1 *The purpose of the instrument was to determine the meridian altitude of the sun. The observer (who stood with his back to the sun, hence the name "backstaff") looked from sights close to the point A, through the wooden slit at B, to the horizon. The sun at S shone on the arm C which cast a shadow on B, and the positions of C and A were then adjusted until the shadow just touched the slit and thus the image of the horizon. Halley's improvement was to place a lens at C, so that an image of the sun might be formed at B and thus permit the instrument to be used in cloudy weather when no satisfactory shadow could be formed.*

tain. The two young men, even with such assistance as the East India Company's commanders may have provided, must have had some trouble transporting their instruments over the rough country and up to the point Halley had selected, a point which in later years was to overlook Napoleon's tomb.

In choosing St. Helena Halley had been considerably influenced by the reports of travelers who claimed that the climate of the area was such that he would have every expectation of clear skies and good observing conditions. But he was grievously disappointed, for very often the skies were cloudy, rainfall was heavy, and climatic conditions were more unfavorable even than in England, which has never been noted as a country especially kind to

the observational astronomer. He records that, during the whole
of the first August he was there, he hardly had one night when
the skies were clear and, at best, not more than one hour's observing
could be done on any one night. The first half of September was
equally bad and often the mountainside was enveloped in fog, mist,
or cloud with, so Halley comments, the north wind blowing hard
most of the time. It was only by using every available opportunity
when the skies were clear, even for only a short time, that he managed to make any headway at all. "I did not go to bed when I could
see the Sky was in a state to permit study," he reported in the preface to his *Catalogue*.

The unfavorable climate of St. Helena was not his only burden.
The governor of the island, a Mr. Gregory Field, treated Halley with
a singular lack of civility—indeed, he seems to have been generally discourteous and arrogant. His incivility cannot have been
caused by Halley's behavior, as this was very favorably reported on
by the East India Company's agents, and the surety of twenty
pounds deposited with the company for their transportation was
returned. No, it is clear that Field did not treat Halley and Clerke
with "all respect & kindness" as he was ordered. His "ill-living" and
generally unpleasant behavior in fact formed the substance of reports which reached England, and seemed so serious to the court
of committees that it was decided on February 20, 1678, that Field's
continuance as governor would not only prove an embarrassment
but might also prejudice the island's prosperity. He was dismissed
and sent home on the next ship. What precisely Field's misdemean-
ors may have been we do not know since almost all the papers referring to him are missing from the contemporary files.

In spite of Mr. Field, clouds, fog, and rain, however, Halley and
Clerke managed to do much useful work. By November 1677 Halley
was able to write to Sir Jonas Moore and not only report progress
on cataloguing the stars but also to send him some observations of
an eclipse of the sun and one of the moon, with a comment that
"mighty winds, and extraordinary motion of the Clouds" had been
troublesome and had adversely affected the precision of the results which could be obtained. In this letter Halley says that he

has found "three Stars of the first Magnitude* that never appear in England," and goes on to remark that there is no Pole Star to be found in the Southern Hemisphere. He also describes the two large "clouds" or nebulae which appear like detached parts of the Milky Way and notes that they are ". . . in Moon shine, scarce perceptible." Halley describes his observations of the transit of Mercury across the face of the sun, observations that he was later to turn to great effect in an effort to determine the sun's distance. Already he was aware of their importance, and in the preface to his *Catalogue* he mentions that he has compared his results with those made at the same time in Avignon by Jean Charles Gallet (fl. 1675) and sent to Cassini but, being uncertain about the accuracy of Gallet's work, he was unable to obtain sufficiently precise results for the sun's distance. But "I can say in truth," he commented, "that if one can find the true position of the . . . intersection of its [Mercury's] path with the Ecliptic,† without difficulty my observation will provide the parallax‡ of the Sun."

Halley never lost sight of his main task of making observations of star positions, and although he had also intended to observe the positions of the planets, he had to forego this due to the bad climate. The poor weather, however, did allow him to make other careful observations, the most significant of which were those concerned with his pendulum clock. He found that in order for it to keep correct time as it had done in England, it was necessary for the length of the pendulum to be shortened. This we now know is because the earth is not exactly spherical but has an equatorial bulge and that St. Helena lies within this equatorial region, but at the time the cause was not known. These findings were to become of interest to Isaac Newton.

Halley and Clerke returned to London in 1678. The *Biographia Britannica* gives the date of return as November, but this seems to be incorrect, for in his manuscript diary Robert Hooke has an entry dated May 30, which states: "Halley from St Helena. With Sr. J.

---

* "Magnitude" is, in this context, a purely astronomical term meaning brightness.

† The ecliptic is the sun's apparent path in the sky.

‡ Parallax is a measure of angular displacement of a celestial body from which its distance may be derived.

More & Colwall at toothes." Toothe's was a well-known coffeehouse, and one of the favorite meeting places of the new savants. From other corroborative evidence we can take it that Halley left St. Helena sometime in March 1678 and was back in London before the end of May.

As soon as he returned Halley lost no time in making arrangements for the publication of the results of his expedition. This was an onerous task, for he produced not only a catalogue but also a careful description of the objects he had seen from St. Helena, including the star cluster in the constellation of Centaurus which had never been reported before, as well as a large circular chart or planisphere of the southern heavens. The catalogue had a very full title§: *A Catalogue of the Southern Stars, or a supplement to the Catalogue of Tycho showing the longitudes and latitudes of the Stars, which being close to the southern pole are invisible from the Uraniborg of Tycho, accurately reckoned from measured distances and completely corrected to the year 1677, with those very observations of the heavens produced with the greatest care and a sufficiently large sextant on the island of St Helena which lies in latitude 15°55′ south and longitude 7°00′ west of London. A labour so far needed in Astronomy. To which is added a small note concerning things not unwanted in Astronomy.¶* The book became known simply as *A Catalogue of the Southern Stars*.

It is a masterly work by any standards, and is the more surprising considering the author's youth. In the long preface Halley makes it clear that, having realized that tables of motions of the planets were inadequate, showing, for example, an apparent motion for Jupiter which was too slow and one for Saturn which was too quick, he determined to try to correct matters. Appreciating that to correct these errors by observation required a careful redetermination of the positions of the stars—after all, it was with reference to such stars that the positions of the planets were fixed—and seeing this being ably done by Flamsteed and Hevelius for those in the Northern Hemisphere, he decided to do the same for those

§ *The Dictionary of National Biography*, Oxford, 1890, XXIV, p. 104, is incorrect here, as well as in a few other details about Halley.
¶ The original title and text were in Latin.

in the Southern Hemisphere. Such an undertaking was long outstanding, for few previous observations had been made before, and
such as there were had no pretentions to any high degree of accuracy. Halley mentions the errors on the globe by the famous
geographer Willem Blaeu (1571–1680) and the work of another
Dutchman, Frederick de Houtman, in Sumatra (although it has
since been found that Houtman plagiarized the observations of a
compatriot who died in Sumatra but seems to have observed in
Madagascar). Halley comments that the observer had little experience in the "Art of Observing," and it is only observations made
by Jean Richer (d. 1696) and a M. Maurice at Cayenne that draw
any respect from him; but, as he also points out, they were not
observing at a sufficiently southerly latitude to see the south cir-
cumpolar stars, and as a result their errors are far too great.

Halley specifically mentions the encouragement given him by
Sir Joseph Williamson, Sir Jonas Moore, and the King, and goes on
to discuss his observations. He also notes that the then accepted
value for the obliquity of the ecliptic* seems to be wrong but that,
because his own observations were concerned only with a part of the
sky, he made no attempt to correct this. The way in which he had
prepared his catalogue meant that it could readily be altered when
a new value for the ecliptic was decided upon.

After mentioning his other astronomical observations on St.
Helena, he closes the preface and begins the catalogue proper. To
this he added some early Greek observations which showed how
inaccurate were the celestial globes of his day. The *Appendicula* or
"little additions" contain his observations of the transit of Mercury
which in the preface he had already remarked could be used to
determine the distance of the sun; his ideas about finding more
accurately the distance of the moon; and, finally, some remarks
about the shape of the moon's orbit and the way in which an accurate knowledge of the moon's position in the sky could be used for
determining longitude at sea. This last theme was an important one
and one to which he devoted much thought and labor during the

---

* The obliquity of the ecliptic is the angle between that line in the sky along
which the sun appears to travel and the celestial equator (the line of the earth's
equator as traced out in the sky).

whole of his life; here it is worth noting that his comments have a particular interest since the theory he used of the moon's motion is based on that of Descartes which he had been taught at Oxford and which was still current.

The book was published sometime in November 1678. In the early part of the month Robert Hooke told a meeting of the Royal Society of Halley's work and showed his planisphere. That the new stellar catalogue should be brought to the notice of the Society's Fellows was in itself an implicit recognition of its worth. In addition to publication in England, the catalogue appeared in France early the next year in a version translated by Augustin Royer with the title *Catalogue des Estoilles Australes,* and Gottfried Kirsch also included it in his *Ephemerides* for 1681.

As a compliment to Charles II, who had supported his idea of an expedition, Halley soon prepared a copy of his planisphere and presented it to the King. His gratitude was perhaps a little tinged with hope, as he now required a further favor. Excited by the possibilities of his scheme for observing the southern stars, Halley had rushed away from Oxford, leaving the university before he had completed the appropriate terms of residence at his college and therefore under the regulations he was disqualified from a degree, however good his academic work might have been. To overcome this difficulty he needed a specially prepared royal order or mandamus. On his planisphere Halley regrouped certain of the southern stars from the constellation of Argo into a new constellation which he named *Robur Carolinum* in memory of the oak tree in which Charles II had hidden to avoid capture after the Battle of Worcester.

His efforts were rewarded, for after remaining in London for a while he went to Oxford, probably in the autumn, and on November 12 the provost of Queen's College wrote to Sir Joseph Williamson, who had been so influential in proposing the St. Helena expedition to the King, about granting a degree to Halley. It appears from the letter that Williamson had already asked for this to be done, but the provost replied that he had spoken to the Vice-Chancellor who was ready to comply with Williamson's desires, but expected to find opposition and, therefore, asked that a royal mandate be obtained. The provost then went on to suggest that nothing short of a degree

of Master of Arts would be appropriate. It is clear that on receipt
of this letter Williamson immediately informed the King, for on
November 18 Charles II wrote to the Vice-Chancellor, "Having. received a good account of the proficiency and learning of Edmond
Halley of Queen's College and especially as to the mathematics and
astronomy, whereof he has given good testimony by his observations
during his abode in the island of St Helena, recommending for the
degree of M.A. without any condition of performing any previous
or subsequent exercises for the same." The provost had told Williamson that the Vice-Chancellor feared that not only lack of residence but also the fact that Halley had not sat for the prescribed
examinations would militate against his being granted a degree, and
this point is clearly taken into account in the wording of the King's
letter.

On December 3 Edmond Halley, then twenty-two, received his
degree of Master of Arts. There is no doubt that he deserved it.
Yet he received still another honor—the Royal Society elected him
a Fellow. This election took place on November 30, which was St.
Andrew's Day and the anniversary day of the Society. Halley's pro-
poser was Sir Jonas Moore.

It was in 1678 that Halley began corresponding with scientists
abroad, an activity which he was to cultivate assiduously. His first
correspondent was Hevelius, and Halley wrote to him in November
telling him of his *Catalogue* and sending him a copy, as well as
discussing various astronomical matters. It may well have been at
Flamsteed's suggestion that Halley sent his *Catalogue* to Hevelius,
for Flamsteed thought very highly of Halley's work and even called
him "The Southern Tycho." Hevelius was delighted with the gift
and was also greatly impressed by the younger man's work.

The foundations of Halley's reputation were now laid, and the
next year they were to be consolidated when he visited Hevelius
as a representative of the Royal Society.

CHAPTER 4

The Visit to Hevelius

In the 1670s Hevelius* was the doyen of observational astronomers. He had been born early in 1611 at the important port of Danzig on the mouth of the Vistula. His father, like Halley's, was a rich merchant, with a flourishing brewery and a considerable amount of land, and his education was appropriate to his father's position. He attended the high school and also had a private tutor, Peter Krüger, who was an able mathematician and had a great enthusiasm for astronomy which he communicated to his pupil. It was Krüger who taught Hevelius the elements of planetary motions and the computation of the dates and times of solar and lunar eclipses, and persuaded him to study not only drawing and painting but also the engraving of copper plates for book illustration and the construction of astronomical instruments: a very varied but, to Hevelius, an extremely useful miscellany.

When he was nineteen Hevelius moved to Leyden, where he studied law at the university. He did not neglect science, and still spent some of his time on optics, mechanics, and applied mathematics. His stay in Leyden lasted only a year before he moved on to London where he learned English, though evidently not very well since he never corresponded in it and in later years complained to Henry Oldenburg because not all papers in *Philosophical Transactions* were in Latin. In 1632, after a year in London, he moved to France. He visited both Paris and Avignon, and seems to have wanted to go on to Italy to meet Galileo but his parents wanted their only surviving son to return home. So in 1634 he was back

---

* The family name was Höwelke and there were many variations in spelling, such as Hevel, Hovel, Höfelcke, etc.; Hevelius is the latinized version.

in Danzig where he applied himself to a study of the laws and statutory privileges of the city, one of those bonded together in the Hanseatic League.

Hevelius learned the trade of brewing, and in 1636 was admitted as a member of the Brewers' Guild. The previous year he had married the daughter of another rich city merchant, and it now seemed that he was settled in a business career and would have little time for astronomy. He kept in touch with Krüger, who did what he could to encourage his old pupil, however, and Hevelius's enthusiasm was reawakened by an eclipse of the sun in 1639 which was visible from Danzig. He decided to devote as much time as possible to astronomy, and set up an observatory and began to spend his leisure there. He was intimately involved with the building of his observatory for he made all his own instruments, constructing the frameworks, mounting these on stands of his own design, and engraving large and elaborate scales for them. He even taught himself the specialized art of grinding and polishing lenses and began to build telescopes which, because of the limited optical knowledge of the time, had to be constructed of inordinate length if they were to magnify at all powerfully. Hevelius's largest instrument was 150 feet long and seems to have caused a stir in Danzig when it was erected. But he never used telescopes on his measuring instruments and employed them only for observing planetary and lunar detail and spots on the sun. It was this practice that was to give rise to bitter controversy.

Hevelius's observatory became well known, not least because once it was established he began a regular correspondence with scientific men abroad. Although astronomy was supposedly only his leisure pursuit, his wife helped him by relieving him not only of all household affairs but also by dealing with much of the day-to-day business of the brewery. This happy arrangement lasted only two years, for in 1641 Hevelius was elected a magistrate and his astronomical work suffered as a result. In 1649 his father died and he became the sole owner of the brewery and his leisure was curtailed still further; when, two years later, he was admitted to the city council and often had to occupy the chair at city meetings, his astronomy had to be relegated to the background for a while. Yet such was his enthusiasm that these setbacks merely spurred him on to greater efforts; he increased the efficiency of his observatory and expanded it so that in a few years it became so large that it spread over the roofs of three adjoining houses. At this time Greenwich and Paris Observatories had not been built and for some years Hevelius possessed the greatest observatory in Europe, if not in the world. It became one of the sights to be seen, and was visited by the many delegates and officials who came to Danzig and by John III (Sobieski, 1629–96) of Poland.

In 1662 Hevelius's wife died, and this might have spelled the end of his astronomical career had he not married again. In 1663, although now over fifty, he married Catherina Elisabetha, an attractive girl of sixteen who, like his first wife, was the daughter of a Danzig merchant. Elisabetha was a serious young woman and she soon took in hand household matters, helped in the brewing business, and with boundless energy began to assist her husband in his astronomical work, taking her due share in all observing programs. In spite of the disparity in their ages, Hevelius and his young wife are said to have been very happy together, and when Elisabetha contracted smallpox Hevelius is supposed never to have left the sickbed but to have nursed her faithfully through a dangerous illness which he had never had. They had one son who died in infancy, and three daughters, all of whom grew up and married.

Hevelius's reputation increased to such a degree that the French statesman Colbert persuaded Louis XIV to grant Hevelius an annual pension—an act which may have had political undertones but was doubtless primarily designed to show how great a patron of learning and so how worthy a monarch Louis XIV was, for there is no reason to suppose that Hevelius was in any need of a pension. In 1665 he was elected a Fellow of the Royal Society, an honor which he seems to have appreciated warmly.

He printed, engraved, and published his observations himself, beginning with his *Selenographia* (1647), containing maps of the moon and detailed drawings of its surface features, following this with books on comets and, in 1673, with the first section of his famous *Machina Coelestis*. It was after the publication of this last work that the fact that he used open sights on all his measuring instruments began to be questioned, and a serious controversy arose.

The open sight was rather similar to a rifle sight, although more elaborate, and had been universally used before the invention of the telescope. It was the kind of sight adopted by Tycho Brahe and by Hevelius's tutor Krüger, and Hevelius had continued with it even though he knew that small sighting telescopes were used at Greenwich and Paris and by almost every other astronomer. Flamsteed and Halley both used small telescopes on the movable arms of their quadrants and similar instruments and these, in theory at least, gave to their observations greater accuracy than open sights could do. The reason is not hard to understand. When one observes through a telescope distant objects appear larger, and hence nearer, than they do with the unaided eye; things which are too close together to be discerned as separate by the eye alone can be resolved if a telescope is used. Clearly, then, if a carefully mounted telescope is used on the arm of a sextant, it will be possible to resolve the apparent positions of the stars with greater precision than with an open sight, however good one's vision.

It is obvious that the English astronomers realized this and Robert Hooke, never one to hide his opinions, was at pains to point out publicly the advantages of telescopic sights. He made it part of his second Cutler Lecture† in 1674. Hooke was not an easy man to deal with, for he tended to be bluntly outspoken, and there is no doubt that he annoyed Hevelius by absolutely denying the reliability of open sights, and strongly asserting the superiority of telescopic ones, but Hevelius himself was at least equally as difficult, refusing to make any detailed defense of his methods.

Flamsteed had also expressed his dislike of open sights, and his views, as well as those of Hooke, had reached Danzig. Some of Flamsteed's remarks had been published in *Philosophical Transactions* in July 1673 when he wrote, "We have heard that the celebrated Johannes Hevelius has indeed undertaken the restitution of the fixed stars, yet seeing that he is reputed to use sights without glasses, it is doubtful if we shall obtain from him much more correct

† The Cutler Lectures were a series of lectures endowed by Sir John Cutler, City merchant, four times Master Warden of the Grocers' Company, Fellow of the Royal Society, and benefactor of the Royal College of Physicians.

places than Tycho left us, except where he went very much astray."
Surprisingly enough Hevelius did not resent Flamsteed's comments,
but he was disturbed that yet a second English astronomer and
another Fellow of the Royal Society should support the arguments
put forward by Hooke. It was Hooke's uncomprising remarks that
really upset him.

For his own part Hevelius could not see that either Hooke or
Flamsteed was correct, and to some extent his obtuseness is un-
derstandable. Neither critic had done more than express the principle that a telescopic sight was of higher accuracy than an open
sight; no mathematical analysis nor any precise optical data had
been submitted in evidence. Moreover, Hevelius had by this time
been observing almost continuously for well over thirty years with
instruments of his own design on which the measuring arcs were
engraved with impeccable accuracy and were fitted with devices to
make use of them as precise as possible. Hevelius *knew* he was
doing good work and, in fact, had no doubt realized from his correspondence with Flamsteed that Flamsteed's results, made with
telescopic sights, confirmed his own. What is more, he was equally
well aware of the defects of the telescopes of his day and, whatever
might be their justification in theory, his experience led him to re-
ject them.

Why should he change? He could see no valid reason, and in a
letter to Flamsteed at the beginning of 1677 he wrote,‡ "Let each
allow the other to help on Astronomy at his own risk and by his
own methods, undoubtedly not adopted without good reasons. Let
one forebear to find fault too quickly with the other's work, and
still less to abuse it and make it distrusted. . . . For the rest, I admit
that one man may produce greater and more brilliant results than
another, and for that reason also will merit the greater praise. For
me it suffices if I be but counted among those who, with their utmost power, have willed to try for something, yet might not quite
have attained their ends in all particulars."

At the same time as he wrote this letter to Flamsteed, Hevelius
wrote to Oldenburg, providing some details of his observations.

‡ The original is in Latin. Here we give a free translation.

Clearly the Royal Society held the work of Hevelius in the highest esteem, for it minuted that "It was ordered that Mr Hevelius be desired, in the name of the Society, to finish his catalogue of the fixed stars, and that an intimation be given to him of the agreement of Mr Flamsteed's observations, of which he would, before long, see something in print: and farther, that what Mr Hooke had published against him, was done without any approbation or countenance from the Society." Oldenburg certainly wrote to Hevelius and, although there is no copy of the letter in existence, there is a copy of a later letter in which he tried to show clearly Flamsteed's opinion and make some attempt to pour oil on waters that, as far as the Royal Society was concerned, were becoming a little too troubled. Oldenburg pointed out that at the Paris observatory no open sights were used and that Flamsteed ". . . does hope that you will allow him to enjoy his own opinion." As we have remarked, it was Hooke to whom Hevelius took objection, and later in the letter Oldenburg says, ". . . I hope that you will not think there is much friendship and intimacy between Flamsteed and Hooke that the two are conspiring together to destroy the value of your observations." This was the situation when Edmond Halley entered the controversy.

Halley had returned to England flushed with his success at St. Helena. He was proud of his *Catalogue of the Southern Stars,* and on coming back to London we know that he saw Flamsteed at Greenwich, where he was shown the latest letter from Hevelius. When Halley sent a copy of his *Catalogue* to Hevelius, he enclosed a letter in which he carefully avoided mentioning the open sights versus telescopic sights argument. In referring to his own catalogue he says that he would not object to recalculating the positions of stars given in it by taking Hevelius's figures for star positions in the Northern Hemisphere and in so doing provide a link between the Northern and Southern Hemispheres on Hevelius's values rather than those of Tycho. Halley also invited Hevelius to make what use he liked of the catalogued information, and says how honored he would feel if Hevelius cared to append the information on the Southern Hemisphere to that of his own. This letter did not only contain polite remarks, astronomical information, and much respect for an older astronomer: It ends by informing Hevelius that Halley intends soon to make the journey to Danzig in order to make his acquaintance in person and attempt to understand, by observing with him, his instruments and methods of measuring star positions. In many ways it was a bold letter, and it ends with an apology for his youthful "presumption."

Superficially this letter gives a simple excuse for the proposed visit, but there is evidence that the reason it was sent was that the Royal Society wished to settle a dispute involving one of its most eminent Fellows. As mentioned, Oldenburg had already made attempts to reconcile Hevelius and Flamsteed, even if he had made no effort to do the same with Hevelius and Hooke, and Flamsteed was by then prevented from pursuing the open sight/telescopic sight controversy further. What was needed was for someone to work with Hevelius and examine how he had arrived at the results he had published. This would need not only tact but also considerable familiarity with observing and star cataloguing techniques. Hooke was a brilliant man but was not an eminent observer and, in any event, he would have been totally unacceptable to Hevelius. Flamsteed himself was engaged in making his own catalogue at Greenwich, but if he had decided to go he might conceivably have been refused leave of absence. As it was, he had only limited financial resources and probably could not have seriously contemplated a trip to Danzig.

Halley was an obvious choice: He had observing experience, much tact, and plenty of money. Moreover, he had by then graduated and was free to travel where he would for he had no personal responsibilities. It is also clear that Flamsteed had faith in him as an observational astronomer, not only because of his catalogue but also because he had seen the young man in action when in October 1678 he had invited Halley to Greenwich to observe an eclipse of the moon. Even if the Society did not directly commission Halley to undertake the journey on its behalf, it approved of the visit and sent a letter of introduction signed by Dr. William Croone (1633–84) and "written by command in the name of the Society."

Croone's letter was dated April 3, 1679, and six weeks later Halley was on his way to Danzig, arriving there on May 26. He was warmly welcomed by Hevelius, and after a brief discussion it was agreed that they should both set to work observing that very night. This they did, and during his stay Halley and Hevelius worked every night when the sky was clear enough to allow measurements to be made. Halley stayed for two months, but after he had been with Hevelius for only ten days he felt himself in a position to write to Flamsteed.

The letter is dated June 7, and after telling Flamsteed how interesting a place Danzig was and how visiting it had kept him busy throughout each day, Halley goes on to describe the instruments in the observatory. After telling about a quadrant used to measure the altitude of the sun, he gives details of the large six-foot sextant for determining star positions. The observations with this sextant required two observers, one at a fixed sight laid on one star and the other at the movable sight which was laid on a second star. The accuracy obviously surprised Halley, and he writes: "As to the exactness of the . . . distances§ measured by the Sextans, I assure you I was surpriz'd to see so near an agreement in them, and had I not seen, I could scarce have credited the Relation of any; Verily I have seen the same distance repeated severall times without any fallacy agree to 10″."¶

Halley describes how later he himself tried using the instruments, first at the movable sight, with Hevelius at the fixed one, after which they changed over. The results they obtained agreed to within five seconds. This was an incredible degree of accuracy, for Flamsteed himself, using telescopic sights, claimed an accuracy of only ten seconds, and it was a marked improvement on the precision attained by Brahe, who had observed with instruments of similar general design. It was partly due to using two observers simultaneously, since simultaneous observation would minimize the minute apparent shift caused by the earth's rotation during the time required for one observer to make two observations. Other contributing factors were the way in which Hevelius had graduated his instruments, and the devices he had designed to read the graduations themselves. Halley goes on to claim that the accuracy he and

§ These were not distances in the ordinary sense but the angular separation of one star from another.

¶ Ten seconds of arc or one-three hundred and sixtieth part of a degree.

Hevelius had obtained was nothing unusual for the observatory, saying, ". . . and you will find the same distance 6 times observed on Page 272 of ye fourth book of his Machina Coelestis, so that I dare no more doubt of his Veracitye." Halley also wrote to Sir Jonas Moore, who passed the letter on to Hooke so that it could be read at a meeting of the Royal Society.

Hevelius for his part was overjoyed to have Halley as his guest, and wrote back to Croone saying that he himself had thought of sending someone to observe the southern stars but was delighted that the Royal Society had been of the same opinion and had sent out an observer who had "quite fulfilled their desires and expectations." Halley had gone to St. Helena without any commission from the Royal Society, but no matter, Hevelius was obviously pleased with the young man. Halley showed him some of his own instruments with telescopic sights, and observations were made with this equipment, but the accuracy obtained was in no way superior to that gained with Hevelius's open sights. This is not surprising, for portable instruments are not likely to have the capabilities of a large fixed instrument. However, comparing observations in this way did nothing but confirm Hevelius in his opinion that with their criticisms Hooke and Flamsteed were doing no more than beating the air. He was correct for just that time and place, but wrong in principle. The telescopic sight is certainly capable of finer resolution and hence greater accuracy of position than the unaided eye, and results obtained some years later were to prove this beyond all doubt.

Before Halley left early in July, Hevelius persuaded him to write a testimonial about the instruments and the accuracy obtained at Danzig. In this Halley is generous in his praise and enthusiastic about Hevelius's work. He acknowledges the kindness and consideration of his host, his frankness over all scientific matters, and says that he is pleased to have the opportunity to bear witness to the accuracy of the observations made at Danzig. "I offer myself," Halley wrote, "voluntarily as a witness of the scarcely credible certainty of your instruments, against anyone who shall hereafter call the truth of your observations into question; since I have seen with my own eyes not one or two, but several observations of the fixed stars made with your large brass sextant by different observers, and

some of them by myself, which even when repeated did most accurately and almost incredibly agree, and never differed but in a
trifling part of a minute." It is a charming letter and written by one
who, quite clearly, had found in Hevelius a kindred spirit, an
astronomer who was honest and utterly devoted to his subject.
Hevelius later referred to Halley as "a very pleasant guest, a most
honest and sincere lover of the truth," and printed Halley's testimonial and their joint observations in his book *Annus Climactericus,*
published in 1685, a copy of which he presented to the Royal Society. This book, Hevelius's last published work and really a sequel
to his *Machina Coelestis,* did not appear until six years after Halley's visit and shows the esteem in which Halley's testimonial was
held by the older astronomer.

It appears that Flamsteed felt Halley had been too generous
in his praise of Hevelius's work, for when *Annus Climactericus* came
out, an account of it was given to the Royal Society by John Wallis,
and Flamsteed objected to this and to Halley's testimonial. In his
own defense Wallis wrote to Flamsteed and commented thus on
Halley's remarks: "As to Mr Halley, if you think (as you seem to
intimate) that he hath been too lavish in his commendations, you
must needs think that Mr Hook hath been so in his reprehensions."
The controversy which Halley had hoped to resolve still raged, and
while Hevelius had the young man and his own observations on his
side, he still had to contend with the firm opposition of most other
astronomers.

After Halley left Danzig, matters were made worse by a terrible tragedy which befell Hevelius and his observatory. Two
months after Halley's departure Hevelius's observatory was burned
to the ground, his instruments, many of his observations, and printed
books perishing with it. The disaster was reported to the Royal
Society by Thomas Henshaw one of the founder Fellows, who read
a pamphlet which had been prepared for Hevelius by one of his
friends, M. Capellus, and was dedicated to "the High-born and Most
Excellent Gentleman PETER WYCHE Knight" who was a Privy
Counsellor of Charles II and his resident minister for the Hanseatic
cities. The reason for this dedication to Wyche would seem to be
that Hevelius hoped Charles II, who was Patron of the Royal Society

and had established Greenwich observatory, might provide funds to assist him in rebuilding and obtaining new equipment.

It appears that Hevelius and his wife had gone on vacation soon after Halley's visit and, on arriving at their destination, Hevelius sent his coachman back to Danzig. The coachman unharnessed and stabled the horses and is reputed then to have gone to bed but to have left a candle burning in the stables. Certainly it was this candle that gave rise to the fire, but whether it was purely an act of carelessness or whether a direct act of arson is not clear. Hevelius himself was sure that the coachman, whom he referred to as "the most perverse animal on two legs," was responsible, and in confirmation of his view stated that if the fire had started by accident, only half an hour after the coachman was supposed to have prepared for bed, then four horses "of choice breed and great value" would have been saved.

Whether or not the coachman was really malicious, the damage was tremendous. All the books in the printing press waiting for binding were destroyed, the books already in Hevelius's library were rescued by being thrown out of the windows of the blazing house—although some were purloined by passers-by in the general confusion—and every single observatory instrument was completely destroyed, together with the equipment for making them. To add to the loss, gold, silver, and other valuables were stolen by some of those ostensibly helping to put out the fire, and in a few hours the great observatory, the pride of Danzig, became just a twisted shambles of wreckage and a pile of ashes. Hevelius was heartbroken, but it says something for his enterprise and courage that even though he was sixty-eight he immediately set about building another observatory.

The tragedy was not only a severe loss to Hevelius and the astronomical world; it meant also that the "scarcely credible" accuracy of which the observing instruments were capable could no longer be independently confirmed by another astronomer. It is no wonder, then, that Hevelius hung on tenaciously to Halley's testimonial and printed it, his one vindication, in the *Annus Climactericus*. But Flamsteed and others were unconvinced about the accuracy he could obtain and were certain that telescopic sights were better; they felt the testimonial to be too effusive, and Hevelius grew more and more bitter. When the *Annus Climactericus* arrived in England in 1685 it was found that Hevelius had made a number of mistakes in the published account, for he claimed not only that Halley had been officially sent to St. Helena, whereas he had gone on his own initiative, but referred to Halley's quadrant as a sextant and expressed himself ambiguously about its size. Suspicions were once again aroused and this time Hevelius let his bitterness get the better of him, even going so far as to claim that Halley was sent to Danzig in order only to examine his instruments and had been sent to St. Helena at his (Hevelius's) request. This made Halley angry in his turn, for he had given considerable support to the older man and there had been a friendly correspondence between them in the weeks between Halley's visit until the fire.

Halley's attitude can be seen from two letters he wrote to William Molyneux (1656–98) in 1686, in the first of which, dated March 27, he says, "The Controversy between Mr Hevelius and Mr Hook, as you very well observe does, as Hevelius manages the matter, affect all those observers that use Telescope sights, and myself in particular, and it is our common concern to vindicate the truth from the aspersions of an old peevish gentleman, who would not have it believed that it is possible to do better than he has done, and for my own part I find myself obliged to vindicate my observations made at St. Helena and to rectifie some mistakes, whether willfull or no I cannot say; first he said I was sent by R.S. to St. Helena at his request to observe the Southern Stars (page 14),* whereas it is very well known to all our Astronomers that at my own motion and charge I undertook that voiage above two years, before I had the honour of being a member of the R.S. all which I have declared in the preface to my Catalogue. Again he sais pag. 18 of the preface that I was sent with a sextans fitted with Telescopic sights for no other purpose but rigidly to examine his instruments: Wherein he does me treble injurie . . ." In his second letter about the matter Halley still seems annoyed, no doubt due to remarks made to him at meetings of the Royal Society, for on May 27 he wrote to Moly-

* The references here are to Hevelius's preface in the *Annus Climactericus.*

neux, saying, "As to Mr Hevelius we heare as yet no farther from him, and I am very unwilling to let my indignation loose upon him, but will unless I see some publick notice taken elsewhere, let it sleep till after his death if I chance to outlive him, for I would not hasten his departure by exposing him and his observations as I could do and truly as I think he deserves I should."

It is most unfortunate that the friendship between Hevelius and Halley should have ended in this way. That he was made welcome in Danzig is clear, but a word must be said of the happy relationships which ensued and only became strained when the *Annus Climactericus* with its incorrect preface appeared. Halley's letters to Hevelius written in 1679, 1681, and 1682 are amicable, dealing with astronomical matters of interest to both of them, and in the letter of 1681 Halley respectfully sends his regards to Hevelius's wife; he was even asked to procure a dress in London for her. Perhaps the true feeling in their relationship is best seen in Halley's letter of October 1679 to John Olaff, secretary to the city council of Danzig, when he had heard a rumor that Hevelius was dead. The letter begins, "Words fail me to express the feelings of sorrow which overcame me when the news reached us that Mr. Hevelius had been snatched from us by a death so sudden and so short a time after my departure." Probably the rumor of Hevelius's death had been caused by the destruction of his observatory, and it may well be that many believed the old man had perished in the blaze. Halley, ever hopeful, writes, "We cherish ardent hopes that Mr Hevelius may still survive and that rumour has shown herself false in this particular, though it is but rarely that she deceives us in unhappy things. I quite realise that his heartbroken spouse must be wearing sad-coloured apparel, yet for several reasons I have thought well to send the gown procured for her, first because I am not yet certain that her husband is dead, in which case I judge nothing would be more unwelcome than delay; then I cannot sell it to a dealer without the loss of several Rixdollars,† and I have no doubt it could be sold on your side, if you so desired, at some profit, since it is of silk and of the newest fashion, and I am confident it will highly please

† One Rixdollar was equal to a little more than 4/6d or 54 cents.

Mme. Hevelius, if only it should be granted to her to wear it, and anyhow she will be able to preserve it until her period of mourning is past . . ."

With Hevelius's death the open versus telescopic sights controversy ended. It was an unhappy business and a very serious one at the time, but throughout Halley showed loyalty and moderation. It was he who saw to the matter of new telescope lenses and other astronomical equipment for Hevelius after the fire, even though there is evidence that he had no high opinion of Hevelius's telescopes. Zacharias van Uffenbach (1683–1734) claimed that the Oxford mathematician John Caswell told him that Halley found it impossible to observe with the largest instrument, and had complained that the tubes of the smaller ones bent so much that the lenses would not keep properly in line. This thirdhand account may be exaggerated, for Hevelius used these instruments to make some elegant planetary drawings and completed a fine map of the moon, but it seems clear that he must have done such work under the most difficult circumstances, and perhaps this is what Halley meant in his letter to Molyneux of May 27, 1686, when he says he could expose Hevelius. If after the publication of the *Annus Climactericus* Halley had wanted to take a different attitude to the one he adopted he would certainly have had a number of influential Fellows of the Royal Society behind him. One can only be grateful that he exercised restraint.

CHAPTER 5

The Grand Tour, Marriage, and Domestic Crises

When Halley returned from his apparently successful visit to He-velius he spent a little time with his father in London. He did not remain at home for long, however, and he moved back to Oxford either at the end of October or the beginning of November, as we know from a letter he wrote in reply to John Aubrey, who had tried to interest Halley in astrology.

Throughout his life Halley took a more straightforward ap-proach to astronomy and showed no apparent interest in astrology, but in deference to Aubrey he does not dismiss it out of hand: "As to the advice you give me, to study Astrology, I profess it seems a very ill time for it, when the Arch-Conjurer Gadbury is in some prospect in being hanged for it, however I went to the Library [the university library] and lookt out the booke [Leovitius's *De Coniunctionibus*] you recommended to me which I find to be pub-lished in anno 1557, so that I doubt not but the more moderne Astrologers having more experience of things may have added to him considerably, however upon your recommendation I will read it over." At this time astrology was falling into disrepute, but oddly enough, among the Aubrey manuscripts in the Bodleian Library at Oxford is a horoscope for Halley cast by an unidentified astrologer, and entitled, "Mr Edmund Halley borne Octob. 29. 1656 Lat Lon-don." Kepler, it is true, had cast horoscopes, his most famous being for the soldier-statesman Wallenstein (1583–1634), but there is evi-dence that he himself had little if any faith in their validity, although they were an obligatory part of his duties as a court mathematician.

Halley remained in England for fifteen months, apparently dividing his time between Oxford and Winchester Street. When in London he probably attended meetings of the Royal Society, for on some evenings he certainly went with Hooke and others to Jonathan's, a coffeehouse in Change Alley, mainly frequented by financiers, but also a rendezvous for a number of the Fellows. He had discussions with Walter Pope, professor of astronomy at Gresham College, and at Jonathan's many private questions of mutual interest were argued. Thus on May 16, 1680, Robert Hooke recorded, "At Jonathans. Spake to Halley for Dr. Pope. He told me Flamsteed endeavoured to supplant Dr. Pope and to get an interest for himself." This is an interesting sidelight and is an indication that Flamsteed was striving to find either another post or an additional income besides that of Astronomer Royal, for from his salary he had to provide nearly all his own observing instruments as well as pay an assistant. An income of one hundred pounds ($240) per annum may not have been unsatisfactory in itself, but it was not up to the standard of the circle in which Flamsteed moved.

On July 29 Halley was formally admitted to the Fellowship of the Royal Society, and in September Hooke recommended that the young man be appointed one of the examiners of mathematics for pupils of Christ's Hospital. Christ's Hospital is a school which was founded in 1552 by Edward VI, and at this time Hooke was one of the school's governors, as also were Flamsteed, Wren and, later, Newton, Locke, and Pepys. Sir Jonas Moore also had connections with the school and was in the process of preparing his *New Systeme of the Mathematicks* "designed for the Use of the Royal Foundation of the *Mathematical* School in Christ Hospital," but he died before its completion, and at Flamsteed's invitation Halley collaborated with him in finishing the book which was published in London in 1681. Whether Halley accepted the post of examiner is not known, but if he did it could only have been for a short period, since at the beginning of December 1681 he went abroad again.

This new trip was a completion of his education as a gentleman, for he undertook what was known as the Grand Tour, which was in essence a continental journey through France and Italy. Halley's journey was wider than usual and less concerned with the arts, for as Martin Folkes put it, ". . . having a mind to make the Tour of France and Italy, and to converse with the astronomers and other Learned Men of those parts, he set out for Paris." He was accompanied by Robert Nelson (1656–1715), the son of another City businessman, a Turkey merchant,* who, it appears, also lived on Winchester Street. Nelson was a religiously minded young man, "eminently distinguished for his piety," a Fellow of the Royal Society, and was later to write some devotional works. He was the same age as Halley, and the two men remained lifelong friends.

At the time they left, Halley was intrigued by a bright comet, visible with the naked eye, which he had observed from London in November and which was the talk of the town. Bright comets were and are astronomical rarities: They appear quite suddenly and disappear equally precipitously. We now know that this is because they remain invisible, even in a large telescope, until they are comparatively close to the sun; but in 1680 they were still much of a mystery. Their paths were unknown (although many conjectures were prevalent), and their physical nature was a subject for speculation. The appearance of one bright enough to be seen with the unaided eye was a challenge to astronomers and one which was bound to stimulate Halley.

For a short time the comet was unobservable due to the glare of the sun, but Robert Nelson and Halley saw the comet again while on their way to Paris, after a rough and protracted crossing of the English Channel from Dover to Calais. This was not enough for Halley, and when they arrived in Paris he lost no time in contacting Cassini, the director of the observatory. Born near Nice in 1625, Cassini had studied at the University of Bologna and had been called to Paris in 1669 by Colbert. He gathered around him a number of brilliant astronomers such as Jean Picard (1620–82) and Olaus Römer (1644–1710) and ruled the observatory until his death

---

* Turkey merchants were normally members of the Levant Company, which had been founded in 1605 to trade with the Turks. It established a large warehouse in Aleppo and imported to Britain commodities that had come on the overland route through Persia from India, China, and other Far Eastern countries. It acted also as an export agency for British lead, tin, and cloth, and although the life of the merchants in Aleppo was rigorous, fortunes were amassed in a short time by those who survived.

in 1712, when he was succeeded as director by his son who, in turn, was followed by his son, who completed a century of family directorship. Cassini had been one of Oldenburg's many continental correspondents, and after the latter's death he continued to keep in close touch with various Fellows of the Royal Society. He knew Halley by reputation and from his *Catalogue des Estoilles Australes,* and he made the young men welcome at the observatory.

Halley was naturally interested in the Paris observatory but found the instruments there inferior to Flamsteed's at Greenwich. All the same he carried out observations of the comet, and generally enjoyed his visit. It appears too, that while in Paris he, like John Locke (1632–1704), who returned from France two years earlier, met Henri Justel (1620–93), secretary to Louis XIV, who shortly after emigrated to England to escape religious restriction and became librarian to Charles II.

From Paris Halley moved on to Saumeur (Saumur) on the bank of the Loire, and from letters he wrote to Hooke it is clear that he was there by May. The two letters to Hooke are interesting. In the first, dated January 15, 1681 and written from Paris, after mentioning the rough crossing of the Channel, he thanks Hooke for letters of introduction to Justel, "with whom," Halley wrote, "is the rendezvous of all curious and philosophical matters." He goes on to say that "the general talk of the virtuosi here is about the Comet," and then promises Hooke details of any observations which he could supply† although, as he points out, cloudy weather did not augur well for observing. He asks Hooke for English observations and then goes on to tell of his attempts to obtain books published in France for Sir John Hoskins (1634–1705) and some for Hooke himself. Books of a specialized kind were often difficult to acquire, and Halley promises that if all else fails he will look at the volumes in the library of the Académie des Sciences so that he can make notes about the scientific results they contained. The letter ends with a note that the French are to send an astronomer, a Mr. Varon, "to the Isle of Ferro to make observation of the Satellites [of Jupiter] to determine the Longitude of Paris from the said Isle which by an

† Hooke had already published information on the bright comet of 1677 in his *Lectures and Collections,* London, 1678.

edict of Lewis [Louis] 13 is under the first Meridian." The point
would be of interest to Hooke who, like so many on both sides of
the Channel, was contemplating the ever-present problem of the
determination of longitude and who would doubtless discuss with
Flamsteed and others the question of finding longitude by observing
Jupiter's satellites.

Halley's second letter was dated May 29. It began with details
about books, and Halley tells Hooke that Cassini "let me have the
peruseing of all the books published by theire Royall Academy,
and tells me that they are designed to be printed in a smaller volume and that then he will obtain a Sett of them for the Society . . ."
Some of the books were to have been obtained for Hooke and the
Royal Society by Henry Savile, England's envoy in Paris, who appears to have forgotten all about his commission, so Halley kept
his earlier promise and gives a brief description of each of them.
Then follows a long account of observational results on the comet
and, in view of what Halley was later to achieve in cometary astronomy, it is worth quoting at least the gist of his remarks. "Mon-
sieur Cassini did me the favour to give me his books of yet Comett
Just as I was goeing out of towne; he, besides the Observations
thereof, wch. he made till the 18 of March new stile, has given a
theory of its Motion wch. is, that this Comet was the same with that
appeared to Tycho Anno 1577, that it performes its revolution in a
great Circle including the earth wch. he will have to be fixt in about
2 yeares and halfe . . ."

Astronomical details of the comet follow, and then Halley goes
on to comment that although Hooke may find it difficult to accept
Cassini's hypothesis that the three appearances were of one and the
same comet returning to visibility, it is a remarkable idea all the
same. Halley tried to represent the three paths by constant movement in a straight line—the then accepted idea of cometary motion
—but found this would not do, and that the actual motion was neither really straight nor constant in velocity. Nevertheless he kept
an open mind on this controversial question, and there is little doubt
that Cassini's idea exerted some influence on him when he later
attacked the whole question of cometary motion in detail.

Halley had obtained a French map of the moon for Flamsteed

and himself, but he was not very impressed with it even though it
was drawn to a large scale, for he found the shadows of various
lunar features ". . . not neer soe well done as those of Mr. Hevelius." Halley's broad interests are apparent in the closing pages of
the letter where he compares the populations of London and Paris
in a way which he was later to enlarge upon. His own words illustrate the comparisons he drew: "If you would Compare London
an Paris together as to the Bulke and people I thinke I can give you
and indifferent account of Paris I tooke the pains to pace it verey
carefully and found it from the Observatory to ye end of the Faw-
bury St. Martin north and south it is 3 Englished measured miles
and from port St. Honoré to Port St. Antoine East and west the
greatest length is 2½ miles, soe that I suppose you would Conclude
with me it is not soe great a Continuum of houses as London, but by
reason of theire liveing many in a house it seemeth more populous,
and theire bills of burialls and Christning Confirms it, for the last
yeare 1680 were buried 24411 whereas at London 20000 is reckoned
a high bill, and the Christnings farr exceed ours, haveing been almost 19000, when we have ordinarily 12 or 13000, here they Likewise take an account of the weddings which were 4470 last yeare
or a quarter part of the Christnings very neare now in these weddings halfe as many were married as were borne; and not more;
it will from hence follow, supposing it alwaies the same, that one
halfe of mankinde dies unmarried, and that it is necessary for each
married Couple to have 4 Children one with another to keep mankind at stand. this Notion Occurred whilest I was writeing, . . ." If
ever there was raw material for working out life assurance, this is it,
and the idea did not escape Halley; ten years later he was to publish
a scientific paper on the subject.

At the end of June or the beginning of July, Halley and Nelson
left Saumeur and went on to Rome by way of La Rochelle, Bor-
deaux, and Toulouse, and thence to Narbonne, Montpellier, Avignon, and Lyons. Halley spent the remainder of 1681 in Italy, and
while there obtained from an unknown source some astronomical
observations made in India. These were of use in longitude determinations, and Halley sent a paper on them to Hooke, who published
them in his *Philosophical Collections*, which appeared between 1679
and 1682 as a stopgap for the *Philosophical Transactions* that had

ceased on Oldenburg's death. Hooke gave them the title, "Observations made at Ballasore, in India, serving to find the Longitude of the place, and rectifying very great errors in some modern geographers."

Halley and Nelson did not stay in Rome the whole time but toured the country, visiting the principal cities and other sights which tourists might be expected to find interesting. How long Halley intended to remain we do not know, for he busied himself comparing the Greek and Roman measure of a foot at the Campidoglio, and would doubtless have found other things to do had he not suddenly been called home to England because of family affairs. He left Italy sometime after November 15 but did not return directly, going to Genoa and back to Paris, where he stayed for a short while, ". . . being received with the greatest respect by the most eminent personages there . . ."

Halley's visits to Paris must have made a deep impression, for as late as 1856—175 years after—the famous French astronomer François Arago (1786–1853), who succeeded the third Cassini as director of the Paris Observatory, wrote that Halley left behind him the memory of ". . . a charming man of rare intelligence." From Paris Halley did not travel straight to Calais, but instead went on to Holland and from there back to England. Nelson remained in Rome where he fell in love with the young widow of Sir Kingsmill Lucy, the second daughter of the Earl of Berkeley, whom he married some months later.

The nature of the family affairs which called Halley back to England are now impossible to determine. Eugene MacPike, an indefatigable collector of information about Halley, suggests that this may have been due to a deterioration in his father's monetary affairs. On the other hand, we know that the elder Halley made a disastrous second marriage to a woman who appears to have had little affection for him or his son and who seems to have known only too well how to spend her husband's money. The date of the second marriage is not known, but in view of the happy relationship between Halley and his father the marriage celebrations could possibly have been the reason for the return to England. Perhaps Halley did not return directly from Italy because his father had given

him a date by which he would like him to be home for the wedding
and, finding he had time to spare, Halley decided to use it to the
full. He was back in London on January 24, 1682, for on that day
Robert Hooke recorded his return, as also did John Aubrey, who
added, "He hath contracted an acquaintance and friendship with
all the eminest mathematicians in France and Italie."

Within three months of his homecoming Halley himself was
married. His bride was Mary Tooke, daughter of the auditor of
the Exchequer, "a young lady equally amiable for the gracefullness
of her person and the beauties of her mind . . ." They were married
at St. James' Church, Duke's Place, just outside Aldgate and not very
far from Winchester Street, on April 20, 1682. The choice of St.
James' Church may have had a special significance. It was then a
noted place for runaway marriages—only four years later the rector
was suspended from duty and from his living for three years for
"suffering persons to be married at his church without banns or li-
cence." Why the young couple married in such a way so very soon
after Halley's return to England is not known. He may have known
Mary Tooke before he went on the Grand Tour, but there is certainly no evidence that there was any reason for a hurried marriage,
for their first children do not seem to have been born until some
years later. Perhaps one family or the other disapproved of the
match, although it seems unlikely that this could have been the case
with the elder Halley for there is no evidence that he discontinued
his son's allowance.

The young couple set up house in the outlying village of Islington, and once married and settled down Halley began to take an
increasing interest in the affairs of the Royal Society, for as Folkes
later wrote, ". . . neither the domestic cares, nor the joys of a happy
marriage, could diminish his ardour for astronomy and science . . ."
In July, three months after his marriage, he reported on observations
made during February of a lunar eclipse so that his results could be
compared with those of Flamsteed and Cassini, and it seems quite
clear that he began his measurements of the moon's position very
soon after his return to England. In Islington he set up his telescope
and sextant "the attendance on these being his darling employment," and he began a special lunar observation program aimed at

studying the moon through a complete eighteen-year cycle in order
to provide material for the determination of longitude. He began
on November 7, 1682, doubtless using the clear skies of the severe
winter when during the great frost of December 1683 oak trees were
split, hollies killed, and the Thames covered with eleven inches of
ice. All this time, and until after his father's death in 1684, Halley
had no regular employment, so it would seem that either his wife
brought him a dowry or that he was still receiving an allowance
from his father.

The year 1683 saw the publication of two of Halley's scientific
papers. The first of these resulted from observations he made concerning the planet Saturn and especially on the motion of one of
its satellites, Rhea. He found that the motion of this satellite was
not properly accounted for and so set about making corrections,
submitting his results to the Royal Society; in due course they were
published in *Philosophical Transactions.* It was a paper which
showed evidence of careful and painstaking work, and although it
contributed useful information to astronomy, it was of no long-term
value since later observations were to provide still more improved
results. His second paper, also published in *Philosophical Transactions,* was of a different caliber, and was called simply, "A Theory
of the Variation of the magnetical Compass"; it was concerned primarily with the problem of longitude.

The use of the magnetic compass on ships was regular practice,
but the theory behind it was not understood. Although Gilbert in
his *De Magnete,* published in London in 1600, had put forward the
idea that the earth itself acted like an immense magnet, and although Descartes had developed the theme, very little further theoretical work had been done, and there was a need for some new
hypothesis. A number of natural philosophers had made observations of the variations‡ which a magnetic needle displayed in different places. Sir Robert Moray (1608?–73) and Hooke had drawn
attention to the importance of such observations, while Henry Bond
(fl. 1670) in London, Adrian Azout in France, and Hevelius in
Danzig, had also investigated variation. Halley had noted the be-

‡ The term "variation" was used by Halley and others, and is still used by
mariners. "Declination" is the usual technical term.

havior of the ship's compass while on his journey to and from St. Helena, and was also aware of proposals put forward in 1676 by Henry Bond, who had the idea that the magnetic poles of the earth lay some distance from the geographical North and South Poles and which, he thought, rotated about the geographical poles.

Halley turned all this over in his mind, so that before he produced his first paper on the subject he had carefully acquainted himself with what had been done earlier. Using the various observations available, and settling down to consider the whys and wherefores, Halley propounded in this paper the revolutionary idea that the earth had not two but four magnetic poles, and added the proviso that the behavior of the magnetic needle is governed by whichever pole happens, from time to time, to lie nearest to it. It was a bold attempt to provide a new outlook on an old and apparently intractable problem, caused considerable interest among scientists not only in England but also on the Continent, and enhanced Halley's reputation still further. The paper is also interesting in showing that Halley had a mind which could not only analyze the results of previous work, but could branch out and give a completely new look to a well-known problem, an attitude that becomes more obvious as his later work on this and other problems is traced.

It was at this stage that domestic affairs interfered with his work, and particularly with his program of lunar observations. On the morning of Wednesday, March 5, 1684, Edmond Halley, Sr. went out, telling his wife that he would be back in the evening. Before leaving the house he had complained that his shoes pinched him and made his feet tender. One of his nephews who was at Winchester Street at the time suggested removing the lining, and it was after this had been done that Mr. Halley left, never to be seen alive again. Exactly what happened has not been fully settled, but in a broadside known as the *Gazet*, in an issue published around April 17, there is to be found "A true Discovery of Mr. Edmund Halley of London Merchant Who was found Barborously Murthered at Temple-Farm, near Rochester in Kent." Since Edmond Halley, Sr. was a well-known City merchant, his death under strange circumstances must have caused a stir. His wife, concerned when her husband did not return in the evening as promised, "the next day made all possible Enquiry," and some days later published a note about his disappearance, offering a reward of one hundred pounds ($240) to anyone who would find him either dead or alive.

It was not until five days after he had left home that his body was found by the riverside at Temple Farm and the matter reported in the *Gazet:* "A poor Boy walking by the Water-side upon some Occasion spied the Body of a Man dead and Stript, with only his Shoes and Stockings on, upon which he presently made a discovery of it to some others, which coming to the knowledge of a Gentleman, who had read the Advertisement in the Gazet, he immediately came up to London, and acquainted Mrs Halley with it, withal, telling her, that what he had done, was not for the sake of the Reward, but upon Principles more Honourable and Christian, for as to the mony he desired to make no advantage of it, but that it might be given entirely to the poor Boy; who found him and justly deserved it."

The dead man's nephew went to identify the corpse, which he recognized only by the stockings and the shoes, out of which he had cut the linings. Apparently the face was unrecognizable, one of the eyes disfigured as well as several parts of the body, although the details were never stated. The body had been in the river for some time before it was discovered, but "It was concluded . . . that he had not been in the River ever since he was missing, for if he had, his Body would have been more Corrupted." At the inquest the verdict was one of murder, but no culprit or suspect could be named. The jury's verdict has been questioned by MacPike, because when discovered the body was found to have four stockings on one leg and three, together with a "Sear-cloth," on the other, and also, perhaps, since the *Gazet* hints that the reason for the walk may have been due to "private Discontent." MacPike suggests a truer verdict would be "suicide while of unsound mind," but against this we must set the facts that the body had clearly been thrown into the river long after the elder Halley's departure from home, and also stripped of all its clothes. Any argument on the subject must necessarily be inconclusive.

There is an interesting postscript to the death. The "Gentleman," a Mr. Adams, who informed Mrs. Halley of her husband's

death, was not moved only by "Honourable and Christian" principles, for he later sued the widow for the one-hundred-pound reward.
The case was heard by the notorious Judge Jeffreys, who ordered
that Mr. Adams should receive only twenty pounds ($48) and that
the remaining eighty pounds ($192) should be paid in trust for John
Byers, the poor boy who had first discovered the body. The funeral
costs amounted to almost one hundred pounds ($240) in themselves
and this, together with the offer of the reward, suggests that the
elder Halley and his wife were not in financial straits as has sometimes been thought, although in the *Biographia Britannica* it is
claimed that the elder Halley's fortune had by this time been somewhat reduced.

The Adams case was not the only court appearance made by
the second Mrs. Halley, who married again and became a Mrs.
Chester or Cleator (the name, even in the court proceedings, is not
clear). Ten years later Edmond had to take legal action against his
stepmother to defend his patrimony, and this was no doubt primarily due to his father dying intestate. By 1694, however, Halley
was making great headway in his career, even though he had no
official appointments at that time. How much the death of his father
upset him is purely a matter of conjecture, but in view of the very
happy relations he had with him in his youth and his father's continued encouragement and financial support it must have been a
considerable blow, especially in view of the unpleasant circumstances which surrounded it.

CHAPTER 6

The Royal Society and the Principia

The ebbing and flowing of the tides has been familiar to mankind from earliest times. Yet the mechanism that causes them remained a mystery even as late as Halley's day. Galileo made an attempt to solve this problem, and by the middle of the seventeenth century it had been realized that the moon played an important part; yet no one knew exactly how it operated, even less why it should exert any influence. The way the new philosophers set out to seek a solution was to gather as much information as they could, and from this hope to discover some hypothesis that would fit the observed facts. On July 15, 1678, the Secretary of the Royal Society received a letter from a Mr. Francis Davenport at Tonkin in southeastern China, who gave details of the irregular tides there which had excited interest because of their unusual characteristics. Davenport's letter, together with some remarks by Halley, were published in *Philosophical Transactions.*

There was a sand bank in the bay at Tonkin and it is clear that, to begin with, Davenport thought that the irregularities were due to this and to the inlets of the bay itself. The important thing was that having once noticed the irregularities, he kept careful watch on them and found that inconsistencies existed within the irregularities themselves. The inconsistencies occurred at different seasons of the year and particularly during the monsoons. After thinking this over he suggested that perhaps the irregularities were due either to the motion of the moon or to the moon and the monsoons together. At the end of his letter he included a table of the dates, times, and

other details of the tides themselves. It is from this point that Halley
took up the challenge.

Beginning with the evidence that the tides at Tonkin differ
from what would normally be expected, Halley notes that there
seems to be a tidal "flux" every twelve hours but that there is only
one proper high tide every twenty-four hours. He points out that, in
addition, there are gaps even in this sequence, the gaps occurring
twice a month and at an interval of about fourteen days, with the
highest tides of all at seven-day intervals. This was a complex phenomenon that required careful analysis, but Halley was able to produce a theory to satisfy the facts. In analyzing the observations he
noted that the rising moon gave high tide during one half of the
month and the setting moon high tide during the other half of the
month. He then argued that it was the moon and not the monsoons
which affected the tides at Tonkin, and also that the form the tides
took was due to the apparent motion of the moon in the sky as
viewed from there.

Halley took matters further and proved by careful calculation
(although these calculations are not reproduced in *Philosophical
Transactions*) that the increase in the tides depended upon the position of the moon with respect to those points in the sky where the
sun's path and the celestial equator cross, and was able to express
this dependence by a precise mathematical formula. Admittedly
this paper, although given the title of a theory, was not in any way
a theory of why the moon had these effects, but it did establish the
moon's influence and was a useful contribution on which Newton
drew for his full theory of the tides, published as part of his great
Principia with which Halley was to become intimately connected.

At the beginning of 1684 Halley turned his attention to Kepler's
laws of planetary motion. In particular Halley wanted to know *why*
the time a planet takes to travel around the sun and the average
distance that it lies from the sun are in the mathematical power
ratio of 2:3. Supposing the sun attracted the planets with some
force—a supposition already made by others—then, he asked himself, what form of attraction would account for Kepler's 2:3 ratio.
After some calculation he arrived at the idea that this would occur
if the sun attracted each planet with a force that depended on the

inverse square of the distance between the sun and the planet—
that is, a force which fell off by four times if the distance were dou-
bled, nine times if the distance were trebled, and so on. Halley's
difficulty was that he could not discover how to prove this geometri-
cally, and a proof was obviously needed. He discussed the problem
with other Fellows of the Society, and especially with Hooke and
Sir Christopher Wren. He found that Hooke had reached the same
conclusion but, in addition, claimed that he had obtained a geometrical proof. He promised to show the proof to Halley and Wren,
who added the stimulant that if either Hooke or Halley could prove
the case, he would give them a book of their own choice up to a
value of two pounds (approximately $5.00). Time went by and no
proof was forthcoming, so Halley decided to pursue matters further
by visiting Isaac Newton at Trinity College, Cambridge.

Isaac Newton (1642–1727), who was fourteen years older than
Halley, had been born at Woolsthorpe, Lincolnshire, and it was his
family's hope that he would follow his deceased father as a farmer.
His talents lay in other directions, and the only solution seemed to
be to send him to a university. In 1661 Newton went to Cambridge,
where he had the good fortune to come under Isaac Barrow, the
first holder of the new chair of mathematics founded by Henry
Lucas. Even though Newton displayed no outstanding brilliance as
an undergraduate, Barrow seems to have recognized his latent ability, and this he encouraged. During 1665, when the university was
closed because of the spread of the plague from London, Newton,
experimenting at home at Woolsthorpe, laid the foundations for his
mathematical and scientific work on planetary motions, gravitation,
and light. On his return to Cambridge he was elected a Fellow of
his College, and in 1669 Barrow resigned his chair so that Newton,
although only twenty-seven, might be appointed to it.

Newton was a shy man and reticent about his work, so his abilities only gradually became known, and then usually by chance. By
1672 his experiments on light and optics had not only led him to
formulate a theory in which he proposed that white light was a
mixture of light of all colors, but also to design and build a telescope
that used a mirror in place of the front lens and thereby overcame
most of the defects of the customary long tube refracting telescopes

used in astronomy. The telescope aroused some interest in Cambridge and news of it came to the ears of the Royal Society, which asked Newton to build them a replica. The outcome was that Newton was elected to the Fellowship and invited to prepare a paper describing his work—something, he confessed, that he would never have done had he not been specifically pressed to do so. The paper was prepared, published in *Philosophical Transactions*, and a storm of controversy arose over his theory of light and colors, a storm which made the shy Newton determined to be even more reticent about his other ideas. Yet although he was strongly disinclined to publish and become embroiled in further arguments, his reputation was now established and something of his mathematical prowess was also known. So it was not unnatural that when Hooke and Halley failed to solve the problem of proof of an inverse square law, Halley should think of going to Newton.

In August 1684 Halley paid his first visit to Newton, a visit which was to have results so far-reaching that they can be said to have altered the whole course of physical science. The two men discussed the problem of planetary motion, and Newton was not only able to agree that an inverse square law was correct, but also to claim, as Hooke had done, that he had a mathematical proof. He then began to look through his papers for the details which, he said, he had thrown aside once they were complete. Yet hunt though he would, Newton could not find them, so he promised to work it all out again and send it to Halley as soon as possible. Newton was as good as his word, and shortly after Halley's visit the proof was brought to London by a Mr. Paget (1656–1703?), who was the mathematics master at Christ's Hospital and who had also been to Cambridge to see Newton. Halley was overjoyed at receiving the proof, the elegance of which much impressed him, and he realized that in this field Newton far outstripped his contemporaries. He decided to travel to Cambridge again and this time to talk to Newton even more fully. He found that Newton's proof of Kepler's 2:3 ratio was really only part of a much broader idea of Newton's. Yet Newton, revolutionary though his ideas were, had let matters rest; he had done nothing to bring them to the attention of the scientific world. Halley, while talking to him for the second time, fortunately appreciated their immense significance, and realized too that it was imperative that Newton no longer hide them among his miscellaneous papers—and perhaps lose them again. He persuaded Newton to weld together the different strands of his work in a great treatise which would bring Newton's name and the name of British science before the world at large.

To solve some of his problems, Newton had developed a new type of mathematics—the use of what he called fluents and fluxions or, as we now say, the differential and the integral calculus. At this time it was so specialized a concept (although other work was proceeding along similar lines on the Continent) that if the method had been used to make known his discoveries, the proposed book would have been inaccessible even to the majority of scientific readers, and Newton's proofs would not have been considered by most of his contemporaries as proved at all. Geometrical proof of the type sought by Hooke and especially by Halley was the kind expected by mathematicians, and it was geometrical proofs that Newton agreed to provide.

It was during Halley's second visit to Cambridge that the idea of a book setting out all Newton's new principles was born, but in addition to this Halley extracted a promise from Newton not only that the book would be written but that it would be written as soon as possible. It was an immense task, and it occupied Newton exclusively for almost eighteen months.

At a meeting of the Royal Society on December 10, 1684, Halley reported on his second visit to Newton and informed the meeting that Newton had promised to publish his results and, in order to guard the priority of his discoveries, that he would be sending his mathematical proofs in to the Society for their receipt to be registered. This was duly noted in the Society's records, where it is also minuted that Halley and Paget were to keep Newton in mind of his promise.

At this meeting Halley mentioned that Newton had already prepared a summary of his ideas in the form of a tract, *De Motu Corporum*. It is now uncertain whether this is what Paget brought to Halley; whatever the document was, Paget and Halley saw it was duly registered by the Society. It consisted of five problems and four theorems concerned with the nature of planetary orbits where the planet moves freely under a central force (the sun), and two more difficult problems dealing with planetary motions through a medium that offers resistance. Newton's ideas were registered, his priority of discovery made certain, and by February 23, 1685, he wrote to Francis Aston, one of the Society's Secretaries, acknowledging receipt of the registration.

The Royal Society had grown out of informal meetings of scientists and those interested in science at Gresham College. During the disturbances of the Civil War some of those involved had moved to Oxford, and meetings were held there too. At the Restoration in 1660 the meetings were again centered in London, and the Society was formally constituted. In 1662 it received a Royal Charter which was extended in the next year, and again in 1669. By 1685 its work had increased to such a degree that the honorary Secretaries could no longer deal with the correspondence, the business of arranging and reporting meetings and publishing *Philosophical Transactions*. It was therefore decided to employ a paid officer, one who could act as Clerk, and so assist the Secretaries.

A number of Fellows applied for the post, among them Halley, the Frenchman Denis Papin (1647–1712?), and Hans Sloane (1660–1735), whose library and collection of curiosities was to form the basis of the British Museum. The candidates were put up for election on January 27, 1686, and two ballots were held; the first was declared ineffective, and at the second Halley received the greatest number of votes. The decision to create such a post and to run an election had taken time, but as soon as the appointment was made Halley was sworn in to office. Certain conditions attaching to the position of Clerk—that the chosen candidate should live at Gresham College and should be a single man—were waived because, clearly, Halley could not comply with them. The fact that he was now a paid employee of the Society, however, meant that he could no longer hold the position of a Fellow, for while Fellows might have their out-of-pocket expenses it was laid down in the Charter that they could not receive salaries, and, as this condition could not be altered, Halley resigned his Fellowship.

One of his duties as Clerk was to deal with correspondence

with scientists both at home and abroad, and also to edit *Philosophical Transactions*. Martin Folkes (1690–1754), later President of the Society, remarked that the parts of the *Philosophical Transactions* which came under Halley's editorship have ". . . ever been esteemed one of the most valuable of the whole, from the judicious choice he made of the papers there presented; and the great number of excellent pieces of his own, in particular, which are there inserted." Why Halley applied for the post at all is not clear. Although full-time, the salary was not large, no more than fifty pounds per annum. It seems that he did it not so much for the money, but because he felt that the post would keep him in touch with scientific matters and offer opportunities to influence the course of events. Whatever his reasons, he entered on his new duties with vigor, apparently not minding that at the Society's Council meetings he was instructed to sit "uncovered [wigless] at the lower end of the table."

He began by dealing with the arrears of correspondence and by March was busy trying to obtain cooperation and respect for the Society from those who had taken offense at the delays in answering letters and the apparent casualness of the Secretaries. Thus, in writing to William Molyneux at Dublin, Halley says, ". . . I invite you to a communication of what passes in your society, which alwaies had been most acceptable here; and I promise you a faithfull account of what is materiall, that is brought before ye Royall Society . . ." and on the same day he wrote in similar vein to Sir George Ashe, saying, "The Royal Society are so far sensible of the Advantages of the Offer you make them of a Correspondence to be kept between the Gentleman of your Philosophical Society at Dublin and themselves, that they have immediately ordered them and your Self their Thanks for so kind an Invitation; and they assure you for the future your Letters shall be duly answered, and such Matters as shall be thought worth communicating, readily transmitted to you."

Under Halley's clerkship not only did correspondence improve, but the already wide interests of the Society were broadened even more. He almost gave Ashe *carte blanche* as far as communications from the scientific community in Dublin were concerned: "Your new method of demonstrating the knottiest Propositions of Euclid, your new-invented Dial, your Experiments of Injections of Liquors into Animals, and the account of your mathematical Girl, are things that will be very acceptable to us; as likewise whatsoever, whether Natural, Artificial or Mathematical Curiosity comes before you . . ." During 1686 and subsequent years Halley's letters, often long and concerned primarily with scientific matters, continued to pour out, not only in England but to correspondents abroad. Thus we find him communicating with Hevelius, writing to the mathematician Johann Sturm (1635-1703) in Vienna and to the famous biologist and microscopist Leeuwenhoek (1632-1723) at Leyden, to whom a present was sent—probably at Halley's instigation—to show ". . . a mark of their respect & gratitude for the pains you take to obliging them, . . ." Leeuwenhoek's gift was a copy of Francis Willughby's *Historia Piscium,* a book which the Royal Society had published at great expense.

We have already had many indications of the breadth of Halley's interests, and in the letters which have come down to us written in these early years of his clerkship, his insatiable curiosity about things concerned with every branch of natural science was given free rein. In a sense this might be expected, for the interests of Fellows of the Society covered every kind of subject; and while little would be gained from quoting many letters in full, for they have already been published elsewhere (in MacPike), some extracts are necessary to underline Halley's outlook. Surprisingly, he appears to have had a working knowledge of biological matters, and as an example we have only to consider his correspondence with Leeuwenhoek in which he discusses botanical and biological problems with great competence. Thus in a letter dated March 2, 1686, he wrote, "Your letter contains in it a great many particulars, in all which you fail not to add some new discovery or to confirm the old, and especially where you tell them that the Cotton seed contains in it a perfect plant capable to shift for itself without any Oleaging pabulum [fatty food], as is ordinary in the seed of most other plants, to maintain its deriving its infancy, if I may so say, however they think it worth the considering whether those plants you examined might not be somewhat too old, that so the substance designed for nutrition might be dried up and extenuated, so as to pass for leaves or els whether there might be contained within the stem which in your figures you design large, a substance analogous to the yolk of an Egg as it is in the bellies of Chickens and undoubtedly in those insects you mention to have found without a pabulum in their shells, but this only by way of inquiry, and to know your opinion thereon . . . ," and later goes on, ". . . since at this time the Eggs of silk-worms, and the things that happen to them could not by reason of the foregoing hard winters be observed by you, they desire you this spring to view the spawn of ffrogs, and to note ye method yt nature takes in ye production of those animals, for it is reasonable to suppose yt ye generation of most *if* not all oviparous fishes is after ye same manner."

Another of Halley's correspondents, to whom many letters were written, was John Wallis, his old mathematics professor who still held his chair at Oxford. Like Halley, Wallis had broad interests, and included medicine among them. In letters to him, a number of medical matters and medical curiosities are mentioned, as well as things concerning mathematics, astronomy, geology, and geography. In a letter dated November 13, 1686, after a normal introduction, Halley goes on, ". . . The sweet earth found at Hogsdon near London has been twice under the Societys consideration, the first time above 20 years since, and now lately it has come before them as a new thing, till the former account was found upon their books. Tis there sd that there lived upon that spot one that used to distill great quantities of Oyle of Turpentine, who digging accidentally, and finding a stiff clay, imagined that it might be capable to hold his Oyle of Turpentine, and accordingly he put into a hole in the ground a very great quantitiy of that Oyle which it seems being more penetrating than Water, in one Night soakt all into the ground . . ."

Next Halley refers to medical matters raised first by Wallis himself: "The child you mentioned to have seen with six fingers on a hand & as many toes on each foot, is a great curiosity, especially if they be so contrived that the hand be not thereby made less fit to do its office. Nor is the quantity of Water found in the Dropsicall maid less prodigious, it being hardly conceavable how the

Muscles of the Abdomen should be distended to so great a Capacity." He then enlightens Wallis about news of a medical curiosity from France, a "little Man," thirty-seven years old with a large beard and but only sixteen inches high who had been presented to "the French King," or so the Society had been told. Many letters to Wallis contain no *materia medica* at all, and Halley seems only to have mentioned them as and when they arose either in letters from Wallis or in correspondence with the Society. As his letters show, Halley, as Clerk, was always ready to provide his correspondents with everything he could which might be of interest to them and help them in their work.

From what has so far been said, it is possible to gain the impression that from his appointment as Clerk Halley's time was entirely taken up with his duties of attending meetings, taking minutes, and dealing with the Society's correspondence. But this is far from the case, for in 1686 he produced a spate of papers, and output continued in 1687. During 1686 Halley and Hooke worked together and, in March and April, made careful telescopic observations of occultations of Jupiter. These observations, like Halley's of the moon from Islington, were made with the problem of navigation in mind, only in this case, by checking those instants when the moon passed in front of Jupiter and occulted it, the apparent position of the moon could be accurately determined. Lunar occultations are still observed today, although the celestial bodies used are usually the stars, and again the purpose is still to correct computations of the moon's orbit. Hooke's and Halley's results were published in *Philosophical Transactions*.

The same year saw the advent of three of Halley's original papers, the first of which was meteorological and dealt with the changing height of the barometer and its relationship both to the elevation of the observer above sea level and changes in the weather. Today this may seem an obvious and simple problem, but in Halley's day the reasons for changes in barometric pressure were neither well known nor properly understood. Some work had been done by Torricelli (1608–47) in 1643 and by Pascal (1623–62), who had taken a barometer up the Puy de Dôme in the Auvergne, and they had established the fact that a column of mercury remained in a barometer due to the pressure of the earth's atmosphere. Halley's paper was a useful contribution to knowledge at a time when facts were at a premium. His "attempt to discover the true reason" for decrease in the height of mercury at places with various elevations and the correlation of changes in the weather with barometric pressure resulted in a new hypothesis: that changes in barometric height are primarily due to the variable winds in the temperate zones, which in England have "great inconsistency" due to "the uncertain exhalation and precipitation of the vapours lodged in the air." This hypothesis was in one sense at least not so far from the truth, and the paper set out matters so well that it was later used as a basis of lectures given in Cambridge by Roger Cotes (1682–1716), who was later to prepare the second edition of Newton's *Principia*.

More significant than the paper on the barometer was a second one, also concerned with meteorology, which Halley called "An Historical Account of the Trade Winds, and monsoons, observable in the seas between and near the tropicks; with an attempt to assign the phisical cause of the said winds." In dealing with this subject, so vital in the days of sail, Halley began with the logical, if to us obvious, remark that wind is no more—and no less—than a current of air, and that because the trade winds are always found to blow in the same direction at the same time, they must necessarily be due to the same ceaseless cause. What cause could this be? To Halley it seemed the explanation must be that they were due to the heating effect of the sun. If the entire world were covered only with water then all would be simple but, as he realized, the existence of large continents of land caused variations that were often complex. Halley discussed the effect of these land masses and pointed out that the nature of the ground and the existence of mountain ranges in particular, would play an important part. Dividing the sea areas into three—the Atlantic, Indian, and Pacific Oceans—he considered the nature of the winds as then known and found that the Indian Ocean posed a special difficulty because there the monsoons change direction from northwest to southeast in its northern part only. He had also to explain the more general fact that the trade winds are limited as a rule to a band of some 30° latitude around the earth.

His general thesis that the heating effect of the sun was the cause of these winds was significant, but it did not solve all the problems, so Halley enumerated those that were still outstanding in the hope, as he said, that others would wrestle with them. To make his points clear he attached a meteorological chart to the published paper, the first chart of this kind ever made. The winds are shown by short, dotted lines, so drawn that each elongated dot has a thick front and a thin tail and thus gives an indication of wind direction; in that area near Cape Verde off the west coast of Africa, Halley showed wind direction with the now more customary method of little arrows.

His explanation of the cause of the trade winds was incomplete and not wholly successful. He was by no means the first to have failed to find the full answer, for Francis Bacon (1561–1626), Galileo, and Hooke had also sought a solution, and like Halley each had contributed new ideas. Halley himself also provided an important additional factor—a method of meteorological charting. The final explanation was to come almost fifty years later when Halley was an old man.

It was also in 1686 that the paper on Newton's theory of gravitation appeared in *Philosophical Transactions*. Halley was working closely with Newton on the production of the *Principia* and this paper, entitled "A discourse concerning Gravity, and its properties, wherein the descent of heavy bodies, and the motions of projects [projectiles] is briefly, but fully handled; together with the solution of a problem of great use in Gunnery," is one full of practical suggestions to achieve greater accuracy in firing mortars. Halley's proposals were based upon the way a projectile would travel according to Newton's gravitational ideas. A solution of this particular problem of gunnery had been attempted many times before and various methods had been put forward; none was entirely satisfactory, and most were mathematically cumbersome, requiring a great deal of calculation. Halley laid bare the essentials, showing both how to lay out a mortar in the correct direction to hit a specific target on whatever kind of ground the mortar lay, and also how to adjust its elevation, again from any position, making use of a metal reflecting plate and a plumb line. He also suggested a standardization of mortars themselves, the bombs they ejected, and the charges of gunpowder used. It is a useful paper and underlines the fact that like Hooke and Newton, Halley had a practical streak in his nature, as well as a sound theoretical knowledge.

During the time he was busy as Clerk and also writing these papers for publication, Newton was engaged in preparing his monumental treatise, and Halley with arranging for its printing and publication. To pilot so technical a work through the printer's hands was no easy task, but it was made more difficult by controversies with Hooke and the fact that the Royal Society was at the time in very low water financially. In May 1686 the Council of the Society had ordered the book to be printed, but by 1687, when some of Newton's manuscript was ready for the printer, it was clear that the Society could not meet the costs involved. To make things worse, the work which, at Halley's instigation and with his encouragement, Newton had begun to write, had grown from a book of no great size to a very substantial volume.

The Society turned to Halley for help, and for his part he was determined that Newton's book *must* be published since he, if no one else, fully realized its immense significance and the vast grasp of mathematical physics that was contained in its pages. He therefore agreed not only to see the book through the press and to check all the proofs, but also to pay the printer himself. He did this in spite of the fact that although he should have been receiving a salary of fifty pounds ($120) per annum from the Society, he was not paid the whole sum in cash. Willughby's *Historia Piscium* had not sold as the Society had expected and large stocks of the book were left on their hands; this as well as arrears in the payment of subscriptions by many Fellows, meant that means other than money had to be found to pay the Clerk. As a result Halley received some of his salary in cash, but the balance in copies of the apparently unsalable *Historia Piscium;* the Council minutes state that "Mr Halley should have fifty copies of the History of Fishes instead of the £50 ordered him by the last meeting of the Council" and then a further twenty-five copies were given to him in consideration of arrears of salary still outstanding. What he did with these copies is not known, but it would seem likely that he made arrangements with booksellers to sell them. It is clear then that Halley must still have had a considerable private income to enable him to pay for the *Principia* and support his family while his rather meager salary was seriously in arrears.

Halley went ahead with the publication of Newton's work, which it had been decided was to be called *Philosophiae Naturalis Principia Mathematica* (*The Mathematical Principles of Natural Philosophy*), or the *Principia* as it has come to be known. A glance at the correspondence between Halley and Newton from May 1686 to July 1687 will show something of the work Halley had to do in order that the first edition of the *Principia* could be published. The first letter, dated May 22, 1686, begins with Halley's remarks on the Society's first steps in agreeing to publication: "Your Incomparable treatise . . . was by Dr Vincent [one of the Society's more senior Fellows] presented to the R. Society on the 28th past, and they were so very sensible of the Great Honour you do them by your Dedication, that they immediately ordered you their most hearty thanks, and that a Councell should be summon'd to consider about the printing thereof;" but unfortunately the President, Samuel Pepys, was in attendance upon the King and the vice presidents had gone into the country to enjoy a spell of good weather so that ". . . on Wednesday last ye Society in their meeting, judging that so excellent a work ought not to have its publication any longer delayd, resolved to print it at their own charge . . . ; and that this their resolution should be signified to you and your opinion therein be desired, that so it mighte be gone about with all speed. I am intrusted to look after the printing it . . . , only I would first have your directions in what you shall think necessary, for the embellishing thereof, and particularly whether you think it not better, that the Schemes [illustrations] should be enlarged, which is the opinion of some here; but what you shall signifie as your desire shall be punctually observed."

So far so good. Newton had received the Society's warm approval for the *Principia* and, to his obvious satisfaction, Halley was to read proofs and to deal with the minutiae of detail involved.

Later in this letter, however, Halley has disquieting news which he had to impart to Newton as tactfully as possible. He wrote: "There is one thing I ought to inform you of, viz, that Mr Hook has some pretensions upon the invention of ye rule of the decrease of Gravity . . . He sais you had the notion from him, though he Owns the Demonstration of the Curves generated thereby to be wholly your own; how much of this is so, you know best, as likewise what you have to do in this matter, only Mr Hook seems to expect you should make some mention of him, in the preface, which, it is possible, you may see reason to praefix. I must beg your pardon that it is I, that send you this account, but I thought it my duty to let you know it, that so you may act accordingly; being in myself fully satisfied, that nothing but the greatest Candour imaginable, is to be expected from a person, who of all men has the least need to borrow reputation."

Newton replied, thanking Halley for letting him know about Hooke's claims and referring Halley to Sir Christopher Wren, with whom Newton had discussed the question of planetary motion and an inverse square law as far back as 1677. In a later letter Newton points out that Hooke, Wren, and himself knew of the inverse square law by 1678 so that there was really no point in Hooke claiming that Newton had it from him. In a very long postscript to that letter, in which he also gave his blessing to the first proofs of the first part of the *Principia,* Newton turns on Hooke, having been told ". . . by one who had it from another lately present at one of your meetings, how that Mr Hooke should there make a great stir pretending I had all from him & desiring that they would see he had justice done him." Newton claims that Hooke had published some ideas of Borelli as his own; it is clear that he was heartily sickened by the whole matter. Indeed, he was so determined to avoid any further controversy that in the main body of his letter to Halley, Newton, whose *Principia* was by this time designed to be published as three books or sections under the cover of one volume, writes, "The third I now designe to suppress. Philosophy is such an impertinently litigious Lady that a man had as good be engaged in Law suits as have to do with her. . . . The first books without the third will not so well beare ye title of *Philosophia na-*

turalis Principia Mathematica & therefore I had altered it to this *De motu corporum libri duo:* but on second thoughts I retain ye former title. Twill help the sale of ye book wch I ought not to diminish now tis yours."

While Halley appreciated Newton's concern for the sale of a book of which he had to bear the financial risk, the suggestion that a third of the volume should be suppressed—a part which contained analyses of cometary orbits, of planetary motion, the cause of the precession of the equinoxes, the nature of tides, the computation of the masses of the sun and the planets, as well as much else—profoundly disturbed him. For the general scientific reader one could well say that the third book was the most significant part of the volume. Every iota of Halley's persuasive powers was now needed to avert what seemed likely to be a philosophical disaster of the first magnitude.

On June 29, 1686—as soon as possible after receiving Newton's tirade against Hooke—Halley replied in the following words: "I am heartily sorry, that in this matter, wherin all mankind ought to acknowledge their obligations to you, you should meet with anything that should give you disquiet, or that any disgust should make you think of desisting in your pretensions to a Lady, whose favours you have so much reason to boast of. Tis not shee but your Rivalls enviing your happiness that endeavour to disturb your quiet enjoyment, which when you consider, I hope you will see cause to alter your former Resolution of supressing your third Book, there being nothing which you can have compiled therein, which the learned world will not be concerned to have concealed; These Gentlemen of the Society to whom I have communicated it, are very much troubled at it, and that this unlucky business should have hapned to give you trouble, having a just sentiment of the Author therof."

Having thus expressed his own hopes as well as those of the Society that Newton would complete and agree to publication of his third book, Halley goes on to say that he had visited Wren to enquire whether it was from Hooke that the "notion" of the inverse square law had first come. Wren's answer was that he himself had tried to solve the inverse square problem, but eventually gave up as the mathematics defeated him. Wren also mentioned

Dr Halley.

1. This portrait of Edmond Halley, executed by Richard Phillips, was "lost" for a long time. It was identified from an engraving made from the portrait (but in reverse) by George Vertue since, before cleaning, the inscription was obscured. Vertue made his engraving in 1721; Halley was then almost seventy, but certainly appears here to be younger. The portrait was acquired and identified by the National Portrait Gallery, London, in 1964.

2. An eighteenth-century engraving of the island of St. Helena. Except for a short time in 1673, from 1600 onward St. Helena was a British possession and used as a watering station. In spite of the date of the engraving, it would appear that the island was little different when Halley visited it in 1676.

3. Halley's planisphere of the southern stars, dedicated, as the legend shows, to King Charles II. Just to the right of the center is the new constellation of Charles's Oak, Halley having taken some stars from the constellation Argus, which is shown here as only part of a ship. In the upper corners of the planisphere are details of the transit of Mercury that Halley had observed in 1677; in the lower corners are geometrical constructions showing how the stars on the planisphere may be linked to the stars of the Northern Hemisphere. Halley gave a copy of this planisphere to Hooke on October 31, 1678. The copy shown here is now the property of Sir Edward Bullard.

4. Hevelius and his wife observing. This sextant requires two observers, one to keep one sight of the instrument on a given star (as Madame Hevelius is doing) and the other using the moving sight to line up with a second star whose angular distance from the given star is to be determined. This very instrument is probably the one used by Halley and Hevelius together. From Hevelius's *Machina Coelestis*, Gedani, 1673.

EDMVND. HALLEIVS LL.D.
GEOM. PROF. SAVIL. & R.S. SECRET.

5. In spite of the legend at the top of the painting, this shows Halley at about the time he was thirty years old and was Assistant Secretary or Clerk of the Royal Society. Painted by Thomas Murray and now in the possession of the Royal Society, Halley is shown holding in his hand a sheet of paper on which is a graphical solution (the intersection of a circle and a parabola) that he devised for determining the roots of a biquadratic equation.   ROYAL SOCIETY

D.ISAACVS NEWTON EQVES
REG. SOCIETATIS PRÆSES. AN. 1703.

6. A portrait of Isaac Newton by Charles Jervas, now in the possession of the Royal Society. It was probably made when Newton was about sixty and Halley in his late forties.   ROYAL SOCIETY

7. Halley's chart of the trade winds and monsoons. Published in *Philosophical Transactions*, the chart is notable for depicting the winds by dashed lines, widely spaced at the rear and pointed in the wind direction. It was the first meteorological chart of this kind.

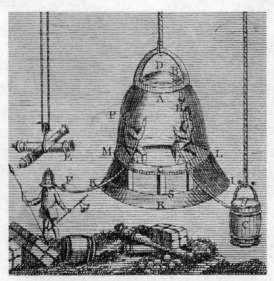

8. Halley's diving bell and diving helmet. No illustration of the equipment accompanied Halley's paper on the subject in the *Philosophical Transactions,* and although he made one very rough manuscript sketch for his own use, this engraving seems to be one of the very few pictures that have survived. It appeared in W. Hooper's *Rational Recreations,* published in London, in 1782. The diving bell A has a strong glass top D and a valve at B which is operated from inside the bell at H, permitting the escape of used air. LM is a circular seat. C is a barrel, cased with lead and containing air. The connection between the barrel and the bell is by means of a pipe of oiled and waxed leather; a weight on the pipe holds it below a hole near the base of the barrel when the barrel is lowered from the surface. The hole permits water to enter the barrel as it is lowered, thereby compressing the air inside. When the pipe is below the hole no air escapes, but when the pipe is taken into the bell and raised above the water level in the barrel, fresh air is admitted to the bell. The diving helmet F is in this instance constructed of lead with a thick glass window.

9. The artist of this unusual portrait of John Flamsteed without his wig is, unfortunately, unknown. NATIONAL PORTRAIT GALLERY, LONDON

that Hooke had repeatedly claimed to have succeeded, but he had never been convinced by any of the computations Hooke showed him. Halley then mentions that he has spoken to Hooke and ". . . plainly told him, that unless he produce another differing demonstration, and let the world judge it, neither I nor any one else can belive it."

So Halley was able to vindicate Newton's originality, but realizing that more than plain vindication was needed and that Hooke's claims had been exaggerated, he attempted to pacify his older colleague by pointing out that matters had been presented in a worse light than the events warranted. Hooke, it seems, neither applied to the Society for justification of his position nor did he claim Newton had received the whole solution from him. He had merely taken umbrage at the praise lavished on Newton's work, and the fact that even his great friend Sir John Hoskins—vice president of the Society and in the chair on this occasion—made no mention whatsoever of his work. According to Halley, Hooke and Hoskins had "utterly fallen out" after this and, after the meeting, Hooke's protestations made at a coffee house received little sympathy.

Having told Newton the whole story, Halley finally appeals: "Sr I must now again beg you, not to let your resentments run so high, as to deprive us of your third book . . ." Whatever may have been the rights or wrongs of Hooke's claims, it is clear that he had not been able to produce a convincing proof, and it is certain that the majority of the Fellows of the Royal Society did not set any great store by his claims. In addition, there were those who had misrepresented Hooke's cause to Newton, and Halley's tact and frankness were the only possible way out of the dilemma.

Newton's anger was mollified, and in his reply to Halley he writes how he realizes that Hooke ". . . was in some respects misrepresented to me . . . ," and Newton set to work on the third book of the *Principia*. The whole affair had left an unpleasant taste in Newton's mouth, and we find later letters to Halley in which Hooke's claims are again mentioned and again disposed of. Halley wisely left the controversy well alone and proceeded to make all haste in obtaining copy from Newton and arranging for its printing, no doubt on tenterhooks that Newton might change his mind again over the third book or that some tactless remarks of Hooke might again spark off a new set of troubles.

Newton had every confidence in Halley. As work on the printing of the *Principia* proceeded, we find him writing to "his Honoured Friend Mr. Edmund Halley" and ". . . I am very sensible of ye great trouble you are in at this business, & ye great care you take about it. Pray take your own time."

The *Philosophiae Naturalis Principia Mathematica* was published, under the imprimatur of Samuel Pepys as President of the Royal Society, in July 1687. Halley referred to it as a "divine Treatise," and from the end of February until publication date had laid everything else aside. His opinion of the book has been echoed ever since; it has even been referred to as the greatest work on natural science which Man has ever produced. Perhaps this is not surprising, since in the *Principia* there appeared for the first time a logical and mathematically rigid system correlating the laws of behavior of celestial bodies with the laws discovered for the behavior of moving bodies on earth—a synthesis of immense breadth that embraced the whole physical universe and was to have the most profound repercussions throughout the learned world. Such a book had long been needed and now, at last, it had arrived.

Newton paid tribute to Halley in the preface: "In the publication of this work the most acute and universally learned Mr. *Edmund Halley* not only assisted me in correcting the errors of the press and preparing the geometrical figures, but it was through his solicitations that it came to be published . . ." For his part Halley prefixed a number of verses to the book. The verses,* like the text, were in Latin. Halley's opinion of the work is best expressed in his own words, taken from his review in *Philosophical Transactions:* "It may be justly said, that so many and so Valuable Philosophical Truths, as are herein discovered and put past Dispute, were never yet owing to the Capacity and Industry of Man."

In the second edition of the *Principia* published in 1713 some changes were made in the verses by Richard Bentley (1662–

---

* These verses are reproduced with an English translation in MacPike, *Correspondence and Papers of Edmond Halley,* Oxford, 1932.

1742), cleric, scholar, critic, and Master of Trinity College, Cambridge. Bentley did not ask Halley's permission to do this and John Keill (1671–1721), later Savilian Professor of Astronomy at Oxford, remarked in a letter to Charlett, a fellow supporter of Halley who was also at Oxford, "You know there is a new edition of Sir Is. Newton's Principles. Published before them there was a copy of verses of Dr Halley's, which in the new edition Dr Bentley has made bold to emend, and alter in several places, without asking his leave; I am of the opinion the emendations are not near so good as the original: some of them are intolerable." The verses were again changed in the third edition, which came out in 1726. It seems that Newton had hoped that Halley's original would be restored intact but Pemberton, the publisher, ignored his wishes.

On the instructions of the Royal Society a copy of the first edition was presented to King James II, and its presentation was accompanied by a paper from Halley which gave a general account of the book, a course of action which was obviously necessary in view of the *Principia's* highly specialized nature. Halley's description of the book is masterly. It gives particular emphasis to Newton's work on the cause of the tides as deduced from the principle of gravitation. This was a diplomatic choice of subject when it is remembered that the King, as Duke of York, was Lord High Admiral during the reign of his brother, Charles II, and had at one time commanded the British fleet in the war with the United Provinces. A letter accompanied the paper, and contains the flowery phraseology at which Halley, when necessary, was so adept: ". . . being sencible of the little leisure wch. care of the Publick leaves to Princes, I believed it necessary to prsent with the Book a short Extract of the matters conteined, together with a Specimen thereof, in the genuine Solution of the Cause of the Tides in the Ocean. A thing frequently attempted But till now without success. Whereby Yor Matie. may Judge of the rest of the Performances of the Author."

Halley then offered his services as an expositor: "If by reason of the difficulty of the matter there be anything herein not sufficiently Explained, or there by any materiall thing observable in the Tides that I have omitted wherein Yor. Matie. shall desire to be satisfied, I doubt not but if Yor. Majesty shall please to suffer me to be admitted to the honour of Your Presence, I may be able to give such an account thereof as may be to Your Majesties full content . . ." There is no evidence that the King availed himself of Halley's offer, but at least the *Principia* was at Court and provided with a duly explanatory text as well. As a matter of fact Halley's summary was so worthwhile that it was later printed and published in *Philosophical Transactions*.

The publication of the *Principia* took by storm those in the learned world able to understand it. To Halley the scientist, we shall ever be in debt for his major part in getting Newton to write the book and seeing it through the press, and we must not forget the ironical fact that he had to pay the bill himself for printing what was to be the greatest of all scientific treatises. Halley's efforts have been well expressed by Augustus De Morgan (1806–71), who wrote, "But for him, in all human probability, the work would not have been thought of, nor when thought of written, nor when written printed." This is the sum of Halley's achievement.

CHAPTER 7

Science and Sea-Diving

It is impossible to assess Halley's place in the science of the seventeenth and eighteenth centuries without spending a little time looking at the wide range of his general scientific work. Too often he has been thought of only as Newton's amanuensis and the discoverer of a comet, yet his contemporaries recognized him as a genius, an opinion which was echoed in the last century by such men as De Morgan and David Brewster (1781–1868), and in our own time by others who have themselves achieved distinction in original research. To call him a genius may be controversial, but perhaps only because the word means different things to different people. Since Halley's interests were broad, it may be felt that he cast his net so wide that he was unable to deal with anything in depth. He was certainly a product of his age, a man whose essays into every field of physical science were as wide as those of his contemporaries; this was also true of Hooke, or Wren, or even of Newton himself, who spent only a small fraction of his life on the subjects that gave rise to the *Principia*.

Looking at Halley's scientific papers and his unpublished scientific work is one way to see him in action, and we shall begin in 1687, the year the *Principia* was published. Even though he was Clerk to the Society and was dealing with the time-consuming business of producing the *Principia*, he nevertheless managed to publish three original papers. The first of these was purely mathematical, and concerned the algebraic analysis of solid geometrical figures; Halley felt that previous solutions of the problem were either too complex, too inelegant, or both. He successfully achieved a comparatively simple solution which delighted other mathematicians and appeared in two successive issues of *Philosophical Transactions.*

Of the two remaining papers of 1687, one on the evaporation of sea water by the sun appears to be of little consequence although Halley subsequently made considerable use of its conclusions. His third paper is historically the most interesting, since its implications developed later, and the ideas expressed in it were to add to Halley's difficulties when he brushed with ecclesiastical authority. The paper, which deals with evidence for the variations of latitude, was innocuous enough on the surface. Halley compared observations recently made in Nuremberg with those obtained some centuries previously, and came to the conclusion that the changes in the latitude of Nuremberg over this period were so small that any significant alteration would only become evident over a very long time indeed.

The significant part of the paper follows. Halley considers the suggestion made by Hooke that the biblical flood had been caused by a gradual shift of the earth's poles, which caused the biblical lands to come under the bulging waters of the equator. Halley argues that due to the Nuremberg observations the only conclusion to be drawn using Hooke's hypothesis is that the flood must have occurred in the very distant past and long before the time which theologians accepted for the creation of the world. Halley was not at this time disposed to argue with the theological time-scale, so he suggested that the flood must have been caused in some other way and by some outside factor. He was thinking of a physical phenomenon and suggested that perhaps a comet or some such body had brought about the deluge by its close approach to the earth. As he remarked, biblical and pagan accounts showed the deluge to have been sudden, and the only physical explanation would therefore appear to be the gravitational upheaval such as a comet might provide. The theory had other implications, as Halley at once saw, for it ". . . would always include a change in the length of the year, and the eccentricity of the earth's orbit, for which we have no sort of authority." In the event we know that Halley's cometary hypothesis was at fault since the mass of a comet is not great enough to have the effect he supposed, but his rational scientific approach was valid enough.

The subject was a new departure for Halley and the first fruits of a new rationalistic approach to biblical evidence. In this approach he was at one with Newton. Newton took a great interest in the dating of scripture and analyzed the authenticity and authorship of the Pentateuch, and immediately after writing the *Principia* he seems to have devoted himself to both subjects.* Newton's work was not published until after his death, but in this respect Halley was rather less cautious. In December 1694 he read to the Society another paper on a physical explanation of the deluge, but his full ideas did not appear in *Philosophical Transactions* until 1724. This delay of thirty years would seem to be due to Halley's brush with the Church in 1691, when he was refused a chair at Oxford because of charges of religious and moral apostasy. Certainly the physical causes of the deluge might be discussed at a meeting of the Royal Society, but in view of his previous experiences he probably felt it would be more diplomatic to leave publication until the storm had completely blown over.

This paper of Halley's which was not published until 1724 was titled, "Some Considerations about the cause of the universal Deluge." Halley discussed his own ideas in the light of the biblical account, and here he displayed an almost modern outlook on the authority of the Scriptures, remarking that in Genesis the "exact circumstances as to point of time shew, that some records had been kept thereof, more particularly than is wont in those things derived from remote tradition, wherein the historical minutiae are lost by length of time." The Scriptures might, as the Church claimed, be divinely inspired, but as Galileo and others had felt, their inspiration must surely be on religion and not on their scientific and factual content. Halley boldly suggested that Scripture here is not infallible, as was usually accepted: ". . . I doubt not," he writes, "but to all, that consider the 17th chapter of Genesis impartially, it will pass for the remains of a much fuller account of the Flood left by the patriarchs to their posterity, and derived from the revelation to Noah and his sons." He goes on to develop this critical approach by discussing certain difficulties in the Genesis account, not least

* For an informative discussion of some aspects of Newton's theology see Leonard Trengrove's paper in *Annals of Science*, vol. 22 (1966), 277 f.

the traditional story of the ark and its animals, the collection of which as well as their behavior seems to him to be highly improbable. From every point of view Halley found that, as far as he was concerned, his hypothesis that the deluge was due to gravitational disturbance caused by the close approach of a comet seemed to be the only logical explanation. With what seems now to be good enough reason, he concludes that if this were indeed the cause, then the omission of details from Genesis is not to be wondered at because of the primitive scientific knowledge of the time.

With a general approach of this kind Halley was in some danger of being labeled a heretic, since he was in fact claiming that Moses, to whose authorship the Book of Genesis was usually ascribed, had only received his facts from oral tradition, and an incomplete oral tradition at that, not from divine revelation. In the twentieth century this approach seems natural enough, for some centuries of biblical criticism have had their effect, but in the late seventeenth century such an attitude of mind was dangerously novel.

The second paper on the deluge was not Halley's only paper delivered to the Society at a meeting which failed to find its way directly into *Philosophical Transactions*. Late in February and at the beginning of March he read papers on magnetism: They give us a further insight into his scientific acumen. These were "Trying the Force of ye Magnet at Several Distances" and "An Experiment, of the Force of the Magnetic Needle, and its Variation," and were written because Fellows had been carrying out experiments to discover the force exhibited by a magnet at varying distances. They had done this by placing a small bar of iron at varying distances from a piece of naturally magnetic material (lodestone) which was placed in one pan of a pair of scales, and had then noted what weights were needed to balance the magnetic force. Halley comments "That this experiment shewes that a Scale is not an instrument nice enough to discover the true proportions desired," and then presents his own solution, which was as simple as it was ingenious. He proposed having two lodestones, one fixed at a set distance from a pivoted magnetic needle, and the other movable, its distance from the pivoted needle being carefully measured. With this experimental arrangement, the comparative magnetic forces of the two lodestones could be determined as the movable lodestone was placed at varying distances from the fixed one. The forces could be computed using a geometrical construction based on the positions of the lodestones, and Halley describes the procedure in detail. The *modus operandi* being laid down, the experiment was tried, and in the second of the two papers the results are given in terms of the swing of the magnetic needle. In order to isolate the experiment it was carried out in "the middle of the area of the Quadrangle of Gresham College," and in this way Halley ensured that any surrounding blocks of iron which might influence the results were as far away and equally distributed as possible. Even so, difficulties were experienced and inconsistent readings obtained due, perhaps, to the insufficient sensitivity of the magnetic needle. The paper comes to no conclusions about the diminution of magnetism with distance.

As always, astronomy was Halley's main interest; whatever his other preoccupations it was never completely neglected, and he became involved in the preparation of ephemerides (collections of astronomical tables). As far back as the end of 1685, the year of his appointment as Clerk, an ephemeris for 1686 had been published, and an account of it was given in *Philosophical Transactions,* explaining that ". . . there being then great want of proper Ephemerides of any tolerable exactures, those which had been done before having been complained of by Mr Flamsteed in his tables of the Eclipses of Jupiter's Satellites; therefore several gentlemen well skilled in these things had engaged in this undertaking, and had executed this present Ephemeris from tables of their own . . ." Anthony à Wood was certain that Halley was not only one of the "well skilled gentlemen" concerned, but also played a leading part in the production.

During 1688 Halley was busy with his work for the Society and in the preparation of five unpublished papers; domestically, children arrived into the Halley household. How many children were born to Edmond and Mary Halley is unknown; infant mortality was high, and it would not be stretching the imagination too far to assume that their whole family did not reach maturity. We do know, however, that in 1688 two daughters, Margaret and Catherine, were born. There is no evidence that they were twins and if they had been, one of the writers of Halley's obituary notices would surely have mentioned the fact, so it must be assumed that one was born early in the year and one toward the end. Little more is known of them except that they were still alive after their father's death, Margaret living until the age of fifty-five and Catherine until seventy-seven. Catherine married twice, first to a Mr. Butler then, after his death, to a Mr. Henry Price, who supplied so much material to the compiler of the article in the *Biographia Britannica*. On Halley's death Martin Folkes wrote that ". . . the Daughters are both living in great Esteem, the one is single, and the other has been twice handsomely marryed."

The five unpublished papers of 1688 are all concerned with various aspects of the phenomenon of heat. The first, read before the Society on January 11, discusses a new type of thermometer in which ". . . the Degree of Heat may be Measured by the Amount of Vapour given off by a liquid." The gist of Halley's idea was that by noting the amount of vaporization which occurred on heating, one could obtain a measure which was directly proportional to the heat involved. He clearly hoped that in this way one might obtain an insight into what degrees of heat meant. The matter was not solved in his papers, and in the middle of March we find that he had turned back to the mercury thermometer to experiment on the "Expansion of Liquors by Heat."

At the end of March he again addressed the Society on "A New Thermometer and the Rarifaction of Liquors." In this, a longish paper, he discussed the behavior of air under the influence of heat and the method of graduating what was, in effect, an air thermometer. He followed this up toward the end of April with an attempt to find an explanation for the rising of water vapor in air, ". . . one of the hardest phenomena in nature to be explicated, considering the manner of the one is at least 800 times more dense and ponderous yn yt of the other." Halley's investigations took the form of a series of experiments, although he does state that ". . . it is evident, by the great ascent of these vapours yt they are become nearly of the same specifik gravity with the Air." It may seem surprising that an astronomer should concern himself so much with matters of this kind, but such an apparent anomaly will be resolved if it is remembered that his interest in heat and vaporization must necessarily have been stimulated by the geophysical papers which he published, and that in the seventeenth century physical science was not separated into such specialized fields of study as it is today.

These papers were no more than part of a spate of work that he carried out with an almost demonic enthusiasm, and the Journal Books of the Royal Society at this time have hardly an entry which does not refer to some observation or experiment in which he was involved. Halley's interests continued to be extraordinarily broad. In 1688 he reported on a type of fern (*adiantum*) which he had observed while on St. Helena and on "a curious observation" which, as Clerk, he had received from a Mr. Watts, "who keeps the Physick Garden at Chelsea," from which it is clear that the necessity of sunlight for sustaining green plants was by then noted, even if not understood, although Halley made some pertinent suggestions for conducting experiments to see if any other influence might be at work. Further entries show Halley bringing to the notice of Fellows matters as diverse as the silting up of a port, a comparison of English, French, and ancient Roman weights and measures, and the discovery of sea shells which he had found on the cliffs of Harwich ". . . which seemed to demonstrate that that bedd had once been the bottom of the sea, notwithstanding its being so much above it now."

In spite of this diversity, we still find him taking an interest in the perennial problem of finding longitude at sea, discussing the use of the pendulum clock for determining longitude on shore but concluding that ". . . it would be scarce possible to find the Longitude at sea sufficient for sea uses, till such time as the Lunar Theory be fully perfected." Here Halley, like Newton, was mistaken, but at the time it was difficult to conceive of anyone making a sufficiently accurate timepiece.

The clerkship of the Society had considerable administrative duties attached to it, and it seems clear from the minutes of council that more office accommodation was needed. In consequence, in a minute dated May 30, 1688, we find Halley and a Mr. Perry ordered to inquire whether the lodgings of the Divinity professor at Gresham College were to be rented and on what terms. Mr. William Perry, F.R.S., is an unknown quantity, and all we can say is that no doubt acting on information received, Halley and his colleague were able to make certain that Professor Wells, who held the Chair, no longer required his rooms, for at the next council meeting held on June 30 it was "Ordered that Mr Perry and E. Halley do make a conclusive bargain with Mr. Wells, the Divinity professour for his Lodgings in Gresham Coll."

Throughout this time Halley received no remuneration from the Society while he was engaged in dealing with meetings, writing letters, and caring for the day-to-day business. Not until October 22, 1690 did the council order "that the Treasurer do pay to E. Halley one hundred pounds being two years Salary due to him on Jan. 27, 1688/9," that is, the salary for the years 1687 and 1688, the date 1688/9 signifying what we would now, on our present calendar, call 1689.

The Society's financial difficulties may in some measure have been due to the existing political situation. James II had ascended the throne in 1685 but there was little enthusiasm for his succession. As Bishop Burnet recorded in his contemporary history, "Few tears were shed for the former nor were there any shouts of joy for the present King. A dead silence, but without any disorder or tumult, followed it [the proclamation] thro' the streets." James was a Roman Catholic and began to fill significant posts with those of his own faith and to make precipitously other tactless moves. Protestant refugees arrived from France in a steady stream after Louis XIV revoked the Edict of Nantes in 1685, and fears grew of a similar situation arising in England; these were heightened by the Queen's pregnancy in 1688, and there seemed every likelihood of a Roman Catholic monarchy being perpetuated. Matters were finally resolved when James abdicated and fled the country on the arrival of William of Orange, husband of James's Protestant elder daughter, Mary. In February 1689 William and Mary were proclaimed joint monarchs.

During the upheaval loyalties were divided. Samuel Pepys, for instance, President of the Royal Society from 1684–86, was torn between his personal regard for James, with whom he had come into close contact as Secretary of the Admiralty, and not compromising himself in the eyes of the new regime or seeming to support the Roman Catholic cause for which he had no sympathy. This dilemma must have been common to a number of Fellows, not all of whom would have been able to extricate themselves from this situation. In consequence some may have gone into exile, if only temporarily, and so been out of funds, while others may have retired to the country and not thought it worthwhile continuing to pay their subscriptions. These reasons probably hold good for the temporary suspension of the publication of *Philosophical Transactions* at this time.

There is a story that Halley ". . . was far from being an unmoved spectator" and that after the Bloodless Revolution he "continued to express . . . with his usual warmth and openness . . ." his indebtedness to both Charles II and James II for all the favors he had received. His views reached William III, who was "a little alarmed," thinking that the opinion of "a person of so great a reputation, and so conspicuous in the learned world . . . should not be neglected; but upon a nearer enquiry, being truly informed that the warmth of our author's [Halley's] zeal for the rejected prince, was the pure effect of his gratitude, and without any mixture of particular dislike to his successor, and especially observing he was continually employed at his telescope, determined not to disturb his speculations; being satisfied from his character, that his close attachment to them, would effectually prevent him from pushing his affection any further at most than drinking a health."

A brief glance at Halley's participation at meetings of the Society, as recorded in its Journal Books, will allow us to see how, with his practical flair, there were few things of a mechanical nature about which he could not make pertinent suggestions. In March we find him ordered to look into ". . . the Contrivance of the pulling Clocks and Watches that repeat and strike the hour and quarter . . ." and, a week later, explaining to the meeting ". . . the secret of the Repeating Clocks . . ." In July he produced a chart of the mouth of the River Thames which corrected ". . . severall very great, and considerable faults . . ." in the charts then available. In the same month he reported on a scheme to build a lighthouse on the Goodwin Sands and also on the reason why, when houses were blown up by gunpowder—as occurred during large fires and especially during the Fire of London in 1666—the windows of those nearby nearly always fell outward into the street and not inward, as was popularly supposed. In October he gave the Society details on refining silver and on the thickness of gold, which covered the "best guilt wire," the latter calling for some considerable exactitude of measurement, considering that Halley found the gold film to be "but 1/134,560 part of an inch." Incidentally, this work has a theoretical interest since, following Robert Boyle, Pierre Gassendi (1592–1655), and Newton, Halley assumed that material bodies were composed of atoms, and made some suggestions about their size: "those particles are necessarily less than 1/2433000000 part of the cube of the hundred part of an inch, and probably many times lesser, if the united surface of the Gold without Pores of Interstices be considered." In other words he had computed their maximum size from the thickness of the gold film which allowed none of the silver underneath it to show through. He also told the Society that in his opinion crystals might also give a clue to atomic sizes.

It is obvious from the extraordinary variety of Halley's contributions during his time as Clerk that he was acting in a similar capacity to Hooke who, as Demonstrator, had earlier been obliged to produce at least one experiment for each meeting of the Society. With Hooke this gave rise to his *Micrographia*, published in London in 1665; but in Halley's case it seems to have led to the criticism that he had a grasshopper mind.

And so during 1689 we find him discussing at a number of meetings the composition of sea water and also carrying out observations of a biological nature and reporting to Fellows about the behavior of sea mussels and a particular cuttlefish found in the waters around St. Helena; a means for "keeping flounders all the year long for sale in corfs [baskets kept in water] in the salt-marshes on the sea coasts"; and how, during the "late great frost," he had watered rosemary with soap suds and by this means enabled it to thrive and "bear the hard winter well." As far as his own subjects were concerned, in February he read a paper on the mathematical question of infinite quantities, with special reference to the infinite extension of solid surfaces, while in October he reported on observations he had made of the eclipse of the moon which had occurred the month before, using among other instruments a wooden quadrant borrowed from Hooke.

In 1690 Halley was doing much the same kind of work, although biological and natural history observations do not figure to the same extent as they did in the previous year, no doubt because of his concentration on the question of evaporation from the sea and the heating effect of the sun. It is interesting to note that it was during this year that he spoke to the Society on "some queries, which he conceived to containe the principall difficulties, that are found in our Theorys of Light Pellucidity, and Refraction," a subject which also intrigued Newton, who was to publish his famous *Opticks* in 1704.

Among the entries in the Society's Journal Book for this year is one which shows an unselfish and amenable aspect of Halley's nature. Under the date July 23, we read that "Halley produced a Pocket book of his wherein among other Mathematicall things there is long since written a proposition lately published in the Acta Lipsiensia by one Mr Bernouilli, who values himself upon the Invention . . ." Jacob Bernouilli (1654–1705) was a member of the amazing family which for three generations produced a succession of mathematicians of international repute. Bernouilli published these particular proposals in the leading German scientific journal —the equivalent of *Philosophical Transactions*—and his work concerned a certain property of sections of a cone and was very similar to Halley's proposition. Because Bernouilli published first, the honor of discovery rested with him and the fault was Halley's since he had never published his results, being content with submitting them to the Society. There is no evidence whatsoever that Halley took offense at Bernouilli's claim to priority and the Journal Book records no recriminations. In this Halley acted in a way that was to put to shame even Newton, whose arguments with Gottfried Leibniz will be mentioned later.

In 1691 much that Halley had been turning over in his mind came to fruition. Six scientific papers appeared in *Philosophical*

Transactions, while others were prepared and read before the Society, but remained unpublished. So much occurred, and of such significance, that it will have to be dealt with piecemeal, beginning with the published work. First to appear was "An Account of the Circulation of the watry Vapours of the Sea, and of the cause of springs." In this paper Halley collected together his thoughts on questions of a geophysical kind. With it he made yet another basic contribution, showing again the importance of a solid scientific approach to matters which were too often the subject of ill-disciplined speculation. The value of the paper lay in its description of what he considered to be the physical mechanisms that occurred during evaporation and subsequent precipitation, and so provided a sound hypothesis that lent itself to further investigation.

The second paper in 1691 was very different from those so far mentioned; it dealt with early history, yet another of Halley's interests. The paper was entitled "A Discourse tending to prove at what time and place, Julius Caesar made his first descent upon Britain." The problem facing Halley was this: It seemed that Caesar had not accurately stated the time and place of his first landing. How then was an accurate determination to be made? As an astronomer, Halley looked for evidence in that field and found that even the hour of the landing could be determined by examining the available accounts of Caesar's expedition and calculating the time of an eclipse of the moon which occurred on this occasion.

Having solved half the problem, he then had to tackle the question of where Caesar had first set foot in the country. He noted that Cassius, in his account, had used an expression which was generally accepted as meaning that the first battles took place in the fen country of Lincolnshire. Halley was not content with this, for Lincolnshire did not seem to be a suitable part of Britain for such an invasion; therefore he examined the works of other authors. He came to the conclusion that the acceptance of Lincolnshire—widely held in his day—was due to a mistranslation which should more correctly be rendered "at the water's edge" and more legitimately be interpreted as near the South Downs. This interpretation was much more consistent with an invasion from Gaul, and since

Halley's day historians have agreed that it was on the southern coast of Britain that Caesar first landed.

The third paper concerned the question of determining the sun's distance using observations of Mercury or Venus as they cross the solar disk, a question of immense importance and one to which Halley contributions have made us forever in his debt. We shall discuss it more fully in the next chapter. The fourth paper of 1691 was again a historical exercise, but this time on a subject rather more closely allied to science, since it dealt with the famous *Historia Naturalis* of Pliny the Elder (A.D. 23–79). This well-known and much used work on natural history was a compendium of scientific knowledge of Pliny's day. It had a great vogue during the Middle Ages and earlier, even though Pliny was uncritical and based much of his information on hearsay and travelers' tales, giving accounts of the phoenix and the unicorn equal status with those of the lion and the elephant, so unsuspectingly preserving the facts and fables, magic and useful arts of the days of the very beginning of the Christian era. Halley's paper, which dealt with emendations and notes on three errors in the generally known text of the book, again shows his critical and scientific approach to questions of this kind and provided some useful facts for contemporary zoologists.

Halley's last paper for 1691 was a mathematical one in which he discussed "several species" of infinite quantity and their relationships. During the year he also addressed the Society on experimental measurements he had made on the refraction of light by diamonds and by the naturally occurring mineral Iceland Spar, which exhibits some unusual optical effects, and discussed a rule for finding the point of focus of lenses of various kinds.

Halley's unpublished papers for this year continued to be extremely diverse and included "A Way of Estimating the Necessary Swiftness of the Wings of Birds to sustain their Weight in the Air," in which he discusses experiments made with a pigeon, "The Manner of Computing the Weight or Force of the Winds . . . ," and "An Attempt to Measure the Strength or Force of Running Water," together with papers discussing the refraction of light, and the height to which bullets could be shot and fountains made to operate, with some details of the physical principles involved. Other, and perhaps the more important papers, show Halley's abilities not only as a physicist but also as an engineer.

Mention has already been made of an unpublished paper of 1689 concerned with deep sea diving, and in 1691 no less than four more papers appeared on the subject. These were not filled with idle speculations but were the result of actual experiments which Halley carried out. The first inkling we have of his interest in these matters comes in the unpublished paper of March 6, 1689, "A Method of Walking under Water." He writes: "To walk on the bottom at a considerable depth of Water and to be there at Liberty to act, or manage one's self to the best advantage as if one trodd upon the drie ground, is without doubt a contrivance of great use in the saving things lost in Shipps or otherwise under water. What I can learn has been yet done herin, is first by plain diving or the power of suspending respiration for a considerable time, so that a man shall be able to continue under water severall minutes of an hour. This faculty is by long habit acquired, and there are many very excellent at it among the pearle divers in the West Indies, who have lately been made use of to very good purpose in the recovering of plate lost in the Spanish wrack [wreck], but it is a very short time that a man can endure the want of Air; and besides the pressure of the water when the depth is considerable, does very much incommode the diver, especially if he stay anything long, so that it is said the blood will gush out at their ears and noses. To remedy this the Diving Bell has been invented wherein there is considerable quantity of Air contained near the bottom of the water to save the trouble of coming up to the topp for breath, the diver when he can bear it no longer retreating to his reserve of air for succour, where having refreshed himself he is again fitt to go about his business: But in this case the diver is obliged to do all he does holding his breath, which must needs take away the Liberty of action, and grows still more and more uneasie till such time as he can indure it no longer. Therefore how to obviate this inconvenience and to contrive a means to be under water and to move there breathing all the while, as I have contrived it, may be a consideration not unworthy of this Hoble. societie."

Next Halley describes his method, which was to construct a

spherical or cylindrically shaped hollow copper or wooden vessel, open at the bottom and with a height twice as great as its diameter. To make it heavy enough he specified heavy lead or brass wheels fitted to the bottom; these would ensure that the contrivance would sink, but what of the air contained in it? This is next discussed, and Halley concluded that at a depth of a little over thirty feet the air would be compressed so that it filled only half the vessel, at one hundred feet it would take up only a quarter of the space inside and the virtual weight of the vessel would be such that it became ". . . immovable to the strength of a Man unless we can drive out this water." This could be done, he suggested, by sending down barrels containing air under pressure which, being taken into the vessel, could be opened, the water inside the main vessel taking the place of the compressed air in the small vessels. Halley believed that by this means the water could be kept to below the diver's knees. Because of the small amount of water contained in the vessel, the diver could move it about on its wheels without difficulty as he walked along the ocean floor. Moreover, if the diver "be provided with such boots as the fishermen use he may be cloathed and stand dry on the bottom of the sea, tho' it be 20 fathoms deep." Halley's only reservation concerned the suitability of the compressed air for breathing, but he concluded that it seemed likely that all would be well.

It is obvious from this paper that Halley had carefully examined the whole problem, and his suggestions are practical enough. Next he made tests to see if his ideas offered a useful solution. In June 1691 we find him at Pagham in Sussex, a small seaport on the south coast, carrying out experiments from a naval frigate. Halley's first experiments did not go quite smoothly, for he writes in a letter to Abraham Hill (1635–1722) dated June 22 that on arriving at Pagham he found that the tarred ropes, although new, had been burned with over-tanning and needed to be replaced. In addition the diving vessels, or casks, as he then calls them ". . . prove not so well as expected."

In August, however, he was able to report progress to a meeting of the Society—indeed, he had no option, for the Society had instructed him to report his results, perhaps, one can legitimately surmise, because they had been instrumental in persuading the Admiralty to agree to use one of the Navy's frigates. His diving tub (it seemed to undergo a colorful variation of name) was cone-shaped, being three feet across at the top, five feet across at the bottom—which was open—and five feet high. It needed a weight of 1¾ tons to sink it, but no longer had the wheels he first proposed. Within the bell was a bench about a foot from the bottom ". . . for the men below to sitt on when they should be cold and whereon a man might sett with all his clouths at any depth drie" while Halley also made a window at the top and provided a valve in the crown of the bell to let out the "hott and effete air unfitt for farther respiration."

Not content with designing the device, Halley himself descended in it, and his description is worth repeating: "When we lett down this engine into the sea we all of us found at first a forceable and painful pressure on our Ears which grew worse and worse till something in the ear gave way to the Air to enter, which gave present ease, and at length we found that Oyle of Sweet Almonds in the Ears, facilitated much this admittance of the Air and took of the aforesaid pain almost wholly." The bell was lowered about fifteen feet at a time, and the water which had entered was driven out before proceeding further. This removal of the water "wherein consisted the principall invention I can bost of" was performed by lowering an ironbound lead-covered cask of about forty gallons' capacity. This cask, lowered from a boat on the surface, had a stoppered hole in the bottom and a valve in the top. When lowered under and into the bell, the air contained in the cask was released by opening the valve, water rushing in to take its place through the stoppered hole which was also opened. Every fifteen feet the procedure was repeated.

The experiment reported to the Society was certainly a successful one, for Halley records, "By this means I have kept 3 men 1¾ [hours] under the water in ten fathoms deep without any the least inconvenience and in as perfect freedom to act as if they had been above." Later he goes further, "This method of keeping men under water has no limits, for if the bell be made greater and the Air Cask proportionable any number of men assigned may be suppleyed with breath for as long a time and at as great a depth as shall be desired and by what we have found at 10 fathom I see no reason to doubt but a man may be well enough in 20 or 30 fathoms without harm." The cask method of supplying air and removing water was cumbersome, even if otherwise satisfactory, however, and a month later Halley told the Society of improvements which he had devised. Halley's improvement, or "invention," as he so rightly called it, was the diving suit. Made of leather with a helmet, the suit had a pipe from the diving bell to receive air for breathing, and a second pipe to take the respirated air back to the bell. Later he fitted a girdle of lead to the suit. A similar system was devised to allow a lantern to be used by the diver, and by this means ". . . I can unlade a shipp at the botom of the sea without breaking her . . ."

Some designs of diving equipment had been put forward earlier by the French physicist Denis Papin, but although Halley probably knew of these, his own ideas were not only improvements, but also went further and even included a primitive form of depth gauge and a method of protecting the ears under pressure. No wonder that he asked the Society ". . . to conserve to my self the right of priority of Invention on your Testimony and Register, being as I conceive like to be of great Use . . ."

Even while carrying out his experiments Halley found time to note odd, extraneous facts, such as the colors of light and of objects seen in the bell, and the transmission of sounds under water. Newton was later to make use of Halley's observations of light below sea level in his *Opticks*.

Further developments of the diving equipment were made in October; the valve on the barrels was replaced by a weighted pipe (see Plate 8), and since Halley found it cold working under the sea, he "fortified" himself with "a double or triple flannel or knit woolen westcoat and excluded the water by a well liquored [oiled] leather suit made fitt and close to the body." He also invented a device "For Blowing Up the Decks of Ships under Water . . ." These inventions did not remain moribund in the Society's archives, for he formed a public company for salvaging wrecks, a company which was successful for a time and the shares of which were quoted in the newspapers of the day.

CHAPTER 8

The Distance of the Sun

One of the fundamental problems in astronomy is the measurement of distances in space. In the seventeenth century no stellar distances had been determined, and even those of the planets were uncertain. From Kepler's 2:3 power ratio the latter could be computed provided at least one determination of a sun to planet distance could be made. (If T_1 and T_2 are the times taken by two planets to complete their orbits around the sun, and a_1 and a_2 their average distances from the sun, then Kepler's 2:3 power ratio gives

$$\frac{T_1{}^2}{T_2{}^2} = \frac{a_2{}^3}{a_1{}^3}.$$

The values of T_1 and T_2 are readily determined from observation, and if a_1 is known, a_2 can be found.) For ease of computation the distance from earth to sun was the best to find, and in essence the problem seems a simple one to solve. Consider two observatories (see Figure 2), A and B, whose distance apart is known. Then if a represents a point in the sky directly above the observatory at A, and b a similar point above the observatory at B, while S is the sun, it would appear that all that has to be done is to measure at each observatory the angles of the sun from the overhead points a and b; by geometry the angle of the sun—and angle ASB—can be found and the distance of the sun obtained by simple trigonometry.

Unfortunately the operation is not as easy as it appears because, in spite of what the drawing shows, the sun is so very far away that it appears at almost the *same* angle from each observatory. The angle is so small—approximately equivalent to a man six feet tall seen at a distance of eighty-eight miles—that the most delicate

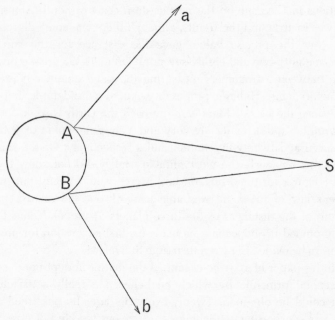

FIGURE 2 *Distance (parallax) determination using two observatories some distance apart.*

measuring equipment is required and, what is more, errors due to mistakes in measuring the distance between the observatories and in timing the precise moment of observation will vitiate the results. In the seventeenth and eighteenth centuries measurements of such precision were hardly practicable, and no one realized this better than Halley. Clearly the only answer was to avoid direct measurement and observe a body closer than the sun; this meant observing the distance of the planet Mars or, preferably, Mercury or Venus. Once the distance of one of these was determined, then calculation would permit the distance from the earth to the sun to be computed.

Halley's solution involved measuring the distances of either Mercury or Venus, although at Paris Cassini had initiated measurements on the distance of Mars. Cassini had arranged to measure the angular distance of Mars from the vertical in Paris while his colleague Jean Richer (Giovanni Richer, d. 1696) made similar observations in Cayenne on the northeastern coast of South America. This was in 1672 and the results, although there was some disagreement over the precise value, gave the distance for the sun as between eighty-two and eighty-seven million miles. So great a divergence between astronomers measuring the same quantity was not satisfactory, and Halley's proposals were of considerable importance since the closest Mars can approach the earth is some forty-eight million miles, while Mercury and Venus can come to within fifty-seven and twenty-five million miles respectively. Of the three, Venus was obviously the most suitable. Halley did not know these precise figures for the orbits of Mars, Mercury, and Venus, but from Kepler's law of ratios he was able to work out the relative proportions of the distances of the three planets. It was on Venus that Halley pinned his hopes and he made his first suggestion for observations to be made after his return from St. Helena.

In his paper of 1691 he examined the matter in depth and gave the general principle by which he believed a really satisfactory result could be obtained. Twenty-five years later he published another paper exhorting astronomers to carry out the kind of observations which he explained in considerable detail, based on the principles given in the paper of 1691.

Halley did not merely suggest a straightforward and simple set of measurements of Venus. The importance of his proposal was that it confined observing to those times when the planet appeared to transit or cross the sun's disk. This does not occur frequently, even though Venus passes between the earth and the sun every nineteen months, for the simple reason that the orbit of Venus is tilted with respect to the earth's orbit; a glance at Figure 3 will make it clear that only when Venus is near the points N and M, and, in addition, when these points lie between the earth and the sun (i.e., when the earth is close to "m" or "n"), can transits occur. Consequently they are infrequent, but when they do happen they are usually in pairs. For Venus the time between one transit of a pair and the next is about eight years, but the time between one pair of transits and the next is very much longer and is never less than 117 years. It was at these comparatively rare moments, the sight of which, Halley stated ". . . is by far the noblest astronomy affords . . ." that he suggested

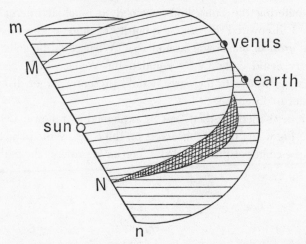

FIGURE 3   *The inclination of the orbits of earth and Venus. Only when Venus is close to M or N and the earth near m or n respectively, can transits across the sun occur.*

such observations be made, and devised a method for carrying them out.

It is true the principle had been hinted at earlier by a young English astronomer, Jeremiah Horrox (1617?–41), but it is to Halley that credit must go for providing a full discussion of the matter and a detailed observing program based on his observation of a transit of Mercury while he was on St. Helena. A transit offers particular advantages since there are four instants when useful observations can be made: noting, first, the instant when Venus appears to touch the edge of the sun; second, the moment when it seems to have fully entered the sun's disk and begun to move across it; then, third and fourth, the equivalent positions on the other side of the disk when it appears to just touch the inside edge and then the outside edge. Halley appreciated that if observations of these instants were made by at least two observers, each at a different and preferably distant observatory, then the distance from the earth to the sun could be directly determined with considerable accuracy.

Here he was drawing upon his observations of Mercury on St. Helena, where he had used a twenty-four-foot telescope and had ". . . very accurately obtained . . . the very moment in which Mer-

cury, entering the Sun's limb, seemed to touch it internally . . .
Hence I discovered the precise quantity of time . . . and that without an error of one single second . . ." What could be achieved for
Mercury could certainly be equaled for Venus which, because it
approaches nearer to the earth, would present a larger disk and so
be easier to observe.

Halley's method, then, can be explained as follows: Let A and
B (see Figure 4) be two observers on the earth, V the planet Venus
and S the center of the sun's disk. Then *aa'* represents the path which

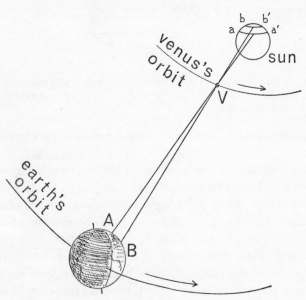

FIGURE 4   *Method of observing the transit of Venus and obtaining the
distance earth to sun.*

Venus will appear to have in transit when observed from A, and
bb' will be the path as seen from B. It will be noticed that *bb'* is
shorter than *aa'*, and it therefore follows that the observer at B will
see the transit more quickly than the observer at A. The job of the
observers is comparatively simple: They have only to note the four
instants already mentioned and time these as accurately as possible.

Once the observers had noted the precise instants of transit, they had to find the actual size of the sun, which can be deduced directly from the observations. Halley's method of doing this was ingenious. From the times obtained by the observers for the transit, the relative lengths of *aa'* and *bb'* can be found, and it is then a comparatively simple matter to compute the vertical distance between these lines in terms of the diameter of the sun's disk. Suppose it is found that the distance between *aa'* and *bb'* is some fraction of the sun's diameter, say, for argument's sake, 1/155th part (for in actual observations the lines are closer together than shown in Figure 4). We can then calculate this distance in miles if we know the distance between A and B. Since the difference in latitude between A and B is known (from the geographical positions of the observers), the north–south distance between them may readily be calculated from the known diameter of the earth. From Kepler's ratio we can calculate, as did Halley, that the distances from the earth to the sun and from Venus to the sun are known to be in the ratio 10 to 7 (approximately); it then follows that the ratio (earth to Venus):(Venus to sun) will be (10–7):7, or 3:7. If we say that the distance between points A and B comes out to about 2400 miles, the actual distance between *aa'* and *bb'* must be 2400 × the ratio (Venus to sun : earth to Venus) or 2400 × 7/3, that is, 5600 miles.

The transit times have shown that the distance between *aa'* and *bb'* is only 1/155th part of the sun's disk, and it therefore follows that the diameter of the sun is 155 × 5600 miles, or 868,000 miles. The diameter of the sun is now known to be 864,100 miles, and the example given here provides too high a value, but it illustrates the principle involved. With the actual diameter of the sun known, and its apparent diameter in the sky known also—it covers rather more than half a degree—it is only a matter of simple trigonometry to work out the actual distance of the sun from the earth. The larger the separation between *aa'* and *bb'* the better, since the greater the difference in the duration of transit times between the observers at A and B, the less significant are any small errors in the timings themselves. This is another reason why Halley chose Venus in preference to Mercury, for Mercury would give a smaller separation between the lines *aa'* and *bb'* than would Venus.

The principles of the kind of measurement for obtaining the

sun's distance having been laid down, Halley continued to think about the problem and in 1716 his paper in *Philosophical Transactions* was really a detailed observing program for a transit of Venus which was to occur in 1761, forty-five years later and long after he himself would be dead. Halley, it must be appreciated, was well aware that there were a number of detailed corrections to be taken into account. A transit lasts for something of the order of six hours, and this is due not only to the time taken by Venus to pass across the sun's disk because of its own orbital motion and the orbital motion of the earth, but also to the fact that during this time the earth is spinning on its axis and so the observers at A and B change their positions. In order that the entire transit from the apparent entry of Venus onto the sun's disk and its exit from it may be observed at one and the same observing position, such a position has to be very carefully chosen geographically. Consequently Halley made a number of calculations, and gave the expected times of the transit and those places on the earth's surface from which it would be both satisfactory and at the same time practicable to observe the phenomenon. In doing this Halley chose as great a separation of the observing stations as possible in a north–south direction, the north–south limits being determined by the fact that too great a separation would mean that Venus would appear above or below the disk of the sun and would therefore lie outside the suitable observing area.

Not everyone agreed with Halley that Venus was superior to Mercury for determining the sun's distance, and a notable exception was the mathematician and theologian William Whiston (1667–1752), who had been interested in some of Halley's work, especially his discussion of the cause of the biblical flood which Whiston mentioned in his *A New Theory of the Earth* published in 1696. He was firmly of the opinion that Mercury would be preferable to Venus, and his comments were published in 1723 by John Senex (d. 1740), a noted map engraver and globemaker. Whiston's work was precipitated by the transit of Mercury which occurred in 1723 and took place within a month of the publication of his book. But Whiston was wrong and his advocacy of Mercury was ignored in England, although not so in France. It was Halley's proposals that were finally taken up and which resulted in much work and many expeditions to view the transits in 1761 and 1769. His hope that "our younger astronomers" would not fail to take advantage of the opportunities was fulfilled.

The main expeditions* which set out to observe the transit of Venus originated in England and France. In spite of Halley's work and exhortation, it was only the interest of the French and, most particularly, of the astronomer Joseph Delisle (1688–1768), which finally prodded Halley's own countrymen into making expedition arrangements. These began in June 1760 on the receipt by the Royal Society of a world map which Delisle had prepared and which showed the areas from which the transit would be observable. Within a month the Council of the Society decided to send "proper persons to proper places" to observe the transit, and also that the Society should "direct the observations." The two most important observing positions were taken from the list of suitable stations given by Halley in his 1716 paper, taking into account certain corrections which Delisle had been able to make in the light of later knowledge.

One of the places chosen was St. Helena, and the other the island of Sumatra. The East India Company agreed to give the Society every possible assistance with the expedition to St. Helena, but expressed grave doubts as to whether the Sumatra trip was practicable in view of the time involved, the distance to Sumatra, and the fact that England and France were still in the midst of the Seven Years' War. They feared that the ship might never reach its destination or, at best, would arrive too late to make any observations. In the event the Society decided to risk such eventualities and successfully petitioned the Admiralty for a ship.

Meanwhile arrangements had to be made to obtain suitable observing equipment. James Bradley (1692–1762), then Astronomer Royal, decided what was necessary but the sum involved, together with the cost of salaries for observers, and the expenses to cover both their passage and their stay, was more than the Society could provide. Accordingly they decided to appeal again to the Admiralty, but it was through the efforts of their President, the Earl

---

* What follows is but a brief summary. For a full discussion the reader is referred to Harry Woolf's excellent *The Transits of Venus*, Princeton, 1959.

of Macclesfield, and the once-powerful but still influential Duke of
Newcastle that the matter was solved and the Society received a
Royal Warrant for the sum needed. It is interesting to note that
pendulum clocks were among the equipment which had to be purchased and one of these, used two years later in determining the
Mason-Dixon line, is still keeping excellent time in the Society's
rooms. The final selection of instruments and the detailed arrangements for their purchase were, at Bradley's suggestion, undertaken by Nevil Maskelyne (1732–1811), who five years later was
to succeed him as Astronomer Royal.

Having decided upon where to observe and what to take, the
next step was to commission the necessary staff. After various arrangements and rearrangements it was decided that Maskelyne, accompanied by an assistant, Robert Waddington, should go to St.
Helena, while the expedition to Sumatra was to be under the direction of Bradley's assistant, Charles Mason (1730–87), and he in turn
was to be assisted by a surveyor and amateur astronomer, Jeremiah
Dixon (fl. 1763); but Mason and Dixon were never to reach Sumatra. The ship in which they left Portsmouth met a French man-of-
war in the English Channel, and after a battle both ships had to
return to their respective ports; in due course Mason and Dixon
made their way to the Cape of Good Hope and observed from
there. There was also a third English-speaking party, for John
Winthrop (1715–79) of Harvard University, in what was then the
British province of Massachusetts, went to St. John's in Newfoundland with two students and the college carpenter, having made his
own arrangements with the governor of the colony.

The French plans were more elaborate and were based on experience observing the transits of Mercury in 1723 and 1753, which
they had carried out in accordance with Whiston's views. Delisle
had met Halley in London in 1724, had discussed the transit of
Venus with him and, like Halley, he had the practical experience of
a transit of Mercury behind him. Delisle slightly modified certain
details in Halley's method: He obviated the need to observe the
entire transit which involved the practical difficulty of requiring the
best weather conditions for a protracted period. Delisle found that
it would be sufficient to observe only the exact moments of first or

second contact of Venus with the sun's disk. Realizing that the observer seeing the longer transit path (*aa'* in Figure 4) would have to commence his observations before his colleague observing the shorter transit path, Delisle found that if the exact time were noted by both observers then the difference between these could be used to determine the vertical distance between the transit paths *aa'* and *bb'*. This method of Delisle's increased the number of possible observing stations and made the likelihood of success greater.

By the time 1753 had come and gone it was clear that the transits of Mercury could not give the sun's distance with the required accuracy. Halley was vindicated and the French settled down to prepare for the transit of Venus, which lay eight years ahead. After much discussion, calculation, and recalculation the French decided to arrange for observations to be made in Siberia at Tobolsk by Jean-Baptiste Chappe (1722–69), on Rodriguez Island off the eastern coast of Madagascar by Alexandre-Gui Pingré (1711–96), in Vienna by Cassini-de-Thury (1714–84), the third of the famous Cassini family, and by Guillaume Le Gentil (1725–92) in Pondicherry on the southeastern coast of India.

Le Gentil failed to reach his distant station through an experience similar to Mason and Dixon's. He left France in late March 1760 and after running battles with the English, his ship finally landed at what was then the Île de France, off the eastern coast of Madagascar. Le Gentil considered a change of plan, but finally in March 1761, a year after he had embarked, he set sail with French reinforcements for Pondicherry, which was being besieged by the British. Le Gentil had three months left before the transit was due, but when near Mahé on the western coast of India the captain learned that both Mahé and Pondicherry had fallen, they turned around and made again for Île de France. On the return journey Le Gentil saw the transit but, being on board ship, could make no astronomically useful measurements.

He was a pertinacious character, however, and decided to stay in the area for another year in order to study the natural history of the surroundings and make some observations which would have at least geographical and navigational use. He wrote to France to this effect, but stayed longer than intended, finally deciding to wait the full eight years so that he would be in a position to observe the second of the pair of transits, which was due in 1769. In due course the time for the second transit drew near and Le Gentil decided his best plan would be to go to the Marianas in the Pacific. He wrote to France again, giving his plans, but received no reply and so decided to take matters in his own hands. He set sail in a Spanish ship, but established his observing equipment at Manila, having learned when he arrived there that ships went to the Marianas only once in three years.

Finally, Le Gentil heard that Paris did not approve of his plan to observe from Manila and he made arrangements to return to Pondicherry, perhaps with relief, for he had become involved in trouble with the governor of Manila, who was notoriously corrupt. He arrived in Pondicherry in March 1768, happily receiving every cooperation from the English. But perhaps the English weather followed their colonists, for during the transit the skies were cloudy, although they were clear again half an hour after it had finished. To add insult to injury, the sky was clear at Manila. Le Gentil remained at Pondicherry for a while, and then slowly made his way back to France. Worse events were now to follow. He did not arrive in France until two years after the 1769 transit, and since no word had been heard of him, he had been presumed dead and his heirs were in the process of dividing up his estate, and he was forced to undertake expensive lawsuits to retrieve it!

Fortunately Le Gentil's experiences were unique, and as a whole the observations of the 1761 and 1769 transits were highly successful. This was to a great extent due to the wide dispersion of both amateur and professional observers. No less than sixty-two stations were in operation in 1761, and by 1769 the total had risen to sixty-three, the majority of which were different from those of the 1761 transit.

It is not too much to claim that because of Halley's appreciation of the problem, astronomy was to be provided with measurements of the sun's distance far surpassing the accuracy of any previous determination. The actual value found after both expeditions was of the order of ninety-five million miles, although later analysis of the results has given a value of ninety-three million miles, which is very close to the figure accepted today (92,870,000 miles). Certainly the method is no longer in use, but this is because it has been supplanted by others such as radar determinations which have rendered purely astronomical methods out of date; but these modern advances cannot detract from Halley's achievement.

CHAPTER 9

Flamsteed and Halley

Halley's work on the transit of Venus and its use for determining the sun's distance ended in 1724 with his discussion with Delisle; but now we shall return to 1691, the year of his transit paper, and take up the story of his career, for in that year he met opposition from the Church. Halley's letter to Abraham Hill, referred to in Chapter 7, mentioned his experiments at Pagham on the diving bell, but its main burden was something else, for in the last half of the letter Halley wrote: "This business [the question of diving] requiring my assistance, when an affair of a great consequence to myself calls me to London, viz. looking after the Astronomy-Professor's place in Oxford, I humbly beg of you to intercede for me with the archbishop Dr. Tillotson [1630–94], to defer the election for some short time, 'till I have done here, if it be but a fortnight: but it must be done with expedition, lest it be too late to speak. This time will give me an opportunity to clear myself in another matter, there being a caveat entered against me, till I can shew that I am not guilty of asserting the eternity of the world."

The situation that had arisen was that Halley's old professor, Edward Bernard, had resigned as Savilian Professor of Astronomy at Oxford, and Halley was one of those who had applied for the vacancy. The appointment had to be approved by the Church. Since the Act of Uniformity in 1662, general assent to the Articles of Religion as drawn up in 1562 and appended to the *Book of Common Prayer* was the necessary requirement of orthodoxy demanded of every member of the university staff. It was a matter that had already caused difficulties for Newton whose views, certainly after he began work at Cambridge, if not before, were such that he found

it impossible to accept the doctrine of the Holy Trinity. The trouble
in Halley's case was that he had been accused of heresy—interpreted
in this instance as holding beliefs which were unorthodox—and as a
caveat had been issued he had to defend himself and prove that
the allegation was false. Bishop Edward Stillingfleet (1635–99), then
bishop of Worcester and one of the referees for the appointment,
was a man noted for his piety and also for his rather rigid views
on the authority of the Scriptures. He was a man who would not
and could not agree to the appointment of anyone about whom
there was even the slightest doubt, without a thorough investigation. What then was the charge against Halley? Was it valid? And
who first made it? These are three questions which must be answered and it will be best to take them separately.

To begin with the charge itself, as far as Halley was concerned
this had to do with his ideas about the deluge. Obviously he did
not believe there was any substance to the statement that he believed the world was eternal—in other words that there had never
been an act of divine creation. This much is certain from the letter
to Abraham Hill. On the face of the matter, then, there should
have been little difficulty, for the charge seemed to be no more
than a misunderstanding of what Halley had been proposing.

But there were more serious undertones of which it seems Halley knew nothing. These arose from charges made to Bishop Stillingfleet who, according to the antiquarian Thomas Hearne
(1678–1735), when he learned that Halley was a "sceptic and ban-
terer of religion," thereupon decided to question him as soon as the
opportunity arose. Halley went to see Stillingfleet, and it is Hearne's
report of this visit that leads us to suppose that Halley knew nothing of this other side of the charges against him, for Hearne states:
"Bishop Stillingfleet fell very foul of the famous Dr. Halley too on
the same account, who came to expostulate with him on the occasion. The bishop began to ask him some questions. The Doctor told
him, 'My Lord, that is not the business I came about. I declare myself a Christian and hope to be treated as such.'"

It is this second part of the charge—the accusation of being a
total disbeliever—that the early eighteenth-century ecclesiastical authorities would have looked on with more severity than the first,

and Stillingfleet was obviously dissatisfied, for according to William
Whiston, he sent his chaplain, Richard Bentley, to investigate the
matter more fully. "Mr. Halley was then thought of for successor,
to be in a mathematick professorship at Oxford; and bishop Stillingfleet was desired to recommend him at court; he scrupled to be
concern'd; 'till his chaplain, Mr. Bentley, should talke with him
about it; which he did. But Mr. Halley was so sincere in his
infidelity, that he would not so much as pretend to believe the Christian religion, though he thereby was likely to loose a professorship . . ." This is Whiston's account, but the writer of the article on
Halley in the *Biographia Britannica* expresses doubts about the validity of the story, pointing out that there is evidence that Halley
from time to time used to tease Whiston about his strict religious
views, and tells of a visit by Whiston to Halley, stating that when
Halley offered Whiston a glass of wine, the latter refused "because
it is Friday," to which Halley retorted that he was afraid that Whiston "had a Pope in his belly."

Certainly Whiston, who drew up this account more than forty
years later when he was almost eighty, was mistaken over one point:
Halley was applying for the chair of astronomy, not mathematics,
but this is of little moment. What is significant is Whiston's state
of mind when he wrote it, and this is clear from the sentence that
follows: "Yet was Mr Halley afterwards chosen into the like professorship there without any pretence to belief of christianity. Nor
was there any enquiry made about my successor Mr. Sanderson's
christianity, even when the university of Cambridge had just ban-
ished me for believing and examining it so thoroughly, that I had
hazarded all I had in the world for it." Since Whiston had first
been expelled from Cambridge and then made to resign the
Lucasian chair which he held as successor to Newton, all because
of his Arian* beliefs which he was ill-advised enough to advocate
in public, he may well have felt bitter and somewhat exaggerated
Halley's attitude. This seems likely when we remember Whiston's
further remark that he had once told Halley, "if it had not been
for the rise now and then of a Luther or a Whiston, he [Halley]

* The Arian heresy, first advocated by Arius in the fourth century, claimed
that Christ had no eternal existence.

would himself have gone down on his knees to St. Winifred or St. Bridget," for there is no doubt that he thought of himself as having a divine mission and anyone who teased him would be bound to suffer.

All the same, there seems every likelihood that Bentley did interrogate Halley and there can be no doubt that their characters would not have been in sympathy. Bentley was rigid in his orthodoxy as Halley was not—Halley's paper of 1724 shows clearly his liberal views—but in addition Bentley had an "utter want of principle and an overbearing tone and manner to all who opposed him . . ." If this comment is felt to be too strong it is only necessary to remember that he not only altered Halley's verses in the *Principia* without leave, but also did the same to sections of Milton's *Paradise Lost*. Moreover, when he saw to the second edition of the *Principia* he kept all the profits to himself, charged Newton for some of the printer's corrections and paid Roger Cotes, who wrote the preface and prepared the index and revised the whole book, not a penny. "He was covetous," Newton later said to his nephew-in-law John Conduitt (1688–1737), "and I let him do it for the money." To be fair, Bentley did much to improve the administration of Trinity College when he was appointed Master in 1700 although, once again, his avariciousness caused trouble and he was suspended from his degrees for a time for extorting fees illegally from his postgraduate students.

Bentley must have crossed swords with Halley during their discussion. He could not bear anyone to disagree with him, and this would have angered Halley and perhaps goaded him into a full dissertation on his views that not every iota of Scripture was necessarily divinely inspired. To a doctrinally rigid churchman this would be anathema and would lead Bentley into supposing Halley to be beyond redemption. Halley did not receive the chair of astronomy, and in 1734 Bentley produced a famous tract, *The Analyst or a Discourse Addressed to an Infidel Mathematician* that has always been taken to be an attack on Halley, who by then had held the Savilian chair of mathematics at Oxford for thirty years.

Whether Halley was truly an infidel, whether in fact he was a scoffer of religion, has never been fully settled, but it seems unlikely. He remained close friends with Robert Nelson and Newton all their lives, and it is improbable that two such strongly religious men would have consorted with him if he had ridiculed their cherished beliefs. In the last century Stephen Rigaud made a careful analysis of the matter and concluded that there was no evidence to substantiate the charge. Nevertheless rumors were current and there is an account that just after Halley had been refused the chair and the Scotsman David Gregory (1661–1708) had been appointed in his stead, another Scotsman called often at a coffeehouse Halley was known to frequent and, after a number of visits, was asked what urgent business he had to make him so persistent. "I would fain see a man that has less religion than Dr. Gregory," he replied.

If Halley lost the appointment due to his supposed religious apostasy, he was certainly considered suitable from an academic point of view. His old college, Queen's, testified, "We judge him to be in every way most fit and accomplished for this performance as well as from our own long experience of his mathematical genius, probity, sobriety, and good life, as also from the very many testimonials of all foreigners eminent in that science," while the Royal Society in their Council Minutes of November 11, 1691, recorded, "It was ordered that the Society do give a recommendation letter to Mr. Halley, signifying their opinion of his abilities to perform the office of professor of astronomy now vacant, as likewise to testify what he has done for the advancement of the said science, and that Dr. Gale [his High Master when he was at St. Paul's and then one of the Society's Secretaries] be desired to draw up the testimonial." In view of statements like these, the religious opposition must have been very strong; the man behind it all seems to have been Halley's erstwhile friend, John Flamsteed.

The trouble between Halley and Flamsteed appears to have started over some tables of high tides at London Bridge which Flamsteed published from 1683 onward. He spent considerable time and much energy on these and made them as accurate as he could. The results were published in *Philosophical Transactions*. But Flamsteed went further and evolved a set of rules so that these tables could, in his estimation, be applied to ports other than London. He had found ". . . there is every where about England, the same difference betwixt the spring and nepe tides that is here observed in the river Thames." In consequence he prepared simple rules so that, observing the time of high tide at any port, one could compare the result with his tables for London, and by carrying out addition or subtraction, obtain the exact account of the time of high tide at any other port. With this rule as a basis he then appended a set of tables which gave high tides for various ports. Newton was interested in the problem, and on the publication of the tables he wrote to Flamsteed for certain further details; to these Flamsteed could provide no exact answer. In any event he misunderstood Newton's question, which queried something that, as Newton said, "you have not observed."

Flamsteed was not the only person whom Newton consulted, for Halley was doing parallel work, and the *Biographia Britannica* states emphatically that Newton discussed the question with Halley and also says that Halley had found errors in Flamsteed's tables for the tides at Dublin. Halley's information about Dublin tides came from correspondence with William Molyneux. Molyneux supplied him with data which was published in *Philosophical Transactions* in 1686, together with some of Halley's own remarks. It is these remarks which seem to have sparked off the trouble, yet they were only the kind of comment which scientists commonly make on one another's work and by means of which theories are corrected and observations confirmed or denied. Halley actually wrote: "This observation makes the tides upon the quarter moons come in later . . . than upon the new and full moons by half an hour, whereas in the Thames as high as London, the quarter moons make high water above an hour and a quarter sooner in this respect, than the new and full, as may be seen in the accurate tide tables of Mr Flamsteed." So far so good, Halley had praised Flamsteed. He went on, however: "But it is hence found that the said tables are not applicable to sea ports, where there is not the same reason for anticipation of the nepe tides upon the quarter moons." In brief, Flamsteed had assumed that tides in a river would be directly and simply related to tides at coastal ports, but his assumption was wrong.

This angered him; he did not like being proved in error

over a matter of this kind and on which he had given Newton advice. So much is clear from the fact that as soon as he had an inkling that Halley had been writing to Molyneux about the tides at Dublin—and somehow he heard about this before the remarks to which he took such strong exception were published—he at once wrote to Molyneux himself, complaining of his "unfriendly action" in giving Halley information. Molyneux's reply is terse: "The only information I wrote to Mr Halley about our tides, was what I wrote to you about three years ago . . . I can assure you there was nothing more, so that you need not mistrust my kindness on that point. He proposed the same queries to me, that you then proposed, and I answered him in the same way, only indeed he added, on the coast of Ireland, whereabouts do the two floods meet. To this I then answered him not, because I had not yet got information . . ." Molyneux's reply to Halley and Halley's comments were published before Flamsteed could receive this letter, and no doubt the fact that Halley had the sagacity to ask a further and important question only served to fan Flamsteed's smoldering anger. He even tried to draw Molyneux into the dispute with Halley, but to Molyneux's credit he would have none of it. Halley, for his part, was upset about the whole affair, for his criticism of Flamsteed's second set of tables had not been meant as a personal slight. Molyneux tried to heal the breach, but Flamsteed was adamant and, in his correspondence with Newton, began to abuse Halley.

This kind of unpleasantness can be seen in two letters. The first, drafted three times by Flamsteed, was sent to Newton at the time of the vacancy in the Savilian professorship; in it Flamsteed exhorts Newton to do what he can to prevent Halley's election, on the grounds that he would "corrupt ye youth of ye University with his lewd discourse." A letter at the beginning of the following year, in answer to Newton's mention that Halley was wondering why Flamsteed had not published his observations, contains the following: "It onely remaines yt I give you the Answer I could make to our suggesting freind when he asks me why I doe not print my observations? tis first I doe not find my self under any obligations to receave Instructions what to doe or be governed by him & his

Associates ye Muss's.† 2, I would not thrust such an incompleat Catalogue on the world as he has done from St Helena nor be obliged
to complement the best reputed Astronomers of our time (as he
has done all of them) by telling them yt had their Catalogues been
extant he would have call'd his a supplement to theirs as he has
done (for want of them) of Tychoes. Nor will I give any one occasion to tell ye world I have erred a 60th parte of what La Hire
has published he does in a star of the Crosiers and one of the
Centaur: that I understand what I have to doe much better than he,
& when & how it will be best for me to publish my own labours,
yt I will not be beholden to him for his Assistance or advise. that
If he wants Imployment for his time he may go on with his sea
projects, or square the superfices of Cylindrick Ungulas,‡ find reasons for ye change of the variation, or give us a true account of all
his St Helena exploits, & that he had better doe it than Buffoone
those to the Society to whome he has been more obliged than he
dares Acknowledge. That he has more of mine in his hands all-
ready than he will either owne or restore, & that I have no esteem
of a man who has lost his reputation both for skill candour & Ingenuity by silly tricks ingratitude & foolish prate. & yet I value not
all or any of the shams of him and his Infidel companions being
very well satisfied that if Xt [Christ] and his Apostles were to walk
againe upon earth, they should not scape free from ye calumnies
of their venomous tongues, but I hate his ill manners not the man,
were he ether honest or but civil there is none in whose company
I could rather desire to be." There were four drafts of this second
letter, so there can be no excuse that it was written in temper.

Flamsteed was a dour, unhappy man, often sick, always strug-
gling to do his work at the Observatory against difficulties, and he
had no sense of humor to lighten his misfortunes. Yet all the time
Greenwich was being built Halley frequently visited him, helping
him with his equipment and later with his observing. Together, using a clock to estimate the time interval between the flash of an ex-
plosion three miles away and the arrival of the sound on Shooter's

† Mus's or Muss's was a coffeehouse frequented by Halley and others from
the Royal Society.
‡ A cylindrical ungula is part of a cylinder shaped like a horse's hoof.

Hill near the Observatory, they even attempted to measure the speed of sound, with tolerable success. The first intimation of any difference between them is to be found in Hooke's diary for January 7, 1676, where he states, "Flamsteed and Halley fallen out," referring, presumably, to a temporary disagreement. Halley was still invited to observe at Greenwich long after this. But Flamsteed loathed levity and hated being teased—a pastime in which Hooke used to indulge—and in July 1675 Flamsteed wrote to Towneley complaining that he was "much troubled" with Hooke, who had been boasting that he had "an instrument or quadrant of 36 foot radius that weighs not a pound and which he can put in his pocket, and things of that sort. . . . I know not how to deal with him . . ." Hooke's claim was preposterous, but one is left with the impression that Flamsteed had, for a moment at least, given it serious consideration. Halley became friendly with Hooke, and Flamsteed strongly disapproved of their association. Again, writing to Towneley in November 1686, this time about Halley, Flamsteed says, "I used him for some years as my friend, . . . since he ran into Mr. Hooke's designs and society I have foreborne all intimacy with him." It seems that Halley's friendship with Hooke was a contributory factor to Flamsteed's abuse, but it cannot have been the sole reason. The fact that Halley probably teased Flamsteed too —his "foolish prate"—must have helped.

Yet this does not seem to have been all. Halley made lunar observations during his time at Islington, and there is evidence that Flamsteed appropriated these to his own use without any acknowledgment. In his copy of the *Principia*, in the section where Newton discusses the moon's motion, David Gregory inserted a note that Newton had told him that Flamsteed had published as his own some tables by Halley and, what is more, Newton claimed to be certain of this because he had seen the originals and recognized Halley's handwriting. A matter of this kind would be likely to lead to enmity, and in a man of Flamsteed's character to exaggerated self-justification. Much of Flamsteed's abuse centers around claims that Halley had the ". . . art of filching from other people, and making their works his own," and Flamsteed developed the habit of referring to Halley as Reymers (d. 1600), an allusion to an astrono-

mer accused of plagiarizing Tycho Brahe's observations. It is highly
probable that Flamsteed's accusations were unfounded for, as will
become clear shortly, in a letter to Towneley written in 1686 Flamsteed condemns himself out of hand.

Flamsteed does not come out of this situation in a good light.
He would make no attempt at reconciliation, even though exhorted
to do so by Newton, and seemed determined to do nothing con-
structive, but instead turned against Halley's friends and acquaintances, including Newton himself. Nothing Halley or anyone else
could do seemed to improve the situation and, in view of the excellent work being done at Greenwich and Flamsteed's later difficulties, it was all doubly unfortunate.

Flamsteed would not leave well alone and in 1692 seized the
opportunity to try to make more trouble for Halley. His chance
came with Halley's publication in *Philosophical Transactions* of his
important and now fully developed theory of terrestrial magnetism. Essentially Halley was faced with finding some detailed theoretical explanation for the variation in readings of the compass, a
variation that causes a slow shift of the magnetic poles as the
years pass, a so-called secular shift which amounts to a few minutes
of arc per year. His "An Account of the Cause of the Change of the
Variation of the Magnetickal Needle, with an Hypothesis of the
Structure of the Earth" was written only after a careful examination of the form and magnitude of the variation, and resulted in
his proposal that the earth had four, not two, magnetic poles. Two
of these he conceived as being fixed firmly in position in the outer
crust of the earth. The other two poles lay, he suggested, within
an inner core, and this inner core, he supposed, also rotated like
the crust itself, but at a slower rate. Such an idea would account
for a change in the position of a magnetic needle, since the needle
would be affected by both sets of poles, and the fact that one pair
lagged behind the other would mean that the direction of the magnetic needle would vary its position as time passed.

By 1692 Halley had analyzed the evidence in greater detail
than he had been able to do in 1683, and his theory met with great
success. In his lifetime it was considered to be one of the most important aspects of his work, and when Michael Dahl (1656–1743)

painted his portrait when Halley was eighty, he depicted him holding in his hand a sheet of paper on which there is a diagram of
the earth showing its four magnetic poles, the outer crust and the
inner core. Unfortunately Halley's theory can no longer be accepted, yet, as Professor Sydney Chapman has pointed out, "Geomagnetism, and especially the Earth's main field and its secular
variation, is rightly regarded as one of the most intractable subjects
for theoretical study," and although Professor Chapman's own work
at the present day has done more than any other to help in arriving at a solution, final agreement among the scientific world still
lies in the future.

The respect and admiration of Halley's colleagues was not
shared by Flamsteed, and he began to try to pretend that the theory
was not original. In a letter to Towneley written as early as November 1686 and three years after Halley's first paper on terrestrial
magnetism, he claimed that Halley was "not ashamed to borrow
where he can, but he blushes whenever he is forced to acknowledge
it. His discourse in the former Transactions concerning the variation of the needle and the 4 poles it respects, I am more than suspi-
cious was got from Mr. Perkins, the Master of the mathematical
school at Christ's Hospital, who was very busy upon it when he died,
and often told me that the needle did not point to any particular
and certain pole but to respective points (which we find betwixt
Mr. Halley's poles) on earth. Mr. Halley was frequently with him
and wrought himself into an intimacy with Mr. Perkins before his
death, and never discoursed anything of his 4 poles till sometime
after I found it published in the Transactions. I charged him mod-
estly with it but he made no answer to the purpose, knowing that
Mr. Perkins had a paper entered on the Journal of the Society,
whereby he may be convinced of his cunning." Here we can see
Flamsteed's condemnation in its true colors, for Perkins' unpublished
paper has little if anything to do with Halley's theory; the conversa-
tions may have been stimulating, but certainly they were no more.

Flamsteed's sly digs at Halley continued after the appearance of the improved theory, but all to no avail. Newton was tired
of them, and Abraham Sharp (1653?–1742), who had been Flamsteed's assistant from 1684 to 1689 and knew his failings as well as

his undeniable qualities as an astronomer, would not be drawn into the controversy. After 1692 Halley's reputation was growing daily, and in continuing his vituperation Flamsteed was doing himself more injury among his scientific colleagues than any harm he could do Halley. The pity of it all is that it would have taken so little to heal matters, but Flamsteed was so set in his course that this proved impossible.

In spite of disappointment over the Savilian professorship, Halley's scientific work went on unabated. There was hardly a meeting of the Society during 1692 which he did not address on some subject, and there also exist a number of unpublished papers for this year. Of these, all but two were in one way or another concerned with shipping. The first, dated January 13, deals with "An Instrument for Measuring the Way of a Ship," and its interest lies in Halley's application of Newton's calculus. His idea was that the rate of motion of a ship could be shown to be proportional to the tilt from the vertical of a heavy body towed from the stern. In this paper he worked out the figures and suggested a design for the kind of body which, if towed, would clearly demonstrate the tilt it was undergoing.

The second paper concerned with shipping was read at the end of March. In this Halley provided what he believed to be a new design of quadrant with telescopic sights for shooting the altitude of celestial bodies at sea. It was ingenious but had previously been devised by Hooke, and a model of Hooke's design was actually found tucked away in the Society's repository; although Halley had come to it quite independently he was quite happy that Hooke should take priority. The third paper discussed "A Method of Enabling a Ship to Carry its Guns in Bad Weather." In bad weather it was the practice to lay up warships when not in use, and as a result the timbers became distorted due to the weight of the guns. Halley's idea was to fit a special tackle of ropes and pulleys to distribute the strain. Hooke in his manuscript diary calls the idea "absurd," but the real reason it was not taken up seems to have been its complexity.

Of the other unpublished papers one merely dealt with a report of the outflow of water from vessels from experiments made by "a

very curious and intelligent man," a Mr. Chamberlain of "Redding,"
but another was more significant. It was "A Description of an Instrument to Observe the Celestial Motions &c. by reflexion, thro' a
Telescope, without elevating the Telescope towards the Object." It
begins with the comment: "The instrument I proposed some time
since, to observe Telescope sights at Sea, and wherin I found Dr.
Hook had gone before me, I take to be of so promising a contrivance yt I have ordered it to be made and adapted for that purpose,
of wood, for tryal and practice, and design one of brass for use."

Next Halley goes on to say that at first he could not bring himself to believe that a plain piece of glass could act as a really satisfactory reflector. Such a piece of glass was built into the instrument
he had proposed, however, for reflecting the bright image of the
sun. When Halley tried a rough model at night he found, to his
surprise, that he could "most distinctly discern all the small spotts
in the Moon." The glass was merely a flat piece of the kind used in
mirrors, and he believed a flat piece, optically prepared, would be
better. Even in his ordinary quality glass Halley saw star images
adequately reflected, and he goes on to say that it is clear that the
quadrant could be used at sea to shoot not only the sun but also the
moon.

He felt, however, that the instrument, or rather a development of it, had other potentialities. It seemed possible, he thought,
"by this method of reflection to keep the moon for many hours
together in a telescope without moving it, only by the motion of the
reflecting plate, which must be made to move either by hand or
clockwork, so as to answer the motion of the Heavens." There follows a detailed description of the technical layout of the proposed
new device. Again Hooke had anticipated Halley. "This (as I since
understand) has been long since proposed by Mr. Hook as a means
of managing a long telescope, viz by reflecting the beams of light
along ye tube, that need not be elevated in position." Halley went
on to remark, however, that no one knew how far Hooke had
pursued the idea, and as the Society possessed a telescope of 120-
feet focal length, it seemed to him that the idea should be put into
operation. In addition he suggested that the "reflecting plate"
should be housed in such a way as to prevent dew condensing on
its surface. To Halley and Hooke jointly, then, must go the credit

for the idea of what is now called a coelostat. Based on the principle enunciated by them both, it is used more particularly for studies of the sun where for technical reasons instruments of long focal length are needed so that a mounting of any other kind is impracticable.

Halley's unpublished papers do not contain all he did in 1692. From the Journal Books of the Royal Society we find that he addressed meetings on the cause of springs and proved that "the Hypothesis that all Springs are from Rains could not well hold"; on a design for "an Engine for grinding long glasses [lenses of long focal length] for Telescopes"; a mathematical law for determining the apparent size of objects seen under water or any other liquid and at any depth provided the refractive power of the liquid be known; a new form of pivot made from glass for a magnetic needle which would allow the needle to "vibrate much longer, and faster, than formerly"; he gave details of the "liquor" for covering his diving suit, consisting of equal parts of beeswax, tallow, turpentine, "and as much Train oyle§ as the rest . . ." He also promised to send to the Society some open, spongy, fretlike interiors of old shells "overgrown with green on the inside" which he found, and described certain kinds of ship's tackle "one whereof he demonstrated to have a fivefold purchase," as well as a model of a grab "made to take things up from the bottom of the Sea, which appeared to lay hold on anything." In November he addressed a meeting on "an Engine . . . whereby he proposed that 2 Men should raise to the hight of about as great a quantity of Earth, as ten Men should fill [it with] below," a device which Halley also claimed could "shoot its load, when at top, and erect itself again, when empty . . ."

Throughout the year he managed to continue his astronomical work. At meetings there were discussions on eclipses and lunar theory, but most important was a subject the Society specifically asked him to investigate and report on. This was the question whether the complete emptiness between bodies in space was unlikely, if not impossible; he suggested that the intervening material might be of such a kind as to be weightless and ordinarily unmeasurable. Such a substance was the ether which had been put forward from time to time in the past, and which was to play such

§ An oil obtained from whale blubber.

a large part in theories of light in the nineteenth century. Halley pointed out that if an ether existed its effect should be measurable, at least over long periods of time. With this in view he examined and compared the observations of the planets made in his own day with those of ancient times. He found some evidence of a resistive substance which slowed down the planets, and remarked that neglect of this had led others to claim preposterous discrepancies in observations by early Greek astronomers. His suggestion about the ether was wrong, but his conclusion about long-term changes was correct and showed that very early observations might be used in contemporary astronomical studies, a fact that he was to put to good use many years later.

There is an interesting postscript to the paper which, although in error, shows at least one effect of his recent experiences with religious orthodoxy. He claimed that the resistance he believed he had discovered would in due course stop all planetary motion with the result ". . . that the eternity of the World was hence to be demonstrated as impossible."

Even though Halley never turned against Flamsteed, he did defend himself against Flamsteed's denigrations of his St. Helena work. In 1692 he read a paper which was "a vindication of his Observations made at St. Helena from some groundless Exceptions of Mr. Flamsteeds, because of a difference found between his Observations, and those of one Pere Thomas made at Siam lately published by Pere Gony at Paris." His defense consisted of a demonstration of the close agreement between his own observations and those of Jean Richer made at Cayenne twenty years before. What is more, he showed that ". . . the principall difference between Pere Thomas and him fall out where he and Richer do perfectly agree." That Halley was annoyed at Flamsteed's abuse is hardly to be wondered at, and the Society's Journal Book records that ". . . Mr. Flamsteed being a Member of the Society he [Halley] desired the Society's leave publiquely to vindicate himself in print from this aspersion, which was permitted him: All personal reflexion being to bee forborn." The last sentence epitomizes Halley's attitude: All he wanted was the right to make known publicly that his observations were what he had claimed them to be, and he had no wish to have a private war with Flamsteed.

CHAPTER 10

Comets and Other Subjects

When he was thirty-six Halley published in *Philosophical Transactions* papers which are generally held to have laid the foundations for the study of social statistics and to have formed the basic actuarial approach on which life insurance is still computed. He was not the first to deal with the matter on a mathematical basis; bills of mortality were regularly issued giving the numbers of burials in a city. John Graunt (1620–74), a tradesman and train band captain* in London, had become interested in the subject, and his *Natural and Political Reflections . . . made upon the Bills of Mortality,* published in 1662, caused a considerable stir, even in court circles. Charles II recommended him to the Royal Society, to which he was elected a Fellow the next year. Graunt's book contained all manner of statistical information: He computed, for instance, that 7 percent of the male population lived to the age of seventy, and that only 1.5 percent of the female population died in childbirth. Some of his statistics were questionable, however, especially such statements as those claiming that no one would live over the age of eighty.

But a start had been made and his speculations particularly interested another Fellow, William Petty (1623–87), who studied chemistry, medicine, and spent a year with the philosopher Thomas Hobbes (1588–1679), eventually becoming professor of anatomy at Oxford. For a time he was a doctor to the Commonwealth army in Ireland, and it was while there that he organized a survey of the country that was social as well as geographical, and from this time on he devoted himself increasingly to political economy. Petty knew

* The train band was a body of civilian volunteers in London and other large cities in the sixteenth, seventeenth, and eighteenth centuries.

Graunt, and at the time Graunt's book was published many believed
Petty to be the real author. The truth may be that he helped Graunt,
but whatever the final evaluation the fact remains that Petty's work
rests secure on his own *Political Arithmetick,* published posthumously in 1690.

It was this book, perhaps, that helped stimulate Halley to think
about the matter again—as we have seen, in Chapter 3, he had
already made some observations in 1679 in a letter to Hooke—so
that when Henri Justel supplied the Society with bills of mortality
for Breslau, Halley thought of looking into the problem himself. In
the words of the *Biographia Britannica,* "they appeared to him, on
examination, to be drawn up with all the impartiality and exactness
. . . required; whereupon he applied himself to make a proper use
of them." Remembering that Halley was a trained mathematician
and that annuity calculations for determining what regular pay-
ments shall be agreed for life are essentially mathematical, it is not
surprising that he should find these bills the raw material for some
interesting theoretical work. The information which arrived in London gave the age and sex of all persons who had died in Breslau
during 1692, and in addition set these out on a month-to-month
basis. Halley computed a table showing the values of annuities
which an insurance company should provide, the intervals in his
table being made for five-year periods and continuing up to the
age of seventy. This he believed to be sufficient, ". . . leaving it to
the ordinary arithmetician to compleat the calculation, whenever
bills of mortality should be given for a suitable large number of
years." Even now five-year intervals are considered adequate.

Technically the paper is interesting for the annuity table it
contains and the many facts Halley draws from it—finding the number of men of military age, for instance—and also for his suggestion
that geometrical shapes can be used for the solution of annuity
problems. From a biographical point of view it is enlightening, for
it shows his outlook on his fellow human beings. His own words,
written as comments to the table, cannot be bettered: "how un-
justly we repine at the shortness of our lives, and think ourselves
wronged if we attain not old age. Whereas it appears hereby, that
the one half of those that are born, are dead in seventeen years

time. So that instead of murmuring at what we call untimely death, we ought with patience and unconcern to submit to that dissolution, which is the necessary condition of our perishable materials, and of our nice and frail structure and composition: and to account it a blessing, that we have survived perhaps many years that period of life, whereat the one half of the race of mankind does not arrive. A second observation I make from the same table is, that the growth and increase of mankind is not so much stinted by any thing in the nature of the species, as it is from the cautious difficulty most people make to adventure on the state of marriage, from the prospect of the trouble and charge of providing for a family; nor are the poorer sort herin to be blamed, since their difficulty of subsisting is occasioned by the unequal distribution of possessions, all being necessarily fed from the earth, of which so few are masters; so that besides themselves and families, they are yet to work for those who own the ground that feeds them. And of such does by very much the greater part of mankind consist, otherwise it is plain that there might well be four times as many births as we now find. For by computation from the table, I find that there are nearly 15,000 persons above 16 and under 45 years of age, of which at least 7,000 are women capable to bear children; of these, notwithstanding, there are but 1238 born yearly, which is but little more than a sixth part, so that about one in six of these women breed yearly. Whereas were they all married, it would not appear strange or unlikely, that four of six should bring a child every year. The political consequences hereof I shall not insist upon; but the strength and glory of a King consisting in the multitude of his subjects, I shall only hint, that above all things celibacy should be discouraged, as by extraordinary taxing and military service, and those who have numerous families of children to be countenanced and encouraged by such laws, as the *jus trium liberorum†* among the Romans; but especially by an effectual care to provide for the subsistence of the poor, by finding them employments whereby they may earn their bread without being chargeable to the public."

These remarks are of interest. On the one hand he appreciated

† A law concerned with privileges for those having three or more children.

the political need for a substantial population, and on the other he shows a desire to have an effectual employment system so that the poor are not a burden on the public. These are the views of a man to whom poverty was a stranger, and his remarks about work for the poor do not seem to have been made with the idea that continued unemployment is a soul-destroying condition as was appreciated by another scientist, Count Rumford (1753–1814), exactly a century later.

The publication of his thoughts on annuities stimulated other work, and his ideas did not pass without criticism. In 1736 a Mr. Weyman Lee attacked Halley's rules on annuities in "An essay to ascertain the values of leases and annuities for years and lives," but this was answered by a pamphlet published three years later under the initials H.B.I.T.S. and called "Observations on an Essay . . . Wherein Dr Halley's method is particularly considered, and rules laid down for estimating the chances of the duration of lives, and the value of annuities for years and lives, in a letter to a friend." In the main, though, Halley's work was followed up without contention, the first full treatment of annuities being published in 1743 soon after his death, by the French mathematician Abraham De Moivre (1667–1754?). But it is worth noting that when the charters of the Amicable Society were drawn up and published in 1790, Halley's table from his *Philosophical Transactions* paper was printed in full.

In 1690 Halley, probably busy with his diving experiments, made it known that he would be leaving London; this we find from the Society's Council minutes, which for November 19 record: "Mr. Cramer and Mr. Sharp do attend Mr. Waller as Secretary, and that his report of their abilities do determine, whether of the two shall be accepted as a Deputy to E. Halley during his absence." But he was soon back, and on January 21, 1691 Waller reported to the council ". . . that he had not done any thing in relation to Mr. Cramer and Mr. Sharp by reason that E. Halley was returned to London and entered again into his place as Clerk to the Society."

It was at this time that the *Philosophical Transactions* was in difficulties. As previously mentioned, it was neither printed nor published from 1688 to 1690, and only after Halley's return at the beginning of 1691 was republication considered. On January 28 ". . . it was resolved that there shall be Transactions printed, and that the Society will consider the means for effectually doing it. And Dr. Tyson, Dr. Sloane, Mr. Waller and Mr. Hook were desired to be assistent to E. Halley in compiling and drawing up the Transactions." The *Philosophical Transactions* came out once more in 1691, Halley still acting as editor, but there were only three issues; and at the end of the following year, 1692, after only one issue had appeared, Halley resigned his editorship. Once again the Society considered whether publication could continue, and in the minutes of the December Council meeting it is recorded that "Halley offered that if it shall be undertaken to print a book of Philosophicall matters such as the Transactions used to consist of, that he would undertake to furnish de proprio five sheets in twenty." In other words, although he no longer wished to edit *Philosophical Transactions* he was willing to provide a quarter of the published material himself. At this time the Society was regular in paying his salary as Clerk, and it cannot have been on this score that Halley resigned his editorship.

Halley had a very productive year in 1693. Through the medium of *Philosophical Transactions* he published no less than five other papers in addition to the one on the Breslau mortality tables. As usual some papers were more significant than others. There was one on thermometry in which he investigated the suitability of different fluids for use in thermometers and the points that should be determined for the upper and lower limits of the thermometer scales, but the results were inconclusive. Then he considered the heating effect of the sun at various latitudes and a way of analyzing the observational results mathematically. But more important than either of these was his study of the solar and lunar tables of the tenth-century astronomer Albategnius (al-Battani, d. A.D. 929). Albategnius had made corrections to the apparent paths of the sun and moon and provided tables which were an improvement on those of Ptolemy. Halley's paper gave amendments to these, one of which was of considerable importance to seventeenth-century astronomers. By a careful discussion of eclipses as a guide to the moon's apparent motion, Halley inferred that over the years there was a gradual acceleration in the average rate of the moon's orbital motion, a conclusion which indicated that the moon's orbit and its average distance from the earth were altering as time passed.

To arrive at this result took some time, and although in 1693 he published only his corrections to Albategnius's tables, he continued to work on the problem for two years before he was in a position to publish his conclusion of a secular acceleration, which was later confirmed by other mathematicians, notably Tobias Mayer (1814–87). Only in the present century has the physical cause been proved to be a tidal effect.

His last two papers published in 1693 deal with optical matters. Both are of interest, for in one Halley set out in a couple of pages various "Queries" concerned with the nature of light and its behavior when passing through what he called "diaphanous" bodies. It was not a paper full of new ideas but rather a list of questions that had raised themselves in his mind, probably after reading Christiaan Huyghens' (1629–95) *Traité de la Lumière,* which had been published in 1690. A paper of this kind may now seem a little quaint, but in the seventeenth century and well on into the eighteenth, a list of queries was a means of drawing the attention of other scientists to the problems in a particular field of study. Newton, in his *Opticks,* followed this approach, and his questions stimulated a considerable amount of theoretical as well as practical work.

Halley's second optical paper was more elaborate and original and aroused considerable interest when it appeared; it was produced in answer to a request from Molyneux, who reproduced it as an appendix to his own book on lenses and the refraction of light.‡ In essence, it was a method of using algebra to solve the problem of finding the point at which lenses of different kinds bring light to a focus, and although the technique is now well known, in Halley's day no widely applicable system was available, particularly for thick lenses, until this paper appeared. Because of the generalized form in which Halley expressed his results, its field of subsequent application was enormous, so that it not only appeared in *Philosophical Transactions* and in Molyneux's book, but also in a

‡ William Molyneux, *Dioptrice Nova,* first edition 1692.

supplement to a posthumous edition of David Gregory's *Catoptrice et Dioptrice Sphaericae Elementa*. The paper was of use not only in providing a powerful method of dealing with a specific optical problem, it served equally well as advocate for the new algebraic methods instead of the hitherto universally adopted geometrical techniques.

In 1693 Halley's growing reputation as a man of science was underlined by a visit he received from James Houghton (d. 1705). Houghton, a Fellow of the Royal Society, was an active writer and reformer who concerned himself with improvements in agriculture and trade, and published a weekly journal, *A Collection for the Improvement of Husbandry and Trade*. Houghton was at this time trying to assess the number of acres in each English county, but he was unable to discover how to do this, and, more particularly, make an estimate of the total land area in the country. Halley attacked the problem, found the answer, and published his results in the issue of Houghton's journal that appeared on January 20, 1693; it is worth seeing how he managed to deal with the question in view of the fact that, as he stated, even the best maps were probably in error by "a million or two of acres."

Halley's method of determining the total acreage was simple: He weighed pieces cut out of a map, the weighing being carried out "in nine scales" (in nine sections). Halley began by weighing the largest circle he could cut from the biggest map of England available. This first section covered a distance of 69⅓ miles, and Halley could readily calculate that it must therefore contain 9,665,-000 acres. Since the circle was only a quarter of the weight of the map covering the whole land area of England, he arrived at a total acreage of 38,660,000, claiming that this would probably be no "wild conjecture." In the event it was surprisingly close to the present figure of 37,475,000, giving a difference of a little less than 1¼ million acres—a total error of just over 3 percent.

Using the same map and the same method, Halley went on to determine the number of acres per county, taking as his standard a piece of map representing 40,000 acres and weighing approximately one grain. The total he obtained for all counties amounted to 39,-938,500 acres, an increase of a little more than 3 percent over his previous figure but rather more in error with modern determinations. Houghton seems to have been satisfied and at a later date turned again to Halley, this time to solicit his help in determining the price of bread of various kinds. Halley prepared a table giving the weight of a penny loaf, taking into account the kind of loaf, the price of wheat, and the baker's profit.

In all its long history the Royal Society has never had a Clerk who was such an "industrious bee" as Edmond Halley. His output of papers was phenomenal, his unpublished work prodigious, and his range of interests surprising even for the seventeenth century, when lack of specialization was an advantage rather than a limitation; and although he did not live at Gresham College, where the Society met until it moved to Crane Court in 1710, he certainly carried out experiments there. His work on magnets, already mentioned, was but one of a series of trials that he made, and in 1693 he carried out some studies on the evaporation of water.

These experiments are not of great interest in themselves; but the conclusion he drew from them in a paper published the next year is quite significant. Halley used his results as the basis for a discussion of the evaporation of sea water; he deduced that there must be a gradual increase in the salinity of the oceans. He then went on to propose that from regular measurements of this increase one could compute how long ago the oceans were composed of fresh water. Such a calculation, Halley claimed, would give a factual measure of the age of the earth. This was one of the earliest rational and scientific approaches to a question which had hitherto been answered purely by an examination of genealogies found in Genesis. Approximate results did not lead Halley to suggest an eternal existence for the earth but merely a great age, far in excess of estimates obtained from calculations based on Genesis, and his results and general attitude cannot have pleased the Flamsteeds and Bentleys of his time. Although Halley's arguments do not find favor now, his method of taking experimental facts and using them to work back in time is a technique which is generally adopted today. At later meetings of the Society Halley also suggested that the Caspian Sea was a water-filled depression caused by a comet striking the earth at the time of the biblical flood, and he computed the amount of water involved in the deluge.

Side by side with Halley's excursions into prehistory was a host of other papers on science and mathematics. He became interested in logarithms and their use, and the solution of equations; he discussed developments of Descartes' marriage of algebra and geometry, the areas under curves, and problems of applied mathematics, including something more on gunnery. The earth's magnetism still claimed some of his attention, and he prepared a map of the South Pole on which he drew variations of the compass using a technique which he was soon to develop in a far more satisfactory fashion. Weather phenomena such as rings around the sun and moon and mock suns or parhelia also intrigued him; while he also tried his hand at cartography, producing a survey of Hugh Myddleton's (1563–1631) New River—a canal and aqueduct that had been constructed in 1613 to bring water from Ware in Hertfordshire to provide London with a supply of clean water—and mathematically analyzed long sea routes using both the map projection devised by Gerard Mercator (1512–94) as well as the customary navigational charts. Astronomically he discussed the apparent motion of the sun, and spent time adapting some tables of eclipses and other phenomena of Jupiter's satellites published in Paris by Cassini and Römer so that they could be used for the meridian of London and dated by the Julian calendar, which was still current in England. He reported on geological observations on the Isle of Wight, on a London windmill used for raising water, and he even presented the foot of an eagle "with its talons very sharp and large" to the Society's repository. Everything of interest came under his jurisdiction as Clerk.

A side of Halley's interests that is less known is his concern with archaeology. Perhaps it was engendered by his curiosity about the early stages of the earth's history and particularly of the flood, or possibly in part as an outcome of his classical and Hebrew scholarship. Whatever it was he does not seem to have been able to pass by without comment any Latin inscription or passage in a Roman author concerned with place distances or datings of battles and conquests. Probably his most extensive discursion into this field was his paper in *Philosophical Transactions* for 1695 on "the ancient state of the City of Palmyra." In 1678 and 1691 English Turkey merchants with trade connections in the Middle East had visited the ruined oasis city, supposed to have been built by Solomon. Reports and descriptions of the 1691 visit were sent to Halley, and he not only collated them but tried to find earlier references in classical literature. In November 1695 he was able to give an interim report to the Society and, a month later, provided further details, including an analysis of an inscription found there; the interest his work aroused led him to prepare his paper for *Philosophical Transactions*.

It was clear to him that Palmyra had been a city of considerable wealth owing to its geographical situation, for it was an oasis on the overland trade route between Syria and Babylonia (Iraq). Its ruins were impressive, with a large temple, huge triumphal arches, and colonnaded streets, and it is little wonder that it fired Halley's imagination. His paper seems to have awakened widespread interest, not only among Fellows of the Royal Society, for in the middle of the next century three British antiquaries made an extensive study of the ruins and published their results which, for more than a hundred years, were reprinted in shortened form in almost every encyclopedia.

As far as Halley's astronomical career is concerned, 1695 was most notable because it was then that he began a program of calculation which, more than anything else, was destined to make his name remembered by later generations. This was his work on cometary orbits. The success of his research, to be published a decade later in 1705, was important from many points of view and regarded highly by his contemporaries. Yet at the time it was considered as only a part of his general contribution to science, to be valued no more than his suggestions about using the transit of Venus to determine the sun's distance, his study of terrestrial magnetism, or his lunar observations and research into lunar theory. Only since his memory has faded and his cometary prediction was dramatically proved correct has this one contribution been inflated at the expense of his other achievements. To see this nevertheless important side of Halley's work it will be as well to consider it completely here, but to appreciate it fully something must first be said about comets and the views of them current at the time Halley entered on the scene.

Comets had been observed from the earliest times. They were unlike the normal celestial phenomena since their appearances were short-lived, lasting at the most for a few months, yet as if to counteract this they were the most conspicuous objects in the sky, and the most peculiar, with their bright heads and long, glowing tails sometimes spreading across nearly half the night sky. And unlike the sun, moon, and stars, which were regular and reliable in their appearances, comets came suddenly in a blaze of glory and vanished with equal rapidity, presumably to be seen no more. They seemed to follow no set laws, and although objects of study to the philosopher, to the public at large they were considered omens—and almost invariably as omens of disaster. In the earliest historical times and before, as well as during the whole history of Greek astronomy, they were believed to be some unusual phenomenon in the upper air and were classified as meteorological, being coupled in men's minds with such strange effects as lunar and solar halos, falls of meteors, and any other phenomena which were considered close to the earth, yet forever out of reach.

The exact nature of this meteorological rarity was open to a host of interpretations. To some they were optical illusions, to others exhalations of vapor from the earth which became ignited in the upper air, while to the more imaginative and less scientifically minded, comets were the souls of illustrious men being carried in triumph to heaven. Yet whatever their explanation most people, including many philosophers, considered them to be omens of evil. They presaged God's judgment on the world, or they were a sign that bode ill for this ruler or that, and even as late as Halley's day these superstitions persisted. With the view that a comet was a hot and dry exhalation of vapor in the upper air, the idea that they should be followed by a hot, dry spell of weather with the consequent dangers of widespread infection was not illogical, but such reasoning was that of comparatively few men; to most, a comet was a terrifying portent of evil days ahead.

All the same, the philosopher, however much he himself might be worried at the appearance of a comet, could not resist making some attempt to classify them, and in the second century A.D. Pliny the Elder summed up the various types in his *Historia Naturalis*. The classification was not one concerned with whereabouts in the sky—although for astrological reasons this was usually noted—but with appearance. His list is picturesque if not particularly helpful scientifically, for he gives the comets such names as blood-red, bearded, horn like, burning torch, or horse's mane. Dates of appearance as well as a description survive in early records, but not all ancient reports are to be relied upon as descriptions are often confused, so that it is sometimes impossible to tell whether what occurred was an aurora, a comet, or some other temporary occurrence in the sky.

The first truly astronomical analysis of the nature of comets came in the sixteenth century after the publication of Copernicus's hypothesis that the sun was the center of the planetary system, and when the very nature of the universe was in question. The point at issue then was the crucial one of whether a comet was a phenomenon that took place in the upper air or whether, in fact, it was some truly astronomical event that lay beyond the sphere of the moon. As mentioned in Chapter 2, the man to solve this particular problem was Brahe, who observed with the greatest possible care the bright comet of 1577, and also gathered together data from the many observations which were made in Europe at this time—observations which were stimulated not only by the controversy as to where comets really lay but also by the wide popular interest that this very conspicuous object aroused. Brahe examined the data, and although he could give no precise measure of distance for the comet, he was able to prove that it certainly lay farther from the earth than the moon.

The old controversy was ended, but now a new one took its place, for since a comet had been proved to be a truly astronomical phenomenon, its path in the sky must be charted, and considerable argument arose about the nature of its course. On the face of it this may seem a simple enough problem, but a comet is only visible for a short period of time. Before the days of the telescope this amounted to a matter of weeks at the most, and even after the telescope came into use it was a very long time before this period could be appreciably extended. In brief, a comet could be observed for only a short section of its path among the background of stars. Brahe ascribed a circular path to the comet of 1577, and centered it on the sun; but this was based on speculation, not observation. Kepler also attacked the problem, and came to the conclusion that comets really moved at varying speeds in a straight line, yet those who followed him favored a curved path of some kind. Cassini tried forms of circular orbits, while Giovanni Borelli (1608–69) and Hevelius suspected that they could travel in parabolas; in England Seth Ward suggested that comets moved either in circular or elliptical paths. But only when the *Principia* had appeared was the matter placed on a sounder basis, since Newton made clear that a comet must move under the gravitational influence of the sun, and specified precisely the force that was operating. Yet even he was unable to determine the path exactly, and concluded that their paths were parabolic.

The essential difficulty in determining cometary paths is that they are visible for so short a time that the measurements of their apparent position in the sky may take a number of different forms, even if we consider their motion to be under the sun's gravitational influence. Three kinds of path are possible: the parabola that Newton favored, the ellipse suggested by Seth Ward, and the more open curve, the hyperbola. These curves are shown in Figure 4, and it will be seen that close to the sun they very nearly coincide; yet this is the only part of their movement that observation could cover. The problem could have been solved observationally if comets could have been tracked farther out in space (to the right-hand side of Figure 5), but this was the very thing that could not be done.

Newton, who was concerned with gravitational effects, favored the parabola, since this would give a sudden approach, followed by visual appearance when close to the sun, and then a disappearance back into space. Newton realized that an ellipse giving a perpetual return of a comet was theoretically possible, but he seems to have thought the evidence unlikely to support this contention. Hooke, it is true, had followed his master Ward in considering a closed orbit, but he too could do no more than speculate. It is here that

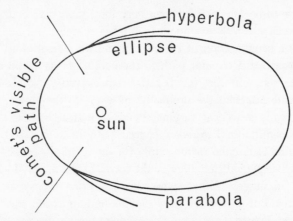

FIGURE 5   *Possible paths of comets. Since comets can be observed only when close to the sun, it is difficult if not impossible to determine whether a cometary path is an ellipse, a hyperbola, or a parabola.*

Halley enters the arena, for in 1695 he began the laborious task of computing the paths of comets using Newton's concept of gravitation and his newly invented calculus.

It is important that the work involved be not underestimated. To compute the path of a comet from comparatively few observations is difficult in the extreme, and it becomes the more complex when in considering such an elliptical path, the calculations have to take into account not only the effect which the earth would have on the path at each circuit of the comet, but also the gravitational effects of the more distant planets when a comet passes near them. Newton himself had very carefully computed the path of the comet of 1680 which Halley had observed in France, but Halley took matters a step farther. In his customary way he went back to earlier times, to the work of previous astronomers, and collected together every scrap of cometary information he could find. Next he assessed these and accepted only those cases where the observations seemed to be of sufficient accuracy to make calculation worthwhile. As Halley put it, this was an "immense labour," for he carefully calculated the paths of twenty-four comets observed at different times. This actually involved him in twenty-six sets of calculations, because he found that it was important to adjust and so recompute his results for the comets of 1680 and 1682. Fortunately, the sixteenth and seventeenth centuries had seen an unusually large number of bright comets, and this gave Halley a quantity of accurate observations.

Halley was the first independent astronomer to apply the law of universal gravitation to a specific astronomical problem, and he kept in touch regularly with Newton. He did not attend to the problem continuously between 1695 and 1705, but in 1695 he launched himself into it with immense vigor, and this was the year during which he had his main correspondence with Newton. Halley reported his results as he arrived at them, and as early as September 28 he had come to the conclusion that the comets with which he was dealing had elliptical paths. His own words show clearly what he was about: ". . . having done the Comet of 1683 [computed the orbit from observations], which I can represent most exactly; and that of 1664 (wherin I find Hevelius has not been able to observe with the exactness requisite,) as near as I conceivd it possible; I fell to consider that of 168%₁ [1680–81] which you have described in your book [the *Principia*], and looking over your Catalogue of the observed places, I find in that of the 25th of January 1681, there is a mistake of 20 minutes, in the Longitude of that day, or 56 minutes for 36, and so I have it in a lre [letter] Mr. Flamsteed sent me when I was at Paris. I thought fitt to advertise this, because you wrote me you designed to undertake to correct what you had formerly determined about the Orb therof; and that day is one of those you have taken to define the orb by. I find certain indication of an Elliptick Orb in that Comet and am satisfied that it will be very difficult to hitt it exactly by a Parabolick. When I have computed all the Observations, I shall send you what I have done."

Since the differences between parabolic and elliptical orbits are so slight close to the sun, Halley was forced to be meticulous about the observational evidence. As his work progressed he became convinced about elliptical orbits and, in particular, that the bright comet that had appeared in 1682 and for which he first computed a parabolic orbit, could be identified with the bright comet of 1531, a consequence that could only be true if the orbit were elliptical. To complete his identification he needed more observations of the 1682 appearance, and Flamsteed was the man to approach for these. Halley knew that he would have difficulty in obtaining Flamsteed's cooperation, so at the end of a letter to Newton he wrote: "I must entreat you to procure for me of Mr Flamsteed what he has observed of the Comett of 1682 particularly in the month of September, for I am more and more confirmed that we have seen that Comett now three times, since ye Yeare 1531, he will not deny it you, though I know he will me." Flamsteed's bitterness was still as strong as ever, and it is tragic that Halley had to write to Newton for this information which, as Astronomer Royal, Flamsteed had no real right to withhold. At all events Newton obtained the required information from Flamsteed, whose observations Halley valued highly. "I . . . would wish that Mr Flamsteed had seen it [another comet, that of 1680] at least once for all the rest are very course observers," he wrote to Newton. Finally he concluded that the 1682 comet traveled in an ellipse, and he started working on new calculations.

In his correspondence with Newton, Halley also discussed the question of the gravitational effect of the large planets Jupiter and Saturn on elliptical cometary paths. "I must entreat you to consider how far a Comets motion may be disturbed by the Centers of Saturn and Jupiter, particularly in its ascent [its return path] from the Sun, and what difference they may cause in the time of the Revolution of a Comett in its so very Elliptick Orb." He experienced great trouble with the comet which appeared at the end of 1664 and the beginning of 1665. Thus he told Newton, "I have with some difficulty mastered that of 1664/5, but I was obliged to have recourse to the observations themselves, and to adjust and compare them together, and recalculate the whole, before I could make them agree with any tollerable exactness, and I suspect that Mr. Hevelius, to help his calculations to agree with the hevens, had added 8 or 9 minutes to the places observed . . ."

But Halley was not satisfied merely to calculate the exact path which would fit those comets for which he had the observations or calculations of astronomers like Hevelius. He critically examined them, computed the cometary paths, and then proceeded to calculate the exact form of the elliptical orbits which the comets of 1680 and 1682 would have on their next revolution around the sun. This was exceedingly difficult since Halley was, as it were, working in the dark. He had to take into account the disturbing effects of Jupiter and Saturn and this, in turn, meant carefully computing exactly where these planets would be at those instants when the comets concerned would be nearest to them in space. Then, once these perturbations were determined, he had next to alter the elliptical paths by a small amount, and then recalculate the exact rate of orbital motion for the next close approach of each comet to the sun. Even this did not clear the problem completely, for having once found the path each comet would take, Halley had to calculate first the earth's position as it would be at the time in question and next compute where in the sky the comet would appear to an observer on earth.

Halley found that the comet of 1680 appeared to have an orbital period of 575 years; the orbit he obtained was extremely elliptical and meant that it moved far away from the sun in space. He computed the date of its next appearance, but more recent research has shown that in this case Halley appears to have been mistaken. He worked out the orbit of the 1682 comet, however, and this he found to be a less elongated ellipse, giving a period of seventy-six years. He also discovered that it was the same comet that had appeared previously in 1531 and 1607, and from his calculations he predicted that it would reappear at Christmas 1758. Knowing that it was highly improbable that he would be alive, Halley appealed to later astronomers to watch carefully for it and give due credit for the scientific prediction of its return, asking them "to acknowledge that this [the predicted return] was first observed by an Englishman." The comet was in fact detected on Christmas Day 1758 and delayed in its return, as Halley had foreseen, by the gravitational attraction of Jupiter and Saturn, although the observed delay was just a little more than the figure he had calculated. Nevertheless, it appeared in that part of the sky Halley had determined more than fifty-five years before.

The successful prediction caused great excitement in the scientific world, which did not fail to acknowledge the Englishman who had computed its return and, in his memory, it was named "Halley's comet." The fact that the prediction was correct lifted the whole subject of cometary astronomy out of uncertainty into the realms of precise astronomical endeavor. Perhaps the aura that has surrounded this discovery is partly due to the romance and in some cases to the superstition that still is attached to the appearance of a bright comet, and partly to the fact that appearances of Halley's comet have so often been associated with political events.

The hard facts belie this political association, for although in the first decade of this century its previous visitations close to the sun were computed back to 239 B.C. (see Appendix II), out of a total of twenty-nine appearances only two have happened to coincide with historical events: its appearance in March 1066, which presaged the Battle of Hastings by seven months and was depicted in the Bayeux tapestry, and its arrival in April 1910, one month before the death of Edward VII. There is some excuse for the Normans and Saxons associating the comet with King Harold's disastrous defeat, for this was at a time when medieval views of comets had nothing to gainsay them, but in the twentieth century to suppose its advent had any connection with the death of an English King in his late sixties, is stretching the imagination too far. Astronomically, however, Halley's comet is a little unusual. It is the only conspicuous comet readily observable without a telescope that has a period of reappearance less than one hundred years, and it orbits the sun with a retrograde motion—a path that is opposite in direction to that of all the planets and other periodic comets.

The results of Halley's cometary work were published in 1705. They appeared first in Oxford under the title *Astronomiae Cometicae Synopsis* and in an English edition *A Synopsis of the Astronomy of Comets,* published simultaneously in London. During 1705 they also appeared in *Philosophical Transactions.* Eleven years later they were printed again, together with his table of "all comets that have been hitherto duely observed" in William Whiston's book for students describing Newton's *Principia* in simplified terms. Yet it was only after 1758, when his comet had reappeared as predicted, that the true value of Halley's research could be seen and its influence on later cometary studies have a real effect. From then onward the discovery of periodic comets using the telescope—for they are most dim objects, invisible to the naked eye when not very close to the sun—was taken up in earnest.

One other effect of Halley's work was to demonstrate the efficacy of Newton's theory of universal gravitation, a fact that was obviously appreciated by Whiston but which was underlined more strongly after 1758. Comets were now amenable to scientific study and mathematical analysis and, at least to those who could understand this, their terror was a thing of the past.

CHAPTER 11

The Mint and Visit of the Czar

In spite of his cometary research and administrative work, the determination of longitude still remained of great interest to Halley. During 1696 this was evident in a paper which contained "his desire that some persons, qualified with skill and Instruments would please to observe the Occultations and Transits of the fixt Stars by the Moon, there being as he conceives no surer method to determine the Longitudes of Places, than by such Observations, especially by the Occultations of Stars on the dark limb of the Moon, which are instantaneous." It was certainly a timely request, for not only would observations give the longitude of positions on land but, once these longitudes were known, would also assist in determining the moon's path in the sky. It is in a sense strange that Flamsteed never made a request of this kind, since his appointment as Astronomer Royal was for the express purpose of solving the longitude problem, but he seems to have been a lone worker who had a grand scheme of his own that he was determined to see through himself, distrusting the accuracy of measurements made by another observer. One is left wondering whether, perhaps, a less accurate solution might not have been a help for a time until greater precision had been achieved, as the kind of accuracy Flamsteed had in mind demanded a very long-term project.

But if longitude largely occupied Halley's thoughts, other subjects, ranging from spruce beer* prepared by Hevelius to bivalve molluscs petrified in marble also engaged his attention, as they were bound to since he was still Clerk to the Society. His interest in history continued and in February, having consulted some original

* Spruce beer was fermented from the leaves and branches of spruce.

records cited by Lord Tarbat, a Fellow of the Society, he reported "a passage in Buchanans history" clearly demonstrating the legitimacy of Robert III, King of Scotland. Again, in early May he read a paper demonstrating "that the Itinerary of Antonius and other Ancient Authors, mentioning the distances of Places, where the numbers are not Vitiated by time might be much relied on, for adjusting the Geographicall Situation of places and Countries of which we have at present but very short accounts particularly that it is not more than 40grs [40°] of Longitude from London to Scandroon, supposing no deflection of the Roads, as is agreeable to the observations of Eclipses made at Aleppo, whereas Geographers generally extend the Mediterranean several degrees too much to the East." With longitude in mind he once more sought early evidence for geographical determination of positions.

About this time Halley became involved in a matter of domestic government policy. By 1685 Parliament and William III had become deeply concerned over the debasement of silver currency due to the widespread practice of clipping small pieces from the coins for resmelting and subsequent sale. Only coins with a milled edge were safe from vandalism; the rest were easy to deface without it being obvious. As a result of clipping, the currency began to lose value, while obtaining silver in this way became an increasingly profitable pastime. As one contemporary historian put it, ". . . in a course of some years, the old money was every year so much diminished, that it at last grew to be less than the half of the intrinsick value; Those who drove this Trade, were as much enriched, as the Nation suffered by it." The King wished to issue a proclamation that the coinage should be assessed by weight alone, but the Exchequer objected, and in due course it became clear that the only satisfactory solution was to withdraw all coins without milled edges and to issue new coins, making the milled ones universal. This was a large and expensive undertaking but it was unavoidable; even though there were severe penalties for anyone found guilty of clipping, these were difficult to enforce and only resulted in such a general alarm about the value of money that there was a drop in the exchange rate amounting to nearly 30 percent. To deal with the great amount of work entailed in recoinage, additional mints were set up, and the cost to the country amounted to the immense sum of over two million pounds ($4.8 million).

The Chancellor of the Exchequer, Charles Montagu (1661–1715), who became the Earl of Halifax in 1714 and who had just been elected a Fellow of the Royal Society, was a great friend of Newton's and in 1696 engineered his appointment as Warden of the Royal Mint. At this time Newton was recovering from a period of intense mental depression and had turned on many of his friends, Montagu among them, claiming that they had betrayed him. The betrayal appears to have consisted of the failure to procure Newton an official position in London, but now Montagu could make amends. During the recoinage there was more than usual need for senior officers of the mint to be men of integrity; as the clipped money was called in, it was vital to ensure that the old coins were not pilfered for melting down, nor that the officers take advantage of what could be a very lucrative situation. Newton's was an ideal appointment, and he acquitted himself so well that three years later he was elevated to the more senior but less arduous position of Master of the Mint.

Five other mints were set up in the country to assist in the recoinage and, through Newton's recommendation, in the late summer of 1696, Halley was appointed Deputy Comptroller of the Mint at Chester, the Comptroller being William Molyneux. This appointment does not seem to have made it necessary for Halley to vacate his post as Clerk to the Society, so while at Chester he continued sending reports on interesting matters to Hans Sloane who, by 1693, had been elected one of the Secretaries. Originally Newton had toyed with the idea of appointing Halley his deputy in the Lucasian chair at Cambridge, but in fact this went to William Whiston, and it would appear likely that Halley had to move at little more than a month's notice, for from a letter dated October 12 and written from Chester Castle to Sloane, Halley begins with an apology about the Society's books which it seems Sloane had sent to him for completion.

"I had hoped," Halley wrote, "to have sent you by this time the Journall book of the Society compleat, but a great glutt of business, at the first opening of our Mint, requiring a constant attendance, has hindered me for some time, so that I must begg your excuse at present, but will speedily return you the Books, filled to the last recess of the Society, by some safe hand. In the mean time the Society meeting on Wensday next,† I have sent you the Minutes of the last Day when the Society adjourned, which you may please to separate from this." There follows at this point a mark and a footnote which reads, "Conceal my letter to this mark," so perhaps in seeing to preparations for his voyage in the Atlantic (Chapter 12) and the rush of departure Halley had left his duties uncompleted.

The letter continues with general information: "There are severall Antiquities in and about this place in custody of private persons, of which I will take care to give you a description; and the scituation of the City is very remarkable; being at the place where the river Dee ceases to flow, upon any other than the spring Tides. And the walls and all publique buildings are of a stone which is afforded by Quarries which are upon the spott, and in many places appear in the Ditch of the Town, which convenience I suppose occasioned the Romans to found the City here, which is square like the Roman Castra, and each side is about 600 or 700 Yards, and here was for a long time the head Quarters of the Legio XX. called Victrix." Halley goes on to say that he had taken his "Magneticall needle" with him and had so far found that the magnetic variation was less than at London, "and as I guess, not fully 4 degrees." He had not had time to draw a meridian line and determine the variation properly but promises to do so.

Later in October Halley promised to accede to the Society's request for more interesting facts, and writes that he will supply ". . . such information as I conceive may be acceptable to them. and particularly where I shall receive their commands to enquire into any matter." He thereupon reports on an altarpiece "dugg up here, about 3 years since" and gives the inscription, or such of it as was still legible, following this with his own analysis of the date of the stone from the internal evidence of the inscription itself, and promising to give further details if required. He also discusses the

† This was presumably the first meeting of a new session after the summer vacation.

peculiar and obviously impossible case of the birth of a puppy to a male greyhound. Halley states that the story was firmly, almost vehemently, believed in Chester and that the puppy was seen alive by a Mr. Robarts, who was a Fellow of the Society and who, in Halley's opinion, "can best judge what credit this uncouth story merits." The story was taken so seriously that the dog was killed and dissected, but found to be quite normal, although Halley, not wishing "to limit the powers of Nature" and on the other hand "not rashly to believe anything" decided to "suspend his opinion."

The Chester mint dealt only in silver coins of small denominations, and Halley hoped that the work would soon be finished, but in this he was disappointed, for he had to spend two years in Chester. He did such observing as he could and managed to get a sight of an eclipse of the moon, but clouds made impossible any accurate assessment of the times of the eclipse. In November he was ill and wrote to Sloane saying how disappointed he was that illness and the short winter nights had prevented him visiting a nearby windmill with horizontal sails and "built severall years since, and now out of use." Later he was able to report that the mill had the unusual contrivance of special "windows" by means of which the wind could be admitted on one side only, and he remarks that "admitting the Wind by a Window and but upon one saile at a time, it did not move without a strong gale of wind, and therefore was so seldome serviceable, as at length to be laid aside as useless and has not gone for some years." Nothing at Chester escaped his notice, and there are reports on the local waterworks system "which makes a good revenue for the proprietor" and the flow of the tidal River Dee.

By the spring of 1697 Halley must have become inured to his surroundings and settled down to make the best he could of his stay, for he organized a party to go to Mount Snowdon at the Whitsuntide holiday and asked the Society "what they would have me enquire into there." The results of the Snowdon expedition were reported in *Philosophical Transactions*, from which we learn that Halley took a barometer with him. Other extracts from his letters to Sloane were published in the same volume; they include "an account of an extraordinary Hail . . . on the 29th day of April . . ."

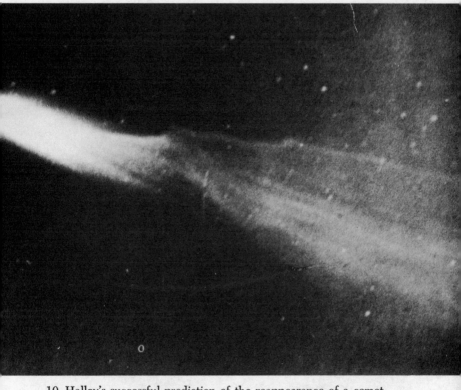

10. Halley's successful prediction of the reappearance of a comet had a profound effect on astronomers and public alike, taking the element of doubt from many cometary paths for the one and removing superstitious fears for the other. This enlarged photograph of the head and nearer portions of the tail taken at the comet's appearance late in April 1910 gives an idea of the changeable and still unpredictable physical appearance of such bodies.

11. The pink had a high narrow poop and bulging sides to increase storage space. Most pinks were Dutch, but the drawing here shows one of the few pinks in the British Navy; whether or not it is the *Paramore* cannot now be determined.

NATIONAL MARITIME MUSEUM, GREENWICH

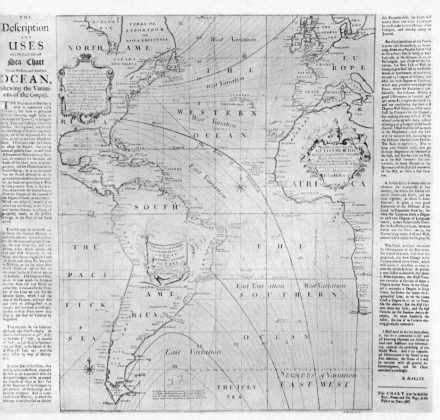

12. Halley's map of the Atlantic, the first map published to show lines of equal magnetic variation. It covers the area over which Halley voyaged (the route of the *Paramore* is shown by a dotted line), and in this copy, the now rare instructions have been stuck on the edges of the map.

AN
ADVERTISEMENT,

Neceſſary to be Obſerved in the

NAVIGATION

Up and Down the

CHANNEL of ENGLAND.

Mr Halley

Communicated by a Fellow of the ROYAL SOCIETY.

FOR ſeveral Years laſt paſt it has been Obſerved, that many Ships bound up the Channel, have by miſtake fallen to the Northward of *Scilly*, and run up the *Briſtol* Channel or *Severn Sea*, not without great Danger, and the Loſs of many of them. The Reaſon of it is, without diſpute, from the Change of the Variation of the Compaſs, and the Latitude of the *Lizard* and *Scilly*, laid down too far Northerly by near 5 Leagues. For from undoubted Obſervation the *Lizard* lies in 49° 55′, the middle of *Scilly* due Weſt therefrom, and the South part thereof neareſt 49° 50′. whereas in moſt Charts and Books of Navigation they are laid down to the Northward of 50°: and in ſome full 50° 10′. Nor was this without a good Effect as long as the Variation continued Eaſterly, as it was when the Charts were made. But ſince it is become conſiderably Weſterly, (as it has been ever ſince the Year 1657.) and is at preſent about 7⅕ Degrees; all Ships ſtanding in, out of the Ocean, Eaſt by Compaſs, go two Thirds of a Point to the Northward of their true Courſe; and in every eighty Miles they Sail, alter their Latitude about 10 Minutes; ſo that if they miſs an Obſervation for two or three Days, and do not allow for this Variation, they fail not to fall to the Northward of their Expectation, eſpecially if they reckon *Scilly* in above 50 Degrees. This has been by ſome attributed to the Indraught of St. *George*'s Channel, the Tide of Flood being ſuppoſed to ſet more to the Northward, than is compenſated by the Ebb ſetting out. But the Variation being allowed, it hath been found that the ſaid Indraught is not ſenſible, and that Ships ſteering two Watches *E b S* for one *Eaſt*, do exactly keep their Parallel. This practice is therefore recommended to all Maſters of Ships, who are unacquainted with the Allowances to be made for the Variation; as alſo that they come in, out of the Sea, on a Parallel not more Northerly than 49° 40′, which will bring them fair by the *Lizard*.

Nor is this the only Danger to which Ships are expoſed in the *Channel*, on account of this Change of the Variation; for this laſt Winter has given us more than one Inſtance of Shipwreck upon the *French* Coaſt and the *Caſketts*, of Ships newly departed from the *Downs*. And though perhaps this were not the only Cauſe of thoſe Loſſes, yet it cannot be doubted but it concurred thereto: For by the late curious Survey of the Coaſt of *France*; compared with what has been done for our own (though perhaps not altogether ſo exactly) it appears that the true Courſe from the Land of *Beachy* or *Dungyneſs* to the *Caſkett*-Rocks, is but Weſt 26 Degrees Southerly; which in former Times, when the Variation was as much Eaſterly, as now 'tis Weſterly, was about *S W b W* by Compaſs, and then a *W S W* Courſe, then called *Channel-Courſe*, was very proper for all Ships bound into the Ocean: But at preſent whoſo ſteers a *W S W* Courſe in the *Channel*, though never ſo near to the Shore of *Beachy*, will not fail to fall in with the *Caſketts*, or rather to the Eaſtwards thereof: It follows therefore, That as the Compaſs now Varies, the Weſt by South Courſe be accounted the *Channel*-Courſe, inſtead of *W S W*, which Courſe, from a reaſonable Offing from *Beachy-head*, will carry a Ship fair without the *Iſle of Wight*, and about mid-way between *Portland-Bill* and the *Caſkett*-Rocks; which are ſcarce 14 Leagues aſunder, and nearly in a *Meridian*. If this Notice be thought needleſs by thoſe, whoſe Knowledge and Experience makes them want no Aſſiſtance; yet if it it may contribute to the ſaving any one Ship, the Author thereof is more than recompenced for the little pains he has taken to communicate it.

LONDON: Printed for *Sam. Smith* and *Benj. Walford*, Printers to the Royal Society, at the *Prince's Arms* in St. *Paul's* Church-Yard. 1701.

13. This broadside on navigation in the English Channel (original is folio size) is very rare, and no copy is possessed by the British Museum. The purpose of the broadside is obvious enough, and although it was published anonymously, a contemporary hand has inserted Halley's name and, as the British Museum has remarked, it is clearly attributable "to no one but Halley." For permission to photograph and use this copy the author is indebted to K. K. Knight, Esq.

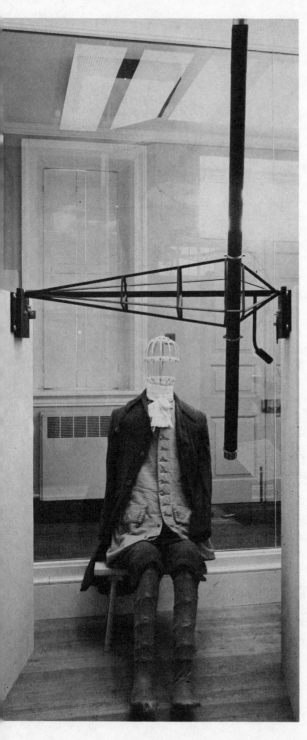

14. Halley's transit instrument, the first to be in regular use in Britain and perhaps the first to be used at all in the country. It may have been constructed by George Graham, but whoever made it, it was built so that its horizontal axis could be precisely adjusted by elevating or depressing one of the bearings. It seems to have had one cross wire in the eye-piece, and this was illuminated at night. It is here shown remounted close to its original position at the old Greenwich Observatory.

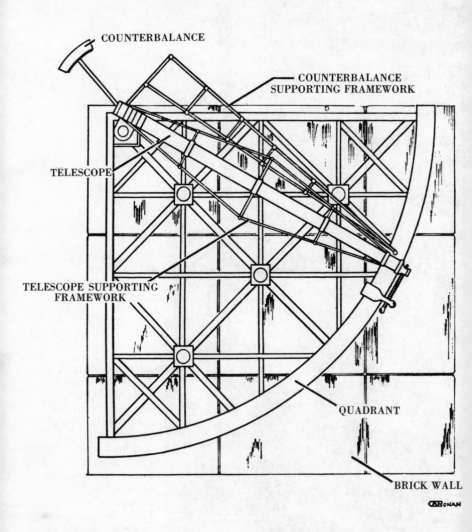

COUNTERBALANCE

COUNTERBALANCE
SUPPORTING FRAMEWORK

TELESCOPE

TELESCOPE SUPPORTING
FRAMEWORK

QUADRANT

BRICK WALL

15. Halley's mural quadrant, built by George Graham and installed at Greenwich in 1725, had a radius of eight feet. This drawing by the author has been prepared after an examination of the remains of the original instrument and the sectional drawings published in Robert Smith's *Compleat Opticks*, London, 1783.

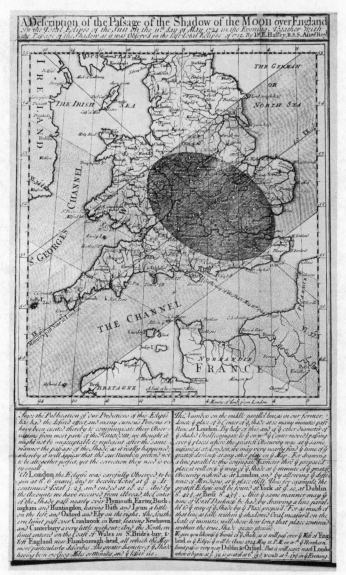

16. Halley made and published three solar eclipse charts. The first gave the predicted (computed) path for the moon's shadow across England and Wales on May 22, 1715; the second the predicted path across England and Wales for May 11, 1724; while the third showed the track of the latter eclipse across England, Wales, and western Europe. The second chart, shown here, is the most interesting of the three since it not only gives the predicted path of the 1724 eclipse, but also the actual path in the eclipse of 1715. The legend at the bottom of the chart is of significance, as it shows Halley's success in stimulating intelligent observations in place of ill-informed and fearful superstitions.

17. Halley at the age of eighty. This painting by Michael Dahl, now in the possession of the Royal Society, was executed in 1736 when Halley was eighty, a year
before the death of his wife and the onset of his slight paralysis. In his hand he
holds a sheet of paper on which there is a diagram of his geomagnetic hypothesis.

and his careful observations of an eclipse of the moon in September. Probably it was difficult during this year to find enough material for *Philosophical Transactions,* for besides these short notes Halley's description of the tidal theory in the *Principia* which he had presented to James II was printed as well.

Halley was forever hopeful that the work at Chester would come to a speedy end, and in late October 1697, in a letter to Sloane, wrote, "I hoped to have waited on the Society by their first meeting after their recess, but as yet the business of our Mint is not in such condition, that I can be spared for good and all; though in a month I guess wee shall have finished our whole coinage, which will be of very near 300000 li [pounds]: and besides I am subpœna'd on a Triall, which will not be till this day 3 weeks. In the mean time my heart is with you, and I long to be delivered from the uneasiness I suffer here by ill company in my business, which at least is but drudgery, but as we are in perpetuall feuds it is intollerable." The kind of clerical and administrative work which the post of Deputy Comptroller involved Halley obviously found tedious, was very different from the scientific stimulus he found as Clerk to the Royal Society, and left very little time for scientific observations, experiments, or even scientific discussions. In addition, his lot was made considerably more unpleasant by what he referred to in his letter as "perpetuall feuds."

The feuds had begun soon after Halley arrived in Chester, and were due to dishonesty over the way the clipped coins were called in. Both Halley and the Warden of the Mint, a Mr. Weddell, took their jobs seriously, and trouble began when they discovered irregularities in the behavior of two of the clerks, Bowles and Lewis. The details of these irregularities are uncertain but probably the two clerks were making money on their own behalf, perhaps by raising the value of the currency brought in for exchange and taking a percentage for themselves; at all events, Halley and Weddell insisted on seeing that the irregularities stopped. This might have been simple enough had not the Master of the Mint, a Mr. Clark, supported Bowles and Lewis, possibly because he himself received something of the clerks' illicit takings. Clark certainly made things difficult for Weddell and Halley, and during an argument with

Bowles and Lewis he took their part by "pretending to take offence at something that nobody else had observed in the company, went and borrowed Bowles his sword, to waylay the Warden as he went home."

But Clark did not waylay the Warden with or without Bowles' sword; in Halley's words, "He appeared, however, on the ground, before the hour, with his man and horses, and staid not after it, by which means they fought not, and I demonstrated the folly of such decisions that went no farther." But if Clark was a braggard, Lewis was a real troublemaker. Not satisfied with throwing an inkstand at Weddell, he persuaded Clark to bring a number of charges against Weddell and Halley, claiming that they had shown preference to certain friends over the purchase of clipped coins, that they added base metal to the silver before the new coins were cast and so carried out a private scheme of devaluation, keeping the balance of silver for themselves. Not content with this, they also accused Weddell of using expressions of a treasonable nature and dangerous to the Government he was supposed to serve. Indeed, it seems that the thwarted men between them accused Halley and Weddell of the very things they had planned themselves.

Halley was vexed and worried by these accusations, and even went so far as to ask Newton to intervene on his behalf with Montagu should the need arise. In due course Parliament voted that the five country mints should continue to operate, and on this Halley wrote to Newton on December 30, 1697, asking "that Lewis may appear face to face with me, before the Lords, there to answer his throwing the standish [inkstand] at Mr. Weddell, the giving the undue preference to Pulford [presumably someone who brought clipped money into the Mint], and some other accusations of that nature, I am prepared to lay before their Lordships. I came to town purposely to charge that proud, insolent fellow, whom I humbly begg you to believe the principall Author of all the disturbance we have had at our Mint, whom if you please to see removed all will be easie; and on that condition I am content to submitt to all you shall prescribe me. Nevertheless as I have often wrote you, I would urge you to nothing, but what your great prudence shall think proper, since it is to your particular favour I owe this post, which is my chiefest ambition to maintain worthily, and next to that to approve my self in all things." This letter also contains both Halley's wish to resign and his desire to prosecute both Clark and Lewis lest they should interpret his resignation in any other way than "a voluntary cessation."

Halley's dissatisfaction with Chester was already well known to Newton. As early as February 1697 Newton had offered to obtain an engineer's appointment for Halley. The exact nature of this post is unknown, but Halley was hesitant, and in replying to Newton said that he wanted to have assurance that the appointment was "durable." Meanwhile, before receiving Halley's reply, Newton also offered him a situation which would entail teaching the mathematical principles of engineering for two hours a day to army officers and field engineers at a salary of ten shillings a week. It seems that Halley turned down both offers, and only in 1698, when the country mints were at last closed down, did he return to London.

It was in this same year that Czar Peter (1672–1725) came to England. His purpose was to study English shipbuilding, which at the time was second to none. It will be recalled, in Chapter 3, that it was at Deptford, southeast of London, that the East India Company had its famous shipyards, and among others it was these that interested the Czar. He was determined to discover all he could about the art of shipbuilding, and actually worked for a while in the yards to acquire knowledge. Peter stayed at Sayes Court in Deptford; it was a large country house with elegant grounds laid out by its owner, John Evelyn (1620–1706), the diarist and horticulturist. Evelyn was not living there at the close of the seventeenth century but had leased the property to Admiral Benbow (1650–1702), and it was Benbow who, with Evelyn's agreement, prepared Sayes Court for the Czar during his stay in England. Peter was young, accustomed to enjoying life and, from stories of his stay in England, had a riotous time at Sayes Court.

But besides his desire for enjoyment, Peter had a serious side to his nature. He was interested in many things besides shipbuilding, not least in the new scientific movement, and requested that one of the able scientists of the day should come to discuss matters with him and answer his questions. The choice fell on Halley; he was known to be an amusing companion as well as having broad scientific interests and considerable engineering knowledge. The scheme worked well. Peter liked Halley's frank manner, found his learning stimulating as well as useful, and enjoyed the company of the man himself. As Martin Folkes put it, "This Great Prince was highly pleas'd with him, treated him with great distinction, admitting him to the Familiarity of his Table, to have the more opportunitys of being inform'd by his enter [entertaining] and instructing Conversation."

Peter's stay in England is surrounded by anecdotes, such as that after a day of discussion and instruction from Halley, this was rounded off by an early dinner (the Czar dined at six in the evening), after which they went into the grounds, where Halley was induced to give his host a ride in a wheelbarrow, on a route that took them into one of the holly hedges so prized by Evelyn. This story is unauthenticated, and W. G. Hiscocks has suggested that the idea that the Czar loved to be wheeled through hedges is due to a confusion between the comments of Evelyn himself made about damage the Czar wrought on Sayes Court and the report on the grounds prepared by William III's chief gardener, George London. There is no doubt that a great deal of damage was done by the Czar's retinue: on the house, new paint and slates had to be provided; inside, sheets and curtains were torn, the kitchen dressers needed replaning, tables and chairs were broken, and pictures destroyed. But the havoc was not confined to the house; plants, including holly hedges, were broken, three wheelbarrows had to be replaced, and there were potholes over Evelyn's precious bowling green and in the grass paths. The total damages cost the Exchequer three hundred pounds ($720). Whether Halley took part in any of the wild behavior is unknown, but it would seem unlikely: He was not even a member of the English nobility and, although he dined with the Czar, the informality probably ended there.

CHAPTER 12

Voyages

The year 1698 marked a turning point in Halley's life. He had returned to London from his unhappy time at the Chester Mint; he
had been invited to discuss all kinds of things that interested him
with the Czar, a man whom he found intelligent and amusing—a
great contrast after the intellectual desert of Chester. Yet other
events, both personal and scientific, were to happen in 1698. In the
first place, it was during this year, on an unknown date, that a son
was born to the Halleys,* and secondly the Admiralty was to take
the unusual step of commissioning Halley, a landsman, as captain of
one of His Majesty's ships.

In Hooke's manuscript diary for 1693 there are two references
to a projected voyage. On January 11 Hooke wrote, "Hally of
going in Middleton's† ship to discover . . ." (here page breaks off),
and on April 12, "Hally & Middleton made proposalls of going into
ye South Sea & Round the World . . . , Buoyed by [John] Herbert.
Hill. &c." From the Journal Book of the Society under April 12,
1693 it is recorded that "The President [Sir Robert Southwell
(1635–1702)] was pleased to propose to the Society a paper lately
offered him by Mr. Benjamin Middleton, requesting the assistance
of this Society to procure for him a small vessell of about 60 Tuns
to be fitted out by the Government, but to be victualled and manned
at his own proper charges. And this in order to compass the Globe
to make observations on the Magneticall Needle, &c. The President

---

* The son, also named Edmond, did not follow his father in a scientific career,
but became a naval surgeon. Subsequently he married a widow some years his
senior, and died at Portsmouth the year before his father.

† Benjamin Middleton, of whom nothing seems to be known except that he
was elected a Fellow of the Royal Society in 1687.

in the name of the Society promised to use his endeavours towards the obtaining such a vessell."

In July 1693 the Navy Board was informed that the Queen (Mary II) was in favor of Middleton's and Halley's proposal. Their plan was to encompass the whole globe from east to west and chart the true positions of coasts, ports, and islands; at the same time they were to record the magnetic declination (variation) and see whether such variations could be used for determining longitude at sea. The Exchequer was in favor of the voyage since it would help in navigation for overseas trade. Arrangements were commenced with all possible speed, and by October Fisher Harding, the master shipwright at Deptford, was in a position to supply details of masts and yards. In the following March he reported a pink‡ ready for launching and on April 1, 1694 received instructions from the Navy Board to launch the vessel and enter her on the list of the Royal Navy by the name of the *Paramore*.§ This small ship had a length of fifty-two feet, a breadth of eighteen feet, and a depth of seven feet, seven inches. Her displacement was eighty-nine tons.

We hear little more of Middleton, and there are no further details in the records for the next two years. But Halley continued to take an interest in the project, and on June 4, 1696 he received a royal commission appointing him master and commander of the *Paramore* together with orders for a regular complement of officers and a boatswain, gunner, and carpenter. The Admiralty issued the commission and directed the Navy Board to obtain security from Halley for payment of the officers and, after a request from Halley that the men should be in the King's pay the better to maintain discipline, he had to give a surety for their wages as well.

The voyage was still looked on as a private enterprise, and

‡ The name for this class of vessel comes from the Middle Dutch "pincke" or "pinke." The Admiralty never possessed more than two of these ships, which were originally of Dutch design. Their particular characteristics were that their bottoms were reasonably flat, allowing the ship to make its way even in comparatively shallow water, and there was only a narrow stern above deck, but the stern and the sides bulged considerably just above the water line and thus the ship could carry more than the normal supply of stores.

§ The name in MacPike *Correspondence* and elsewhere is usually spelled *Paramour,* but in the manuscript logs the spelling is *Paramore,* and this is the spelling Halley sometimes adopted in correspondence with the Admiralty.

Halley was free to decide on the complement of officers; as a result he also requested the services of a naval surgeon and a chief mate, and a crew of ten foremast men and two cabin boys besides the carpenter, gunner, and boatswain. Middleton was still intending to make the voyage, for Halley's assessment of the *Paramore's* complement amounted to twenty, including Middleton and his servant. Sir John Hoskin stood surety for a bond of six hundred pounds to cover wages and other costs for a period of twelve months. In September 1696 Halley went to Chester, but the month before he must have known that this was likely since the *Paramore* was laid up in wet dock at Deptford during August. Only after Halley's return from Chester in 1698 were arrangements for the voyage resumed. In July 1698 the Navy Board was instructed to improve the sailing qualities of the vessel by making her able to carry more sail, and by August she was victualed for a twelve-month voyage. It was a further six weeks, however, before guns were fitted and she was manned.

Halley's main interest was in charting magnetic variation, and under the date of October 15, 1698 the Admiralty issued his instructions. These were explicit, and based on Halley's own recommendations. They were addressed to "Captn. Edmd. Halley Comandr. of his Mats. Pink Paramour,"¶ and in part they ran as follows: "Instructions for proceeding to Improve the knowledge of the Longitude and Variations of the Compasse. . . . You are to make the best of your way to the Southward of the Equator, and there to observe on the East Coast of South America, and the West Coast of Africa, the variations of the Compasse, with all the accuracy you can, as also the true Scituation both in Longitude and Latitude of the Ports where you arrive. You are likewise to make the like observations at as many of the Islands in the Seas between the aforesaid Coasts as you can (without too much deviation) bring into your course: and if the Season of the Yeare permit, you are to stand soe farr into the South, till you discover the Coast of the Terra Incognita, [Australia] supposed to lye between Magelan's Streights and the Cape of Good Hope, which coast you are carefully to lay downe in its true position. In your returne home you are to visit the

¶ The probably incorrect spelling *Paramour* is used in these instructions.

English West India Plantations, or as many of them as conveniently you may, and in them to make such observations as may contribute to lay them downe truely in their Geographical Scituation. And in all the Course of your Voyage, you must be carefull to omit no opportunity of Noteing the variation of the Compasse, of which you are to keep a Record in your Iournall." These, then, were the gist of Halley's orders for what was the first scientific voyage to be carried out under the auspices of the British crown, predating Cook's first voyage by seventy years.

A full record of the expedition is contained in Halley's log,* now in the British Museum. From this we find he set sail from Deptford about noon on Thursday, October 20, 1698, only five days after the Admiralty's orders had been issued. The next day they anchored "in Gravesend reach," and Halley returned to London to settle his account with the victualing office. He reembarked on the twenty-fifth, and four days later we find the entry ". . . we weighed at peep of day and turned it through the Gull [Gulf] Stream where to my great satisfaction I found the weakness of my Crew and that our vessell was very leewardly for all the Shipps out turned us and went away before us." Bad weather followed the next day and Halley found the ship ". . . Leaky and our pumps brought up an abundance of our Sand ballast . . ." The sand choked the hand pumps and Halley decided that the only answer was to return to port and have the ship repaired and the sand ballast exchanged for shingle. He wrote about this to Josiah Burchett, Secretary to the Admiralty, on November 1, 1698, and his letter shows an already good grasp of seamanship. At Portsmouth, the dockyard authorities found Halley's complaints only too correct, and they considered the work so vital that no orders from the Admiralty were necessary before the work could be done. By November 10 the sand ballast was removed and the *Paramore* was in dock, with Halley passing

* Halley deposited the log with the Admiralty which loaned it to Alexander Dalrymple (1737–1808), who published it in full in his *Two Voyages Made in 1698, 1699 and 1700 by Dr Edmund Halley published from the Original Manuscript in the Possession of the Board of Longitude,* London, 1773, and then two years later he incorporated sections of it in his *Collection of Voyages to the South Atlantic,* London, 1775. The log was never returned, and when Dalrymple's house was burned it was assumed that the log perished. Sometime about 1877 the log was sold privately and purchased by the British Museum.

the time taking measurements of the magnetic variation in Portsmouth Harbor. Six days later the shingle ballast was loaded, and
on November 22 he joined Admiral Benbow, who was waiting for
a favorable wind. Off St. Helen's, Isle of Wight, Halley wrote to
Burchett, "Our people were somewhat doubtfull of going alone, for
fear of meeting with a Sallyman [pirate], but if we can keep the
Admirall Company those apprehensions are over. He has promised
to take care of us . . ."

In just over two weeks they were at Madeira, where Benbow
had to leave them. They made their way to the Canary Islands, and
then on to the islands which lie off Cape Verde on the western
coast of Africa. On the way Halley wrote that they "past through
a Streak of Water in appearance turbid, but when in it we took up
some Water, and it was full of Small transparent globules, but less
that white peas intersperst with very small blackish specks. These
globules were so numerous as to make the Sea of a yellow muddy
Colour. There Substance appeared like that of our Squidds . . .
and there were two or three sorts of them."

On arriving at St. Jago they were fired on. As he told Burchett,
"I found there two English Marchãt shipps, one of which calld the
New Exchange, whereof one John Way is Master belonging to London, was pleased, instead of saluting us, to fire at us severall both
great and small shott. We were surprised at it, and believing them
to be pirates, I went in to windward of them and bracing our head
sailes to the Mast, sent my boat to learn the reason of their firing.
They answered that they apprehended we were a pirate, and they
had on board them two Masters of vessells, that had been lately
taken by pirates, one of which swore that ours was the very shipp
that took him; whereupon they felt themselves obliged to do what
they did in their own defence." This misunderstanding was probably
genuine, since pirates often ran up colors they felt would allow them
to get in close to their prey.

Unfortunately Halley was to have considerable trouble with
the crew on this voyage, and the first intimation of it came on February 17, 1699. Halley records, "This Morning between two and
three looking out I found that my Boatswain who had the Watch,
steard a way NW instead of W (we now bearing down W, for the

Iseland of Fernando Loronho†) I conclude with a design to miss the Iseland, and frustrate my Voyage, though they pretend the Candle was out in the Bittacle, and they could not light it." Halley stood no nonsense, however, and the next day they anchored off Fernando de Noronha "having narrowly escaped a Sunk Rock." On the island were nothing but "Turtle Doves and Land Crabs in abundance, neither goats nor hogs nor any people," but Halley mapped it and his plan marks "A Sunk Rock Six Foot Water" off the southwestern coast.

Next they anchored off the western coast of Brazil, and Halley charted the area and noticed errors in the maps available. Here they watered, the Portuguese governor of the area sending down a deputation headed by a sergeant-major and with an interpreter ". . . to invite me on Shore and to persuade me to Water in his Rivers promising to send me a Pilote the nexte Morning." Halley went up to Paraiba, and obtained water, tobacco, and sugar. He was unable to observe an eclipse of one of Jupiter's satellites "but great hight of the Planet, and want of a convenient support for my long telescope made it impracticable" and he had to be satisfied with observing the end of a lunar eclipse. Measurements of magnetic variation were made, and Halley went upcountry to make measures there, leaving the ship's surgeon with the governor as a hostage. They set sail again on May 12.

After this expedition there was more trouble on board. Halley had originally felt it might be necessary to winter in Brazil, yet he had to record that "my Officers shewing themselves uneasy and refractory, I this day [March 16] chose to bear away for Barbadoes in order to exchange them if I found a Flagg [a flagship] there."

By the beginning of April they were near Barbados and sighted the "Topps" of the island. Trouble on board was growing worse, and this time it was the first lieutenant, Halley's second-in-command, who brought matters to a head. "My Lieuten't then haveing the Watch clapt upon a wind, pretending that we ought to goe to Windward of the Island, and about the North end of it, whereas the Road is at the most Southerly part almost. He persisted in this

† Fernando de Noronha, off the western coast of Brazil.

Course which was Contrary to my orders given overnight, and to all sence and reason, till I came upon Deck; when he was so Farr from excusing it, that he pretended to justifie it; not without reflecting language." Halley gave his own orders and saw that they were executed; in due course they landed on Barbados. Longitude determinations were made using observations of Jupiter's satellites, and measurements taken of the magnetic variation.

They moved on to Martinique, "which is much bigger than Barbadoes," then to Antigua and St. Christopher, where they found "Water proving excellent good." After further measures of latitude and longitude and of magnetic variation, they set sail for England on May 10. By June the lieutenant's behavior became so impertinent that Halley put him under arrest and himself navigated the ship back to England. In a letter which he wrote to Burchett on his return to Plymouth and dated June 23, 1699, Halley gives a fuller story of the behavior of the lieutenant than appears in the log itself. "I this day arrived here with his Maties: Pink. the Paramour in 6 weeks from the West Indies, having buried no man during the whole Voiage and the Shipp being in very good condition," then, after explaining that one reason to bring him home so soon was that he had voyaged into the Southern Hemisphere at the wrong season for exploration, he goes on: "But a further motive to hasten my return was the unreasonable carriage of my Mate and Lieutenant, who, because perhaps I have not the whole Sea Dictionary so perfect as he, has for a long time made it his business to represent me, to the whole Shipps company, as a person wholly unqualified for the command their Lopps have given me, and declaring that he was sent on board here, because their Lopps knew my insufficiency." This was not all, as Halley explains. "On the fifth of this month he was pleased so grosly to affront me, as to tell me before my Officers and Seamen on Deck, and afterwards owned it under his hand, that I was not only uncapable to take charge of the Pink, but even of a Longboat; upon which I desired him to keep his Cabbin for that night, and for the future I would take charge of the Shipp myself, to shew him his mistake; and accordingly I have watched in his steed ever since, and brought the Shipp well home from near the banks of Newfound

Land, without the least assistance from him." Why his lieutenant should have behaved in this way, Halley can only conjecture. "I take it that he envys me my command and conveniences on board, disdaining to be under one that has not served in the fleet as long as himself, but however it be I am sure their Lopps will think this intollerable usage, from one who ought to be as my right hand, and by his example my Warrant Officers have not used me much Better . . ." The observations of magnetic variation and for determining longitude had been successful, however, and Halley said he hoped to have the opportunity to report more fully to the Admiralty on these.

On the face of it the mutinous conduct of Halley's second-in-command, Lieutenant Harrison, was due purely to the fact, as Halley suggested, that Harrison was obliged to sail under the orders of a landsman who, to add insult to injury, had all the privileges of a captain. Moreover, Halley had spent the voyage measuring magnetic variation and taking latitude and longitude observations, and of these Harrison had his own ideas. Harrison's objections, however, whether well-founded or not, provide no excuse for his actions. That he instigated trouble with the crew is clear, and the conduct of the boatswain already referred to only confirms this. Yet the real reasons behind Harrison's attitude and behavior only came to light at the court-martial, which took place on July 3, 1699. In 1696 Harrison had published in London a small book, *Idea Longitudinis*, in which he proposed methods of determining longitude at sea. This book had been submitted to the Admiralty, the Navy Board, and the Royal Society. It received unfavorable reports, and Halley was one of those who thought Harrison's ideas were impracticable and incapable of providing a sufficient degree of accuracy.

It seems Harrison never forgave him, but unfortunately for himself he did not appreciate Halley's abilities and underestimated the kind of man he was up against. In his book he referred abusively to the attempts and methods which had already been made to ascertain longitude on board ship, saying that ". . . there are some Persons in *England*, whose Duty it is (being paid for it) to improve *Navigation* and *Astronomy*, and from whom much is expected, and little or nothing appears." Halley had suggested that if the magnetic variation were properly charted it would be possible to use this knowledge to allow longitude to be determined at any point on the earth's surface, but Harrison thought this nonsense, and stated that he, as a sailor, ". . . may prove . . . to be a more Competent Artist in Navigation . . ." than any mathematician. The fact that Halley safely navigated the *Paramore* back to England from Newfoundland without loss of life does nothing to support this contention.

The court-martial took place, and Harrison and his brother officers received a stern reprimand. The sentence could not legally be more because none had openly disobeyed Halley's orders. The only charge Halley could bring was one of insolence, and his own comments on this are contained in another letter of Burchett, written the day after the court-martial: ". . . I fully proved all that I had complained of against my Lieutenant and Officers, but the Court insisting upon my proof of actuall disobedience to command, which I had not charged them with, but only with abusive language and disrespect, they were pleased only to reprimand them, and in their report have very tenderly styled the abuses I suffered from them, to have been only some grumblings such as usually happen on board small Shipps."

But the confidence of Their Lordships does not seem to have been disturbed by the Harrison fracas, and Halley had already received new sailing orders by the date of the court-martial. Certainly their confidence was well-founded; on the first ill-fated voyage much useful information had been obtained, and on his second voyage even more was achieved. It was at this time that Halley resigned his post as Clerk to the Royal Society, since obviously he was going to be away from England for a protracted period.

In one sense this second voyage did not start too well. Admittedly the *Paramore* did not leak and its pumps become clogged with sand; it was refitted and ready by August 23, Halley's commission was renewed, but his crew was still not satisfactory, for he had assigned to him ". . . A Boatswaine with one Arm, who by consequence can be of little service in case of extremity . . . ," and Halley felt himself ". . . obliged to begg the succour of 3 or 4 men more; which as I content my self with a Mate only, will be born on the Shipp with the same charge as in the former Voiage, when I had a Lieutenant allowed me." Some criticism of Halley as a commander had been made by certain of Their Lordships, and before sailing, Halley expressed the firm belief that he would be able, on his return, ". . . to answer the expectations of those who perhaps censure the performances of my last voiage, without examining all the Circonstances."

On Wednesday, September 27, 1699, the *Paramore* set sail for the second time with Halley in command. He was a little later in leaving than he would have wished, but from his log he seems to have been pleased with the progress made. They struck bad weather, however, near the Canaries, and on Saturday, October 14, Halley had the unhappy task of recording in his log, "Yesterday betweene 3 and 4 in the afternoon my poor Boy Manley White had the misfortune to be drowned, falling over board. We brought the Shipp immediately at Stays, and hove out an Oar, but the sea being high and the Shipp haveing fresh way wee lost sight of him, and could not succour him; at 6 I bore away . . ." This tragedy upset Halley, and it is reported that afterward he could never refer to it except with tears in his eyes.

But the voyage had to continue, and eight days later they anchored off the Island of Sal, almost the most northerly of the Cape Verde group. Halley went ashore and found a "Portugese there with some few Blacks Servants, who assured us there was no Salt to be had, the Salt penns being all in the Water, we had leave to Hunt, and our people killed and brought aboard two Cabritos [a species of antelope], one very fatt and good Meate. We saw Turtle in the road, and their Tracks on shore so 4 of our hands stay'd on Shore this night, and next morning they brought off two Turtles, . . . The Portugese promised me some Salt but made me stay till Evening for it, and it was not much above a Bushell when it came, bad Salt mixed with Dirt . . ."

After this Halley moved south to other islands in the group and obtained a store of fresh water. The Portuguese in general were not very friendly, and soon the *Paramore* weighed anchor and set off on the next section of the voyage. All the while Halley was mak-

ing observations of latitude and longitude, and although the log
at this time records no observations of magnetic variation, it seems
from the results he brought back that these were in fact made regularly. Halley took an almost direct southerly course, crossed the
equator, and made for the island of Fernando de Noronha again.
He does not seem to have touched land but to have continued his
southward course. On December 4 there was an occultation of a star
by the moon, and this enabled Halley to obtain his longitude with a
fair degree of accuracy; indeed, his longitude determinations at this
time are fairly accurate, and surpass those made on the first voyage. They reached Rio de Janeiro by early December but by the
end of the month set sail again, still going southward. The farther
south they went the worse the weather became, and on January 18,
1700 ". . . After Midnight it blew extream hard at N.W. with much
Lightning, and again a little before Sunn rise with very terrible
Lightning which seemed to be just on board us but God be thanked
we received no damage by it." They were to encounter considerably
worse weather conditions, and in general, high seas and storms
seem to have prevailed. It also grew cold, and in Halley's cabin
". . . which had been kept from the Air the thermometer‡ stood
but 11 above freezing."

By January 27, in latitude almost 51° south and, as far as one
can judge from Halley's figures, in a position a little north of a
line between the Falkland Islands and South Georgia, they met
". . . a greate Fogg" and, after it had cleared, they saw ". . . severall
fowls, which I take to be penguins . . . being of two sorts; the one
black head and back, with white neck and breast; the other larger
and of the Colour and siz of a young Cygnett, haveing a bill very
remarkable hookeing downwards, and crying like a bittern . . ."
Later they came upon other creatures which Halley describes:
". . . We have had severall of the Diveing birds with necks like
Swans pass by us, and this morning a Couple of Animalls which
some supposed to be Seals but are not soe; they bent their Tayles

‡ Halley gives no details of the thermometer scale he was using, and it may
have been arbitrary. On the other hand, both the Fahrenheit scale and that of
Réaumur (0°=freezing to 80°=boiling point of liquid in thermometer [and
gradually taken as boiling point of water]) were in use.

into a sort of Bow . . . and being disturbed shew'd very large Finns as big as those of a Large Shirk The head not much unlike a Tur-tles." It became colder, the thermometer in Halley's cabin drop-ping to ". . . but 4 above freezing . . ." and the men were allowed their full ration of rum.

Yet worse was to come. They reached almost to latitude 53° south, and on February 1 saw three islands. The thermometer had now moved to below freezing point, and the three islands were unidentified by Halley, not being shown on his charts. One lay northeast, one due east, and the other east-southeast of the *Para-more*, and his description of them is interesting: ". . . being all flatt on the Top, and covered with snow. milk white with perpen-dicular cliffs all round them. . . . The great hight of them made us conclude them land, but there was no appearance of any tree or green thing on them, but the Cliffs as well as topps were very white . . ."

Since these islands were not marked on contemporary maps, Halley had either to conclude that his latitude and longitude were wrong and he was farther south than he believed, or that the islands were huge icebergs. He may have been in error over his longitude, but his latitude measurements cannot have been wildly wrong, and the most likely explanation seemed to be that these were ice-bergs. But it was important to be sure, and Halley decided to ap-proach closer. "In the night it proved foggy, and continued so till this day [February 2] at noon, when by a clear glare of scarce ¼ of an hour wee saw the Island . . . very distinctly to be nothing elce but one body of Ice of an incredible hight whereupon we went about Shipp and stood to the Northward."

The mystery was solved, but the *Paramore* was in dangerous waters. Disaster nearly overtook it the next day in the fog and ice: ". . . between 11 and 12 this day we were in iminant danger of loosing our Shipp among the Ice, for the fogg was all the morning so thick, that we could not see for long about us, where on a Sud-den a Mountain of Ice began to appear out of the Fogg, about 3 points on our Lee bow: this we made a shift to weather when an-other appeared more on head with severall pieces of Ice round it; this obliged us to tack and had we mist Stayes [putting on another

tack], we had most certainly been a Shore on it, and had not beene
halfe a quarter of an hour under way when another mountain of
Ice began to appear on our Lee bow; which obliged us to tack again
with the like danger of being on Shore: but the sea being smooth
and the Gale Fresh wee got Clear: God be praised. This danger
made my men reflect on the hazards wee run, in being alone without a Consort, and of the inevitable loss of us all in case we Staved
our Shipp which might soe easily happen amongst these mountains
of Ice in the Fogg, which are so thick and frequent there."

The *Paramore* now moved a little way north and east and made
for Tristan da Cunha, but even so they continued to encounter fog,
cloud, and cold weather for a while, icebergs passed by them, and
four days later Halley altered course NNE so that they would soon
"recover the warm Sunn, who we have scarce seen this fortnight;
the weather being comonly foggy with so penetrateing a moysture
that our linnen, our Cloaths, our papers &c feel wett with it, even
in our Cabbins." To his joy on February 8 he was able to record
"pretty clear Sunn Shine," and conditions improved even though it
remained cold, and there were still foggy patches. By February 17
they reached Tristan da Cunha, but passed the islands and made
for the Cape of Good Hope. They now experienced "dry comfortable Air," but Halley missed an eclipse of the moon because the sky
was overcast, "as is usuall in these Climates." Later they ran into a
"Terrible high sea" which "threw us so that we had likt to have over-
sett, but please God, She wrighted again."

Halley decided to collect his next intake of water at St. Helena,
for he did not wish to go straight back to England, "fearing to go
hom in the Winter, which would Expose my weak Shipps Compa.
to greate hardships." Matters were not made easier by water getting
through some leaks and into where the bread, flour, and cheese
was stored; six dozen loaves and thirty pounds of flour and cheese
were rendered unfit for use. He persevered in his latitude and longitude observations and also recorded his measure of magnetic variation every day. On Monday, March 11, 1700, the *Paramore* came
close to St. Helena, but was becalmed on the morning of the following day, being unable to drop anchor until noon. From St. Helena
Halley wrote to Burchett, giving a brief account of the voyage and

especially the encounter with the icebergs, one of which could not, he thought, be less than two hundred feet high, to say nothing of what lay below water, and ended by saying, ". . . in this whole course I have found noe reason to doubt of an exact conformity in the variations of the compass to a generall Theory, which I am in great hopes to settle effectually."

From St. Helena he decided to move on and undertake more work, for his crew was rested. The *Paramore* sailed westward, and on April 14 came to the island of Martin Vas, some six hundred miles east of Brazil and north of Rio, but they moved on and anchored off the more westerly Brazilian island of Trinidad, called by Halley Troindada.§ Here they found water, and Halley went ashore ". . . and put Some Goats and Hoggs on the Island for breedg, and alsoe a pair of Guinea Hens I carry'd from St Helena." He also notes, "I took possession of the Island in his Maties name, as knowing it to be granted by the King's Letters Pattents leaving the Union Flagg flying." The island was mapped during their five-day stay, after which they set sail to the northwest, aiming for the Brazilian province of Pernambuco, which they reached on April 29, seven months after setting out from England.

The Portuguese governor at Recife, the capital of the province, was most helpful, but not so a Mr. Hardwicke who, Halley reports, "calls himselfe English Consull." Hardwicke thought they were pirates, would not accept the evidence of Halley's commissions and admiralty orders, and examined two of the seamen. Their account of the voyage tallied with Halley's but Hardwicke would not be convinced, and on May 2 Halley was arrested and the *Paramore* searched. Hardwicke could find no evidence of piracy and therefore released Halley, apologized, and claimed that his action had been taken only to satisfy the Portuguese. But the Portuguese claimed that this was not true, that in any event Hardwicke had no authority to act in the way he had—even though it was they who supplied the guard during the short period of Halley's arrest.

On May 3 the *Paramore* set off northward, running into squalls and gales. Eighteen days later they reached Barbados, with Halley's

§ This should not be confused with the island of Trinidad in the West Indies.

estimated longitude some two degrees different from the present figure. Halley ". . . went up into the Country to Wait on the Governour the Honable Ralph Grey Esqr. who advised me to make no more Stay than was absolutely Necessary by reason the Island had not been knowne so sickly as at present the Bridge Towne Especially and for that reason to take care to keep my Men on board. I order'd the Water Caske to be gott ready and Some of them carried a Shore this evening . . ." On Friday, May 24, they weighed anchor, but while they were getting under sail Halley found himself ". . . Seized wth. the Barbadoes desease, wch, in a little time made me so weak I was forced to take my Cabbin . . ." They anchored at St. Christopher's Island, some four hundred miles northwest of Barbados on the twenty-eighth, while Halley was "in hopes to recover my health," and all was well by June 5. We learn, however, from a letter to Burchett written later, that the plague at Barbados was worse than the bare bones of the log intimate, for Halley describes it as ". . . a severe pestilentiall dissease, which scarce spares any one and had it been as mortall as common would in a great measure have Depeopled the Island . . ." and gives additional details concerning the effect on himself and his crew, "my selfe and many of my men were seazed with it, and tho it used me gently and I was soon up again yet it cost me my skin, my ships company by the extraordenary cure of my Doctor all did well of it."

From St. Christopher's they moved to Anguilla and thence to Bermuda, which they reached on June 20. Here the *Paramore* was refitted for her homeward voyage. A fair amount had to be done, and ". . . our Decks and upperwarks being leaking by being so long in the heats, I hired three Caulkers to assist my Carpenter, who in six days had finished their work, and I gave a new coat of Paint to our carved work which was very bare and parcht." In the log there follows a description of the island and its tides and from which we learn that they set sail on July 11.

Halley now set course for Cape Cod in New England. By July 21 they passed Nantucket, but the seas were high and continued so; in consequence Halley decided to go straight on to Newfoundland, which they reached ten days later in thick fog and "had we not fell in with some French Fishermen we might have been on Shore."

After two more days, when the fog lifted, they found themselves off to the east, ". . . and being come near the English Fishboats they all fled from us, takeing us, as we found afterwards, for a Pyrate; being come into the harbour of Isle of Sphear call'd Toads Cove one Humphrey Bryant a Biddiford man fired 4 or five Shott through our rigging, but without hurting us: here we anchored in 15 fathom water, and I sent my boat to fetch Bryant on board, who excused what he had done, by giving me an Account of a Pirate that had lately cruised on the Coast, and plundered a vessell but a few dayes before. I forgave the affront finding the said report confirmed." All was then well, they landed, cut wood, obtained water, and on August 6 the *Paramore* set sail for England. No more excitements ensued, and three weeks later they dropped anchor in Plymouth Sound. Halley found no orders awaiting him there, so he once again set sail and reached the Downs, where he received instructions to put in to Deptford, and his last entry, dated September 10, 1770, read: "We Deliver'd our Gunns and Gunners Stores and the Pilott being on board by Lowe Water we weighed from Long Reach and Delivered the Pink this Evening into the hands of Captn. William Wright Mastr. of Attendance at Deptford."

The second voyage was over and was crowned with success. Halley had had no trouble with his crew although his experiences, especially in the high southern latitudes, had been anything but uneventful. He gave Their Lordships an account of his voyage and then settled down to prepare for publication the host of observations he had accumulated. In both voyages he had lost only one cabin boy, and the good health of his crews was probably due to some extent to his earlier experience with the East India Company, where he would have learned the value of taking fresh oranges and lemons in the stores to obviate the dangers of scurvy, for they adopted this practice long before the Royal Navy.

It is disappointing that in the log Halley gave no details of the instruments he used nor the method he adopted for making his observations of magnetic variation. The log, in Halley's opinion, may well not have been the right place to do this, but unfortunately he never published any scientific papers in *Philosophical Transactions* discussing his results. All the log provides is enough information to make it seem certain that Halley carried out most of his longitude determinations at sea by means of dead reckoning, perhaps assessing how far he had traveled by use of his device with a brass ball which he had described to the Royal Society in 1692 (see page 129). He also made some observations of the moon's position with respect to nearby bright stars, since he believed this to be a useful method once sufficiently accurate tables of the moon were available, but it does not seem to provide anything approaching the desired accuracy at that time.

Halley used a sextant on board, and his tabulated values of longitude are only given to the nearest minute of arc; since there was the possibility that these figures were subject to errors of anything up to half a minute, the results could not be close enough to solve the longitude problem. He did observe occultations of stars which were useful for correcting lunar theory as well as for determining longitude, but again the precision they could give from a moving ship was not great enough. On shore things were different, and when they called at ports Halley set up his telescope and a pendulum clock for determining longitude by observations of Jupiter's satellites. Using tabulated values of satellite positions to give Portsmouth time, he obtained positions well within the required accuracy of some thirty to sixty miles. Latitude was an easier matter, and sextant measurements of the altitude of the sun by day and the Pole Star or other stars by night would provide considerable accuracy, certainly to within twenty miles or so.

But however he obtained his results, they were expeditiously published, and in 1701 appeared on his large Atlantic Chart, which went through a number of editions during his lifetime. The first edition covered mainly the Atlantic, both north and south, but later editions covered the whole earth between latitudes 60° North and 59° South—a very wide range indeed. The first map was dedicated to the King, under whose patronage the voyages had been undertaken, and was especially remarkable for the way in which Halley showed the magnetic variation. He adopted the simple yet effective expedient of using dotted lines connecting the points where the variation was equal, and these Halleyan lines, as they came to be called, have been used ever since for charts of this kind.¶ Halley himself merely called them "curve lines." In the present century the term isogonic lines or isogones has replaced both Halley's nomenclature and the name Halleyan lines, but the outcome is the same and Halley can without doubt claim to have laid the foundations of modern physical geography. The charts show what a master of practical navigation he was, and illustrate the importance of Halley's accomplishments in contrast with the pettiness of men like Harrison who thought they knew so much but, in fact, achieved so little, and whose names are only remembered because of their contact with the man they despised.

The Atlantic Chart, as it first appeared, had the title "A New and Correct CHART Shewing the VARIATIONS of the COMPASS in the WESTERN AND SOUTHERN OCEANS as observed in ye YEAR 1700 by his Maties Command" by Edm. Halley. An appropriate humble dedication in Latin to William III was included, and an explanation of the curve lines which read as follows: "The Curve Lines which are drawn over the Seas in this Chart do shew at one View all the Places where the Variation of the Compass is the same; The Numbers to them, shew how many degrees the Needle declines either Eastwards or Westwards from the true North; and the Double Lines passing near Bermudas and the Cape Virde Isles is that where the Needle stands true without Variation." At the bottom of the map, which includes the route of the Paramore, two of the peculiar "animalls" which Halley observed are drawn, accompanied by the legend "The Sea in these parts abounds with two sorts of Animalls of a Middle Species between a Bird and a Fish, having necks like Swans and Swimming with their whole Bodyes always under water only putting up their long necks for Air." This statement seems to show a confusion between the two separate species mentioned by Halley in the log as having been seen in this area. As he was a careful observer of everything around him, even if no expert in natural history, it is worth spending a moment to

¶ Lines on a chart connecting points of equal magnetic variation appear to have first been used by Christoforo Borri (fl. 1630), but his work and, indeed, his chart seem to have been but little known.

inquire into the true nature of the creatures which were seen from the *Paramore*.

First it will be recalled that Halley described "severall of the Diveing birds with necks like Swans . . . and which cried like a bittern as they passed us." These could well have been king penguins, which have the ability to stretch their necks quite considerably, and swim with them stretched fully out; this seems to be the most likely answer considering the high southern latitude in which the creatures were seen. Moreover, the penguin does not fly and would fit a description of half fish and half bird while, in addition, it does make a raucous noise which Halley may have thought to be rather like the sound of a bittern. The other animals Halley observed were, in his opinion, not seals, and he described that ". . . they bent their Tayles into a sort of Bow . . . and being disturb'd shew'd very large Finns as big as those of a large Shirk The head not much unlike a Turtles." The main part of this note— the bending of the fins—is an apt general description of a cetacean, but it is the turtlelike head which involves difficulty. Admittedly the log we have is a fair copy of his actual sea log, and it is conceivable that the word "Turtle" is a miscopy of a roughly written "bottle," for there are "bottle-nosed" whales and dolphins in these waters. But one must be cautious, and while it appears certain that he saw either dolphins or whales, and was therefore correct in saying the creatures were not seals, one cannot be sure of the species, although the killer whale presents the most likely possibility.*

After the first printing of the chart, Halley issued a note on its nature and purpose for subsequent editions; this was separately printed on strips of paper which were pasted either at the bottom or the sides of the copies sold. This note was called "The Description and Uses of a New and Correct SEA-CHART of the Western and Southern Oceans, shewing the Variation of the COMPASS." After pointing out that the chart is drawn on Mercator's projection which, Halley suggests, ". . . from its particular Use in Navigation, ought rather to be nam'd the Nautical; as being the only True and Sufficient Chart for the Sea," he describes the scheme of

---

* I am indebted to Dr. L. Harrison Matthews, F.R.S., for a very helpful discussion on these observations.

layout of the curve lines and gives examples of how to read the magnetic variation from the chart itself. There then follows a description of the actual use of the chart, and the fact that the magnetic variation is slowly altering is pointed out. The note ends as follows: "And if by undoubted Observations it [the chart] be found in any part defective, the Notes of it will be received with all grateful Acknowledgement, and the Chart Corrected accordingly."

Under Halley's direction the Atlantic Chart was in due course replaced by the World Chart. Much that appeared on the original was redrawn, the half bird, half fish animals were omitted, and the new and in many ways improved chart was published in 1702. This was dedicated to "his Royall Highness Prince GEORGE OF DENMARK LORD HIGH ADMIRAL of ENGLAND Generalissimo of all her Maties. Forces &c." and contained both a Latin and an English title, a separate insert showing the north polar regions, and two panels in which Halley had placed Latin verses of his own composition, dedicated to Queen Anne.

Although Queen Anne died in 1714, the verses remained for more than a century on the map, which was frequently reprinted. A description of its use was also issued in a way similar to that for the Atlantic Chart, but this time Halley could not assure his purchasers that it was all "according to what I my self found," and pointed out that part was based on observations of other seamen. The map was popular and ran into many editions, English and foreign, and brought Halley's name before an increasing public. In 1744, two years after his death, the curve lines were revised and brought up to date, while another revised edition was published in 1758. Moreover, in the great *Atlas Maritimus et Commercialis* published in London in 1728, the maps contained much information supplied by Halley as a direct result of the work of these two years. The charts are now very rare as they were bought for use and, when they had become unacceptably out of date, were thrown away; few copies were retained even in the libraries of either the learned institutions or the collectors of curiosities. In this chart as well as the earlier Atlantic one, certain errors exist, yet this is not surprising since Halley was not always able to determine longitude accurately. Considering that, as his log shows, he had to calculate it primarily from dead reckoning, it is amazing the errors were not more serious.

With the appearance of these magnetic charts and his already published work on the physics of winds, monsoons, and evaporation of sea water, Halley can truly be termed the founder of modern geophysics, a fact which was recognized by the Royal Society in 1957 during the International Geophysical Year, when it named its permanent scientific base in Antarctica† Halley Bay.

After his Atlantic voyages Halley, now re-elected a Fellow of the Royal Society, set off once more to sea, again in the *Paramore*. This time, however, he plied his art of charting nearer home, being commissioned to determine the tides, headlands, and promontories of the English Channel. The voyage was undertaken seemingly at Halley's suggestion, as we know from a letter to Burchett, dated April 23, 1701. Their Lordships limited the trip to the English Channel and specified the *Paramore*. Their confidence in Halley was strong, but there was a delay in sending him his new commission. Moreover, he had difficulty in obtaining a crew ". . . no men now offering themselves as usuall at other times," and was then told to visit Lord Lucas for men obtained by the press-gang. Lucas informed Halley that his order "for pressing Seamen has been discharged some time since . . . ," and Halley appealed for a few men from the warships, promising "to return them where I had taken them in case the breaking out of a war oblige me to desist from my undertaking." This request was granted, and the Admiralty took steps to see that he got his men. Halley was again disappointed in his mate, however, ". . . who for great wages has been tempted to break his promise with me . . ." and he goes on to say that "I humbly hope their Lopps will think it reasonable to allow me a warranted Master, well accuainted with the Channell in lieu of a Mate . . ."

By June 11, 1701 Halley was ready to set sail, and wrote to Burchett asking for final instructions which, as in the case of the Atlantic voyages, were suggested by Halley himself. His proposals were accepted without question, and on Saturday, June 14, Hal-

† Latitude 75° 31′ South; Longitude 27° 37′ West.

ley set sail from Deptford. Soundings were continuously made and the rest of his measurements were presumably taken in a similar way to those on the Atlantic voyages although, once more, he provides no details. By July 9 the *Paramore* was at Cherbourg, and for the next few days Halley surveyed this area. Magnetic variation was not forgotten, and the voyage proceeded without excitement of any kind, Halley returning to Deptford on October 10, when he delivered the *Paramore* to Captain Wright once again, and the crew was paid off.

Thus quietly and without any fuss, Halley's naval career came to an end. His expenditure on the three voyages amounted to £47.15s. ($115), the largest single items of which were £13.16s. ($33) spent on ". . . presents to severall Portugese Governors and Officers at St. Jago, Paraiba, Rio Jennero and Pernambouc . . ." and £11.10s. ($27.50) to "Peter St. Croix pilot of Jersey for 58 days service on boar the Pink . . . in the Channel . . ." Halley's chart of the English Channel was published in 1702, and he also supplied the Admiralty with details of how further measurements could be made and how, in addition, positions which were inaccessible on an enemy shore could be accurately deduced. In view of the deteriorating relationships with France which were to result in the War of the Spanish Succession in 1702, it is interesting to note Martin Folkes's suggestion that the whole Channel survey, extremely valuable though it was, was a cover which enabled Halley to obtain information about French ports and shipping.

After Halley's voyages the Admiralty had no further use for the pink, and the *Paramore* was sold in 1706 for £122 ($245).

CHAPTER 13

Recognition

The end of Halley's Atlantic voyages marked the beginning of a new phase in his life. Relieved of the duties of preparing material for meetings of the Royal Society and once more elected into its Fellowship, he could spend time in research on those matters which especially interested him. In 1700 he discussed rainbows, including a geometrical analysis of their formation by the dispersion and total internal reflection of light within raindrops—here making use of ideas about light and colors that Newton had formulated and was later to publish in his *Opticks*. This Halley followed up two years later with a study of the closely related phenomena of mock suns (parhelia) and halos, both of which are due to refraction by ice crystals in the atmosphere. Then in 1701, while still busy charting the Channel, he found time to write a paper on Hooke's barometer and its use.

Halley returned from his Channel survey in mid-October 1701, but he was not to remain at home for long: the War of the Spanish Succession drew him openly into the Queen's service as technical adviser. In September 1701 Emperor Leopold of Austria had ratified the Grand Alliance with the English and Dutch, and in October of the next year Queen Anne's Secretary of State, the Earl of Nottingham, instructed the Chancellor of the Exchequer to the effect that "the Queen thinking fitt to employ Mr. Edmond HAWLEY in some matters of importance to her Service abroad, has comãnded me to acquaint yor Lop that shee would have you advance him the sume of two hundred pounds towards his charges in that employment." With letters of authority Halley set out on November 27, 1702, embarking on the Thames and sailing to Holland, whence he made his way across Europe to Vienna. His first task was to advise the Emperor on the fortification of harbors in Istria (now divided between Italy and Yugoslavia) on the northern shores of the Adriatic.

In Vienna he met the English minister, the poet and diplomat George Stepney (1663–1707), from whom he learned full details of what was required of him. Wasting no time, Halley moved on to Istria. In some way which is not clear he seems to have met with opposition from the Dutch, but all the same he surveyed the ports, one of which was Trieste and the other Boccari, and returned to Vienna. This time George Stepney presented Halley to the Emperor to whom he reported on the state of the harbors and provided suggestions for the improvement of their fortifications. Emperor Leopold was pleased and ". . . by the hands of Count Mansfelt [president of the council of war at Vienna] presented captain Haley . . . with a diamond ring of great value, and treated him with all the marks of esteem imaginable." Leopold also sent Halley away with a letter to Queen Anne with praise about his advice and "written with his own hand." Halley returned to England, presumably early in 1703, and may well have made his way back through Italy, Germany, and Holland: the *Biographia Britannica* claims that Halley was ". . . likewise received with great respect by the King of the Romans, by Prince Eugene, and the principal officers of that Court."

Leopold was not only impressed by Halley's advice but also decided to follow it through and so, not long after returning home, Halley was once more sent to Vienna, this time to supervise the actual work. For his second journey Halley traveled along much the same route as before but, on the way, passed through Lower Saxony and visited Hanover, where he "supped" with the Queen of Prussia and the Electoral Prince who was later to become George I of England. Going to Vienna "he was presented the same evening to the Emperor, who directly sent his chief engineer to attend him at Istria." Halley had found Boccari quite suitable and needing no repairs or alterations, but Trieste was a different matter; here repairs were required and some new fortifications needed in order to make it safe for the British warships which were to spend the winter of 1703–4 there. Finally he returned to England in November

1703, but there is one interesting postscript. On January 14, 1704 the Earl of Nottingham wrote to the Chancellor of the Exchequer asking him to pay thirty-six pounds ($86) to George Stepney to reimburse him for this amount which he had paid to Halley, and it was ordered that this sum be paid "out of the secret service." This, coupled with Folkes's suggestion about the English Channel survey, makes it seem highly probable that Halley carried out some technical intelligence work at this period of his life.

We turn now to the very end of 1703 and the beginning of 1704, the year of the Battle of Blenheim, the joint victory of Prince Eugene and the Duke of Marlborough. On October 28, 1703, Rev. John Wallis, Savilian professor of geometry at Oxford, had died, and Halley was put forward as a candidate for the vacancy. What Bentley's views on his proposal were is not recorded, but Bishop Stillingfleet was now dead and Halley's reputation was at its height; he had powerful friends, and his former detractor kept his opinions to himself in this instance. Not so Flamsteed who, on December 18, 1703 wrote to Abraham Sharp, "Dr. Wallis is dead. Mr. Halley expects his place. He now talks, swears, and drinks brandy like a sea captain, so that I much fear his own ill-behaviour will deprive him of the vacancy." But on November 30, 1703 Halley had been elected to the Council of the Royal Society, having received more votes in his favor than Newton. Newton, however, was elected President, an office which he continued to hold consecutively for the next twenty-three years. Halley was now in a position of considerable authority, and in 1704 he was appointed to fill the Savilian chair.

At this time Halley was actively pursuing his scientific work at Gresham College, but in May he went to Oxford and delivered his inaugural lecture. What he said in this lecture we do not know in full, but a letter exists from Thomas Hearne to a Dr. Smith in London, in which Hearne writes, ". . . Mr. Hally made his Inaugural Speech on Wednesday May 24. which very much pleased the Generality of the University. After some Complements to the University, he proceeded to the Original and Progress of Geometry, and gave an account of the most celebrated of the Ancient and Modern Geometricians. Of those of our English Nation, he spoke in particular of Sr. Hen. Savil, but his greatest Encomions were upon

Dr. Wallis and Mr. Newton, especially the latter, whom he styled his Numan etc [his presiding spirit]. Nor could he pass by Dr. Gregory, whom he propos'd as an Example in his Lectures; but not a word all the while of Dr. Bernard . . ." Halley's omission of Bernard's name is a little strange since he had studied under him when an undergraduate, and one can only conjecture that in his opinion Bernard's reputation in astronomy and in geometry was not so great as to warrant even a passing reference. To show their esteem for him the university granted Halley the degree of LL.D.

Having given his inaugural address, Halley did not take up residence immediately; indeed, it seems that he did not move to Oxford for two years, although he did spend some time there. The reason for his delay in moving seems to have been the ill-condition of the house set aside for occupation by the Savilian professor of geometry. There were, and still are, three houses in New College Lane that, after a somewhat checkered history, were acquired by John Wallis and, on his death, passed to his son, who generously gave them to the university. The Master of New College was Charlett, a friend of Gregory's (the professor of astronomy), and between them they persuaded the university to repair the houses. This took some time for, as late as June 23, 1705 we find Halley writing, "I return you many thanks for your repeated favour as well in what relates to my house, wherein I must esteem you my greatest benefactor, as for your kind endeavours to give reputation and value to my small performance about Comets, which in no wais deserves a place in your Catalogue, or to bear the budg [badge] of the Theater." (Halley's *A Synopsis of the Astronomy of Comets* had just been published in its Latin edition from Oxford and had the privilege of bearing the imprint of the Sheldonian Theatre, the official seal of the university press.) The house was at last ready for Halley's occupation with, be it noted, a small observatory on the roof, and it seems likely that he moved there in 1705.*

On taking up his Savilian professorship Halley, in company with David Gregory, set to work on the writings of the Greek geometers.

---

* When the author visited this observatory in 1956 through the kindness of Professor H. H. Plaskett, F.R.S., then Savilian professor of astronomy, it was in a dilapidated state and contained little evidence of Halley's occupation.

The ideas of the Greeks and Romans had interested Halley for some time. In 1696 in an unprinted paper he had discussed and compared their geography with that of his own day and no doubt welcomed this new opportunity which meant that he would come to grips with some early mathematics of considerable importance. Gregory had already prepared an edition of the works of Euclid, and both now settled down to the writings of Apollonios. Apollonios flourished around 210 B.C. and lived in Alexandria, but was born in Perge in the area then known as Pamphylia but now situated in the southwest of Turkey. He had made striking mathematical advances, mainly in the field of curved line geometry, and it was he who invented the names ellipse, hyperbola, and parabola, and showed how each of these curves could be obtained by cutting sections from a cone. It was suggested by Henry Aldrich, dean of Christ Church to both Halley and Gregory that Apollonios's work should be fully translated, being second only in importance to that of Euclid, and that if the two Savilian professors could achieve this it would be to the great honor of the university. Halley and Gregory therefore decided to examine all available material and prepare a definitive edition of Apollonios's work. After three years, in 1708, David Gregory died at the early age of forty-seven, and Halley had to carry on alone. His achievements were remarkable.

Halley's results were published in two separate parts, and the problems he had to face were these: first to translate Apollonios's work from the Arabic and, second to reconstruct those "books" of Apollonios's writings which were "lost." The original Greek was not available, and all Halley and Gregory had to work from were a number of Arabic texts. Even these did not contain the whole of the original, so in addition Halley used some comments in Latin by the fourth-century mathematician Pappus. The works of Apollonios had previously attracted the attention of a number of seventeenth-century mathematicians, notably Isaac Barrow, the Italian mathematician Giovanni Borelli (1608–79), and the Orientalist Christopher Ravius (1613–77). All had published parts of Apollonios's volume on *Conics* but both Gregory and Halley wanted to make what they felt would be a definitive edition, and to deal also with another tract of Apollonios's in the same field—the *Sectio*

Rationis. Edward Bernard had made a start on a Latin translation of this tract but had given up before he had gone a tenth of the way through it, and this alone will give some idea of the difficulties which translators faced.

The tract itself was available only in an ill-written Arabic manuscript with many incomplete diagrams, and Halley knew very little Arabic. David Gregory had revised the portion which Bernard had done and also prepared a fair copy of what there was of the original Arabic. When Halley took over he compared the Bernard/Gregory Latin text with the Arabic original, in this way obtaining a key to the Arabic, and it was from this alone that he managed to decipher the remainder. Halley was assisted in the project by his own profound knowledge of the subject about which Apollonios was writing. The great Orientalist of the day was a Dr. Sykes, and with him Halley discussed his finished result, at the same time bringing to his attention certain passages the sense of which he understood but which he had been forced to interpret rather freely. To Sykes's amazement Halley's interpretation was correct provided one or two small alterations were made to the original manuscript, alterations which Sykes believed were quite valid considering the kind of errors which a copyist might make.

The plan for Apollonios's *Conics* was that Gregory should deal with the first four sections and also with some early comments on that part of the work, while Halley undertook to work on the remaining three sections together with the scraps of information provided by Pappus on the final section of the work, which had been lost and for which no Arabic translation was available. Gregory died after dealing with only a small part of his portion, and the main burden fell on Halley. To help him in his work Halley examined and compared a number of Arabic texts by various famous Muslim mathematicians and notably that of Thābit b. Quarra (826–901). In all the Arabic texts was a note at the end stating that the final section of the *Conics* had not been translated because the Greek text of the section was missing.

To anyone but Halley this would have meant an end to his work, but as the *Biographia Britannica* states, this ". . . was neither sufficient to discourage his industry, nor yet to baffle his ingenuity."

Halley used the comments of Pappus, who had possessed the Greek text of the last and eighth section, and with this, plus his own knowledge of what Apollonios had achieved in the first seven books and of what he must have been trying to achieve in the eighth, Halley reconstructed the missing section. Moreover, by this time he had become utterly familiar with the style of expression Apollonios had used and himself wrote the reconstructed book in this vein. He was eminently successful, so much so in fact that the contemporary view, as recorded in the *Biographia Britannica,* goes so far as to say, "In this performance the elegant taste and manner of Apollonius are so perfectly copied, that the best judges have agreed, the whole eight books, as published by our author, may fairly be esteemed to be the work of the same Grecian master."

In addition to this, which was his main work on classical mathematics, Halley prepared and reconstructed another work of Apollonios's *Sectio Spatii* and worked out a Latin translation of the Greek of Serenus of Antinoeia (fourth century A.D.), another ancient geometer; these he published together with his work on the *Conics* of Apollonios. To complete his studies on early mathematics Halley translated the *Sphaerica*—a discussion on the geometry of the sphere—by Menelaus of Alexandria (fl. A.D. 98). This was an elegant translation and Latin scholars, not only of his own day but also of more recent times, have commended it highly.

His edition of Menelaus was published posthumously in 1758, but the Apollonios appeared in three separate volumes in 1706 (the *Sectio Rationis* and *Sectio Spatii* together) and 1710 (the *Conics* in two volumes). The *Conics* served the world well and provided the only complete edition of Apollonios's work for nearly two hundred years, and it is gratifying to record that in 1710 Oxford recognized his quite surprising achievements by granting him the coveted D.C.L.

There were other matters which claimed Halley's attention at this time. He edited three volumes called *Miscellanea Curiosa, being a Collection of some of the Principal Phenomena in Nature* which was a selection of the more interesting papers that had appeared in *Philosophical Transactions* in the hope that they would reach a wider audience of "inquisitive Gentlemen." They were published

in London between 1705 and 1707 and contained much material by
Halley himself. But more time-consuming was the argument which
had developed between Flamsteed and the Royal Society. In preparing the *Principia* Newton had continually to apply to Flamsteed
for observational details and, as we have seen, because of Flamsteed's antipathy to Halley, the latter had to get Newton to ask for
certain observations on comets. These personal applications were
due to the fact that Flamsteed had failed to publish any of his observations, and opinion within the Society gradually grew that this
was a failure on Flamsteed's part; it was thought that as a public
servant paid by the Crown, he ought to publish his results both for
the good name of the Observatory and, even more, so that other
astronomers might have the benefit of freely consulting them. Need-
less to say, Flamsteed did not agree. He claimed that even though
the Crown appointed him and paid him a salary, this was but a
pittance that had to be supplemented in other ways and, more to
the point, as he had paid for his observing instruments and his
assistants out of his own pocket, such results as he had obtained
were his property and his alone. He would publish them, he said,
as and when he was ready and not before.

We may appreciate something of Flamsteed's feelings, yet it is
clear that his attitude was not one of service to his brother astronomers. In any event Newton, now President of the Royal Society,
became increasingly angry over Flamsteed's procrastination. He
visited Flamsteed at Greenwich in April 1704, ostensibly to dine
with him but, in reality, to ascertain the state of his star catalogue.
Flamsteed claimed that the catalogue was ready for publication
and was asked to submit an estimate of the cost to the Society, a
request which he did not comply with until seven months later.
When at last a catalogue did arrive the Society agreed that publication should be made, and Prince George of Denmark, consort to
Queen Anne, was informed of the decision and generously agreed
to pay for the publication himself.

A Committee of the Society, which included Newton, Wren,
Halley, and others was set up to examine the manuscripts Flamsteed
supplied, and decided that all should be published. The Society
therefore instructed Flamsteed to put his work into a suitable state

for the printer. Flamsteed's next action was not cooperative, for he merely handed over a copy of his observations and the catalogue of star positions which he had worked out from them, at the same time pointing out that the catalogue was incomplete and should not be published. He did, however, promise to submit a "more perfect copy." By May 1706 the printing of the actual observations was begun, but the work proceeded slowly and came to a standstill in 1708 on the death of Prince George. At last the Society, probably at Newton's instigation, decided to take action. They realized that whatever Flamsteed's private views might be, the purpose of the Observatory was not being fulfilled. It had become clear that Flamsteed could not be relied upon to exercise his position without some kind of outside control.

The result was that in 1710 Queen Anne issued a Royal Warrant appointing the President of the Royal Society and those other Fellows whom he should think fit, to act as a Board of Visitors. This Board was given wide powers, among which was the right to demand of the Astronomer Royal that he deliver to them within six months after the end of each year a "true and fair copy" of his annual observations. They also had the right to direct him to make such observations as they might deem desirable and even to inspect his instruments to insure that they were maintained in a condition proper for observing.

Flamsteed's dilatoriness had lost him his freedom. Even so, what can only be termed his pigheadedness at not realizing the importance of the immediate publication of his results, led to further trouble. By order of the Queen in 1711, the printing of his observational results of 1704 was begun again, but Flamsteed himself remained apparently unmoved, and indeed in the intervening seven years had done nothing to get his catalogue into what he considered to be a condition suitable for publication. In the end the Royal Society Committee lost patience with him and, after re-examining the manuscript catalogue which Flamsteed had deposited and noting its grave incompleteness and imperfections, asked Halley to complete it as best he could. Halley supplied whole pages of observations and edited the work so that in 1712 it was published under the title *Historia Coelestis*.

Flamsteed was furious. His own observations had been made with painstaking care and the issue of computed results in his catalogue made him bitter: He decided that somehow, at his own expense if need be, he would publish a complete and corrected edition of his observations. Both he and his wife tried either to suppress the *Historia Coelestis* or appeal that at least it should not be put to use. It was not until 1715, however, on the appointment of a new Lord Chamberlain, that Flamsteed was able to get hold of three-quarters of the total number of copies printed. These, except for the volume containing his sextant observations, of which he approved, he publicly burned "as a sacrifice to heavenly truth." After this fit of passion Flamsteed did apply himself to preparing his catalogue and observations in a form which he believed to be accurate, but they were not published until after his death. They were edited by Joseph Crosthwait, with the help of Abraham Sharp. It is generally recognized that Flamsteed's publication—*Historia Coelestis Britannica*—is a monument to his labors, and it shows what a very able observational astronomer he was. Unhappily his seems to have been a classic case of the scientist and the man being two very different kinds of person.

It is usually claimed that the manuscript catalogue was published in 1712 surreptitiously and without Flamsteed's knowledge, yet there exists a letter sent to him by Halley on June 23, 1711, which makes it clear that such a contention is as far from the truth as it could be. Many have maligned Halley for his part in the proceedings but this is unjust, and it is worth quoting the letter in full to show how fair and honest Halley was in a matter which was neither more nor less than of Flamsteed's own making. The letter runs: "Though I am credibly informed that these sheets have been, from time to time, sent you from the press, yet, lest it should be otherwise, I have now sent you the catalogue of the fixed stars intended to be prefixed to your book; having spared no pains to make it as complete and correct as I could, by help of the observations you have given us, made before the year 1706. I desire you to find all the real faults you can, not as believing there are none, but being willing to have a work of this kind as perfect as possible: and if you signify what's amiss, the errors shall be noted, or the sheet reprinted, if the case require it. Pray govern your passion, and when you have seen and considered what I have done for you, you may perhaps think I deserve at your hands a much better treatment than you for a long time have been pleased to bestow on Your quondam friend, and not yet profligate enemy (as you call me)."

A second controversy into which Halley was drawn began to simmer in 1710, and after this date gathered momentum. The subject was the priority of the invention of the calculus, the question of priority being between Newton on the one hand and Leibniz on the other. Leibniz was born in 1646 in Leipzig and was four years younger than Newton; he was a brilliant mathematician and had been elected a Fellow of the Royal Society in 1673 while he was on a visit to England. His discoveries in the calculus date from this time and were published in the Leipzig scientific journal *Acta Eruditorum* in 1683. We can now look back and assess this quarrel without being involved in the heated arguments and acrimonious feelings of three hundred years ago, and it seems that what really happened was that Leibniz and Newton both came to their discoveries quite independently. Such a situation has arisen in science both before and since, and it must be appreciated that the invention of the calculus was not an isolated flash of insight on the part of either Leibniz or Newton—developments in mathematics had been leading up to it for years. This does not mean that the invention did not require either the exercise of a brilliant mind or the use of a mathematically disciplined imagination, for it needed both, and the question in the eighteenth century was who had first achieved this. Newton had come to his "method of fluxions" as early as 1676, and whether Leibniz gained anything from Newton's work we do not know for certain.

Newton did not publish his results for some time, however—indeed, we have already seen how hesitant he was to make his ideas public—and it was a young Swiss mathematician, Nicolas Fatio de Duillier (1664–1753), who first began to raise the question of originality. Fatio had met Leibniz in 1685 and imagined that he had been slighted by him, so when he emigrated to England two years later he determined to have his revenge. He first ingratiated himself with Newton, and to such a degree that he was considered as a possible editor for a new edition of the *Principia*. It was after this, in 1699, when he had prepared a tract on the motion of bodies in a resisting medium, that he openly attacked Leibniz and accused him of plagiarizing Newton's calculus. Leibniz was angry, but claimed that since Newton had given credit to him in the first edition of the *Principia,* he would doubtless vindicate him. But Newton remained silent, and Leibniz defended himself in the *Acta Eruditorum,* the editors of which refused Fatio a right of reply. For almost five years nothing more happened until Newton's *Opticks* appeared in 1704. In his "Advertisement" at the beginning, Newton stated that he had written to Leibniz in 1679 and disclosed many of his ideas, and he also appended two tracts which constitute his first publication of his mathematical methods. Leibniz countered this by publishing an unsigned review in which he claimed that Newton's method of fluxions was in fact his own calculus merely renamed but with a slightly different notation.

Matters now reached a climax. Leibniz's calculus had been taken up widely on the continent of Europe, while Newton's methods had been used by a number of English mathematicians, and in particular by Halley in his work on comets. Thus both protagonists had their supporters and both factions became irate. Coal was heaped on the fire by John Keill (1671–1721), who published a statement claiming that Leibniz had received the idea from Newton by seeing some letters which had passed between Newton and Oldenburg, when the latter was Secretary to the Royal Society. Leibniz became even more angry and increasingly adamant, and finally protested to the Royal Society, asking that Keill's paper should be withdrawn and an apology extracted from him. Keill refused to acquiesce and feelings began to run so high that the Society appointed a committee to look into the matter. Halley came into the argument as a member of this committee and by helping to prepare the result of their deliberations, which was issued in 1712; it took the form of a publication of the relevant Newton/Oldenburg correspondence in a volume entitled *Commercium Epistolicum,* by means of which it was supposed to be clear that Newton's early knowledge of the subject, as shown by the letters, made his claim of priority a true one. Leibniz still remained unconvinced, being sure that with Newton as President of the Society and Halley as a member of the committee, the conclusion reached was not an unbiased one.

Had Leibniz not died a few years later, the argument would

doubtless have continued with increasing acrimony. The exact nature of Halley's part in this whole matter we do not know, although it is certain that he supported Newton, but Keill seems to have become head of the pro-Newton faction. In a letter to Keill, which Halley wrote at Newton's request, as late as 1715 when a French translation of *Commercium Epistolicum* was printed, Halley referred to Keill as Newton's ". . . avowed Champion in this quarrell." This "quarrell," as Halley called it, still had its repercussions, and for nearly a hundred years English mathematicians continued to use Newton's method of algebraic notation for the calculus in preference to the more self-explanatory and efficient system of Leibniz, an attitude which helped to hold back development in England of this branch of mathematics.

In 1713 Halley became one of the Secretaries of the Royal Society, following Sir Hans Sloane. Halley continued in this post until 1721, and in the course of his official duties we find that in 1716 he had to write to Flamsteed in connection with the observations which it was now commanded he should provide. From this letter we see that Flamsteed was still as dilatory as ever, and Halley wrote to him in a terse and formal fashion: "I am commanded by the president, Councill and Fellows of the R. Society, to put you in mind that you are in arrears to them a Copy of your Astronomicall Observations for the year 1714; and that those of 1715 ending with December last, are now become due to them; both of which they require to send them on or before Midsummer day next [seventeen days from the date of the letter], as you are obliged to do by her late Maties orders, which constituted them perpetuall Visitors of the Royall Observatory, and entitle them to the Copies they now demand." Many such letters were sent to Flamsteed; but this is the only one signed by Halley alone, the others being signed by members of the council. They were made necessary by the fact that Flamsteed refrained from sending his observations to the Society until their continued reminders made him realize that no refusal would be brooked. As Secretary Halley had considerable power in this matter, but he cannot have relished writing to Flamsteed in this way, for while he had every reason to treat Flamsteed as an enemy he never seems to have done so.

CHAPTER 14

Astronomer Royal

Halley was now fifty-seven, his past work had been recognized, and he had achieved a position of eminence in the scientific world. By normal standards he should have been leading a less active life, yet he was still producing original papers and was shortly to engage in the most arduous task of his whole career.

In *Philosophical Transactions* for 1714, he wrote "An Account of several extraordinary Meteors or lights in the Sky" that was nothing remarkable in the way of new knowledge but did provide observational evidence which was of use to astronomers in later years. He made telescopic observations of the star cluster in the constellation of Hercules, and there also appeared a paper on observations of the comet of 1680 made by Gottfried Kirch of Saxony, who was the first to observe it—although unsigned, it was probably by Halley. Next there was a paper about comments published on the Continent on the variation of the compass as noted during his voyage to the Straits of Magellan. But perhaps Halley's most notable achievement in 1714 was his calculation of the exact position of the track of the shadow of the total solar eclipse which was due to occur on April 22, 1715. These calculations were published in the form of a map, many copies of which were sold by John Senex from his premises "at the Globe in Salisbury Court near Fleet Street" and were more accurate than the calculated positions for the shadow given by Flamsteed. Yet all this was merely the beginning of a spate of astronomical work, wide in its scope and profound in its insight.

In 1715 Halley prepared a paper reporting his observations of the April eclipse. These were made from the new premises to which the Royal Society had moved five years earlier, premises at Crane Court on Fleet Street which were then in the middle of London, yet quiet and peaceful. (They are now the center of newspaper publication and have long since been vacated by the Society.) The observations were made from the roof of the building using the Society's instruments, more particularly a quadrant of almost thirty-six-inch radius fitted with telescopic sights and a screw adjustment that allowed the observer to follow the sun with considerable precision. With Halley were the Earl of Abingdon and Lord Parker, Chief Justice of the King's Bench and afterward the first Earl of Macclesfield, both Fellows of the Society who made their own observations. There were two other members of the party, the mathematician Pierre de Montmort (1678–1719) and the astronomer the Chevalier de Louville (1671–1732) who had come from Paris ". . . expressly on this occasion."

Halley's paper on the eclipse is of considerable interest because it shows his well-developed sense of scientific caution. The question which the observations raised was the nature of the corona, the pearly-colored, very tenuous solar atmosphere which is normally invisible due to the glare of the sun, but which can be seen during a total solar eclipse. Although we now know that the corona is part of the gaseous envelope which surrounds the sun, there was no such knowledge at the beginning of the eighteenth century. Halley contented himself with a careful description and equally carefully avoided coming to a decision as to whether the "appendage" was a part of the sun or, as usually suggested, a thin atmosphere surrounding the moon.

His next paper in *Philosophical Transactions* dealt with what we now call "novae" (new stars), which become visible, or at least noticeable, due to a sudden increase in their radiation. These stars had intrigued astronomers for a long time, and in at least one instance—that of Tycho Brahe—had acted as the stimulant for a career of astronomical observation. Halley traced the reports of those that had appeared since 1550 with special reference to one in the constellation of Cygnus which was still visible, although not as bright as when it first exploded into view, and he also dealt with variable stars (those which continually vary their brilliance by small amounts). This served to draw more attention to the subject and was part of Halley's increasing interest in stellar matters.

Yet more significant was his subsequent paper, "An Account of several Nebulae or lucid spots like clouds, lately discovered among the fixt stars by help of the telescope." The nebulae, so called from their hazy, cloudlike appearance, were something new; with very few exceptions they were invisible until the advent of the telescope, and they presented a problem which could only be solved toward the close of the nineteenth century with the development of the spectroscope. In view of the paucity of knowledge in Halley's day, his paper is extraordinarily penetrating, for after discussing the appearance of the objects, which included his earlier observations of a cluster in Centaurus and more recent ones of the cluster in Hercules, he concluded that the nebulae were ". . . nothing else but Light coming from an extraordinary great space in the Ether; through which a lucid Medium is diffused, that shines with its own proper lustre." Considering that we now know that the kind of objects Halley was describing are immense clouds of glowing gas, shining either by their own light or made visible because of stars embedded in them and, in both cases, that the primary energy causing them to glow is due to stellar radiation, Halley's suggestion of a "lucid Medium" was surprisingly accurate. Moreover, his idea that their light covered "an extraordinary great space in the Ether" [space] is only too true, for the volume which a nebula fills is so large that, in general, one can say that the sun and all its planets would be swallowed up even in the smallest.

The next year, 1716, saw no abatement in Halley's scientific work. Although now almost sixty, he was producing a flood of ideas and a host of scientific papers that speak much for his surprising vitality and would have done credit to a much younger man. Some of his work was the fruit of years of observation as, for example, the publication in 1716 of an appendix in the third edition of Thomas Street's *Astronomia Carolina* of "A Series of Observations on the Planets, chiefly of the Moon, made near London . . . being a proposal of how to find the Longitude, &c. By Dr. Edmund Halley." This appendix contained Halley's lunar observations made when he was a younger man, which were followed through for nearly the

eighteen-year sarotic period.* In the meantime Halley was still dealing with the question of the sun's distance, this year seeing the
publication of his final paper on the use of the transits of Venus and
also a paper in which he discussed some daylight observations of
Venus which had been made during the summer. Yet his most important contributions in 1716, besides his appeal to observe transits
of Venus of 1761 and 1769, were his two papers describing the
appearance of aurorae, notable displays of which had occurred in
March and early April.

Halley's descriptions are careful and accurate, but the importance of his papers lies in the explanation he offered to account for
the phenomenon. He noted that the aurora seen on March 6 appeared to have what he called a "crown" of light above it and,
rejecting any of the picturesque but scientifically useless beliefs then
current, he realized that this was purely an optical effect of per-
spective due, as he put it, to the "concourse" of many auroral
streamers each of which stood almost vertical. This suggestion was
confirmed in later years, but it was not the only revolutionary
point he made. He also recommended a method for determining the
height of the aurora which, in principle, is still used; and he gave a
theoretical explanation which is surprisingly modern and, in the
early eighteenth century, was certainly far ahead of its time.

Briefly, Halley suggested that the aurorae were formed by the
escape from below the earth's crust of a luminous "medium," and
went on to propose that once it had escaped, its behavior was governed by the earth's magnetic field. The first part of his hypothesis is now untenable, although it must be appreciated that, in his
own day, the physical universe was populated with hypothetical
media and fluids which could not be directly weighed or measured.
The universe itself was thought to be full of ether—an idea which
hung on tenaciously until the beginning of the twentieth century
—and Halley's proposal that the aurora was just such another im-

---

* The saros is a period of 223 lunations (one lunation is the interval between
one new moon and the next). A total of 223 lunations equals nineteen apparent
revolutions of the sun with respect to that point on the moon's orbit where the
sun appears to cross it. This period is equal to approximately eighteen years,
eleven days, and is significant in calculating the dates of eclipses and thus the
motion of the moon.

ponderable substance was not far removed from the scientific climate of his time. But it was his suggestion that the behavior of the
aurora was due to the earth's magnetic field, or "virtue," as he
called it, which was the most significant point in his theory. This we
now know to be true, but in the eighteenth century it was a completely novel approach to suggest a well-known terrestrial phenomenon such as magnetism as an explanation of what seemed to be a
celestial phenomenon. It is this aspect of his theory that is so
remarkable, and although it may have been Halley's preoccupation
for so long with the questions of magnetic variation and the cause
of terrestrial magnetism that led him to link the aurora with them,
it was nonetheless a penetrating insight into the problem.

In 1716 the *Philosophical Transactions* also contained an account of Halley's ideas and experiences of ". . . living under Water"
but did not contain his designs for a diving helmet which he seems
never to have published himself. During the next year, however,
except for one paper which gave an English translation of a French
publication in which Halley's chart of magnetic variation was much
lauded, the *Philosophical Transactions* contains purely astronomical
papers, one of which was quite revolutionary.

First it must be mentioned that in June 1717 there appeared a
small "telescopicall" comet; being visible only in a telescope it did
not cause much comment, at least among the public at large, but in
view of Halley's researches on cometary paths it was of concern to
astronomers. Halley observed it and reported his results, although
the information he obtained did not provide enough data for him to
attempt any computation of its path and allow for any prediction
of its return. His second paper to be prepared concerned an "Advertisement" to astronomers "of the advantages that may accrue
from the observation of the Moon's frequent appulses [close ap-
proaches] to the Hyades during the three next ensuing years." The
point Halley made in this paper concerned the better determination of the moon's apparent path in the sky. The Hyades, a cluster
of many stars, lies in the constellation of Taurus, and in 1717–19
the moon's orbit relative to the earth lay in such a position that the
moon would appear to pass in front of the cluster. Since the positions of the stars of the Hyades were well determined this, as Halley

appreciated, provided a golden opportunity to observe a number of occultations and thus obtain better data for computing the moon's orbit. His appeal was useful because it drew the attention of astronomers to a series of simple yet important observations. But it was Halley's last paper of 1717 which contained his most novel idea.

Some years earlier, in 1710, he had set himself the task of examining Ptolemy's writings and of going through the catalogue of star positions which Ptolemy had compiled from his own observations and those of Hipparchos, who had observed some three hundred years earlier. Halley noticed that the positions of certain stars listed by Ptolemy were far different from the positions given either by his own observations or by those of others made in the late seventeenth and early eighteenth centuries. It first occurred to him that these differences might be due to inaccuracies in the earlier observed positions but, after due reflection and some computation, he came firmly to the conclusion that the differences were of such a magnitude as precluded this possibility. He decided that there was only one satisfactory answer, namely that the fixed stars were not fixed at all but had real motions of their own. Admittedly the evidence he adduced for this concerned primarily only the three bright stars Arcturus, Procyon, and Sirius, but if these moved, then he conjectured so must the others which, because they were dimmer were in all probability farther away and possessed motions that were less easy to detect.

Halley's deduction was correct, and although it is now known that the stars all have their own proper motions, this was a completely revolutionary viewpoint in the eighteenth century. On the face of it, the evidence seemed rather against Halley's suggestion; the same star constellations had been observed from the earliest times without, apparently, any change in their shapes at all. But what Halley appreciated was that the stars were so far away† that even a large real motion in space of any particular star would be undetectable by the unaided eye, and only the most precise observa-

† He did not, of course, have any actual measurements of stellar distance to help him, only the generally accepted view that even the nearest stars were immensely far off.

tions made a great many years apart could serve to reveal any change. What Halley was able to do was to produce circumstantial evidence, using observations made at least fifteen hundred years apart, which showed that such motions did exist. It is, however, strange to record that this example of Halley's profound insight into stellar astronomy was not recognized, and his paper passed without comment in at least three of the obituary notices prepared after his death. Perhaps this was due to the lack of appreciation of the significance of his discovery, which was not followed up in any concerted fashion until the late nineteenth century, when observational techniques had become much more refined. All the same it is to Halley that credit must be given for discovering that the so-called fixed stars have real motions of their own.

In 1719 an "extraordinary" meteor appeared which was visible from "all over England," and it aroused widespread interest. Halley commented on it and pointed out the unusual height it must have been to render it visible over so large an area. He wrote again on the aurora, this time purely descriptively, noting its position with respect to the magnetic meridian, and discussed some observations of an eclipse of the moon made at the Cape of Good Hope from which he was able to deduce, with some accuracy, the longitude of the cape; he also commented on this method as a means of longitude determination.

On December 31, 1719 John Flamsteed died, and the post of Astronomer Royal became vacant for the first time. This event brought Halley to the fourth and final important phase of his life; he was appointed in Flamsteed's place. As Martin Folkes remarked, "Dr. Halley was recommended by the late Earl of Macclesfield, then Lord Chancellor, and perfectly acquainted with the Drs. Great Merits, as also by the then Earl of Sunderland, Secretary of State, and others, to his late Majesty K. George the First, as the fittest Person to do Honour to the Post of Astronomer Royal and observator at Greenwich; which his Majesty was accordingly pleas'd to give him, by Commission dated the ninth day of February 1720." Thus came full public recognition of Halley's astronomical work, and he entered on his new duties "to apply himself with the utmost care and diligence to the rectifying the tables of the motions of the heavens, and the places of the fixed stars, in order to find out the so much desired longitude at sea, for perfecting the art of Navigation," even though he was now in his sixty-fourth year.

When Halley arrived at Greenwich he found it in a sorry state; Flamsteed's widow had removed all the astronomical instruments and all the furniture, and the place was bare. His first task was to rectify the situation without delay, and it is obvious that he was determined that he was not going to pay out of his own pocket for the equipment needed. He applied to the Crown for assistance, and obtained a grant of five hundred pounds ($1,200) from the Board of Ordnance in order to refit the Observatory. He began re-equipping by purchasing a transit instrument, the first of its kind to be installed in the Observatory and, as is now customary, it was set up in as accurate a north–south direction as possible so that the passage or transit of stars across the meridian could be timed as precisely as possible, such observations providing the equivalent of terrestrial longitude of the position of any celestial body. At about this time Halley also placed an order for a large eight-foot mural quadrant so that he could measure the altitudes of stars, planets, and the moon, and from these compute the celestial equivalent of terrestrial latitude. The quadrant was delivered in 1724, having been built by the famous instrument maker "Honest" George Graham (1673–1751),‡ "well known by his Exquisit Care and Judgement in all works of this sort." The instrument seems to have caused some interest among the knowledgeable, and a drawing showing its details and another giving the general arrangement appeared in 1738 in Robert Smith's *Compleat Opticks;* unfortunately the general arrangement shown by Smith contains some errors, and the author has prepared a complete drawing from the details which Smith provided and after an examination of the actual instrument as it still stands at Greenwich (see Plate 14).

With characteristic boldness Halley not only obtained a grant for re-equipping the observatory, but also set to work on preparing

‡ It is likely that Graham also built the transit instrument, according to a private publication of the National Maritime Museum, which is now responsible for the old Greenwich Observatory. Lalande's claim that Hooke built it seems improbable.

an observing program which he believed would lead him to obtain a means for determining longitude at sea. This was the *raison d'être* of his commission, and he pinned his faith on using the moon for the purpose. The moon's apparent position was still not predictable to the accuracy required, however, and Halley set about the task of completing a new collection of observations for the eighteen-year period of the saros. In the eighteenth century life expectancy was nowhere near what it is now, and Halley's plan to undertake such an observing program at the age of sixty-five was optimistic in the extreme, but at least he could hope to lay the foundations on which his successors could build. He began work on this project in 1722, and actually lived long enough to see it successfully through to the bitter end. Following through the program required dogged determination and a continual application to the task in hand so that during the whole period ". . . he scarce lost a meridian view of the moon, whether by day or night, as often as the heavens would permit."

Halley's lunar observations improved in 1725 when his new quadrant was in regular use but they were not published until 1749, seven years after his death, in spite of earlier prodding by Newton from the Royal Society. Yet in 1731 he was able to announce in *Philosophical Transactions* a method of using the moon to determine longitude at sea with an error of no more than sixty-nine miles at the equator. This was a considerable achievement even though it did not quite reach the standard set by the Board of Longitude. His posthumous tables provided a slightly increased degree of accuracy but again did not bring a close enough solution for naval use, and they have been criticized as inferior in quality to those that Flamsteed made. It has even been claimed that he ". . . undervalued those habits of minute attention which are indispensable . . . in the practice of astronomical observation"—but this seems rather too harsh. The majority of Flamsteed's observational work was carried out when he was a much younger man than Halley, and were virtually finished when he was at the age Halley began his program. When Halley was young, his catalogue had to be prepared using portable instruments under bad conditions, but when he had the opportunity to observe with Hevelius using permanent and so more accurate equipment, there were no discrepancies. Only when his eyesight was less acute and his reactions slower were his observations less than the best. Moreover, it must be appreciated that even if the precision he later obtained was not all it might have been, it proved valuable in showing the practicability of lunar observation for longitude determination and gave a basis on which later Astronomers Royal could build, so that in 1767 Nevil Maskelyne was in a position to publish regular lunar tables for this very purpose.

Ironically, the longitude problem was to be solved in the one way Newton had pronounced impossible, and on which Halley had felt it unwise to pin his hopes—by the production of an accurate seagoing clock. In 1728 John Harrison (1693–1776), a young, self-trained clockmaker, called on Halley at Greenwich and showed him his ingenious temperature-compensating pendulum and a clock mechanism that was self-lubricating, together with proposals for a marine timepiece. Halley advised him that the Board of Longitude was not prepared to advance money for suggestions alone, but gave him a letter of introduction to George Graham and advised him to make a clock such as he proposed. Graham generously lent Harrison some two hundred pounds ($480) without security, and in 1737 Halley had the pleasure of being present as a member of the board when Harrison demonstrated his first marine chronometer. This was a real step toward Harrison's final solution, which came twenty-four years later with the completion of his fourth design of chronometer, although lunar observations were never completely disregarded and were in current use beside the chronometer for a very long time.

In the year of his appointment as Astronomer Royal, Halley published a number of scientific papers and continued to do so, although at a reduced pace, until near the end of his long life. Those of 1720 were primarily concerned with astronomy, only one paper dealing with another subject, namely the measurement of heights above sea level of various places using a newly invented model of the barometer ". . . in which the scale is greatly enlarged." This paper is straightforward enough and was a method of determining altitudes which Halley had advocated before.

Halley's astronomical papers of 1720 are of primary interest. The first of these was a critical assessment of observations made by Jacques Cassini (1677–1756), who had attempted to obtain a determination of stellar distance by observing Sirius, the brightest of all the fixed stars. Cassini had based his choice on the assumption that Sirius was the nearest star to the earth since it was so bright and, using a transit instrument, made careful observations as it crossed the meridian. He claimed that he had detected a shift against the background formed by other stars. If this were true, then Cassini had obtained observational evidence for the Copernican theory which, in spite of the work of Brahe, Kepler, Flamsteed, Newton, and Halley, was still without direct proof. Halley subjected Cassini's results to a rigorous examination and concluded, quite correctly, that the shift was not in fact a measure of distance at all. This was no disservice either to Cassini or to his care in observing, for such a shift calls for the most refined techniques, and no eighteenth-century equipment could satisfy the requirements; indeed, it was not until just after the middle of the nineteenth century that the first successful measures of this kind were made successfully.

Halley's paper, however, did not concern itself solely with Cassini's measurements but also provided a very thorough analysis of the accuracy attainable with transit instruments of the kind then used. Halley went further into this subject in another paper, published later in the year, in which he discussed methods of observing with a transit instrument which was fitted, as was his own at Greenwich, with "cross hairs" in the eyepiece.§

Halley's most important paper in 1720 was concerned with the universe as a whole. This notable contribution to what is now called cosmology was published in the *Philosophical Transactions* in two parts, running consecutively, under the titles "Of the Infinity of the sphere of fix'd Stars" and "Of the Number, order, and light of the fix'd Stars." Both papers are so closely allied that it is convenient

§ Today photographically etched images are generally used to provide sighting points within a telescope. Previously thin wire was customary or, very often and in Halley's day probably entirely, very thin hairs were stretched across the eyepiece mount. These "hairs" were frequently made of dried spider webs which had each strand split in half.

to consider them together, but first we must examine the question at issue. Was the universe finite in extent or did it have no end? It had been suggested that the idea of an infinite universe, which in England had been coupled to the Copernican theory, was untenable because if the stars were infinite in number, then their light ought to be infinite in amount and so the night sky should appear as bright as daylight. Halley very carefully countered this suggestion. He assumed, for sake of argument, that the stars were evenly distributed in space—a reasonable enough assumption to work from—and went on to claim that the light from the more distant ones would diminish to a greater and greater degree as their distances increased: in other words, that the diminution which the light of the stars suffered was not just directly dependent on the distance they were away from the observer, but to some greater factor than that of simple proportionality. The result, he claimed, was that beyond certain distances the stars would become invisible "even in the Nicest Telescopes." This was a plausible answer to the protagonists of a finite universe, and we now know that light does not diminish in direct proportion to the distance of its source but to a greater degree as Halley suggested. Nevertheless his detailed argument appears to have a mathematical flaw which does not seem to have been recognized at the time. But Halley's main point of disagreement with those who supported a universe of finite extent was the gravitational paradox which he believed such a view contained. His argument was simple and direct: He claimed that if the universe were not infinite then there must be some point which could be considered as its center and it would follow that, because of the law of universal gravitation, everything in space would be attracted to such a center and, in consequence, the universe would collapse. Even though there were flaws in Halley's arguments, the interesting point is that he was here again acting as a pioneer, this time in matters which were to have important cosmological consequences through the work of de Chéseaux (1718–51) and Olbers (1758–1840).

As we have said, Halley began his concentrated observing program on the moon in 1722, but it is clear he was preparing for this from the moment he was appointed Astronomer Royal. He found much that needed to be done, and decided that one of the more important tasks was to determine accurately the allowances that must be made in observation for the refraction of starlight by the earth's atmosphere. The exact nature of this correction depends on the apparent altitude of a celestial body and, it must be remembered, this altitude changes continually as each body moves in its apparent curved path across the sky, due to the earth's rotation. Moreover, as the altitude becomes less the refraction changes at an ever-increasing rate. Halley therefore analyzed the whole question and prepared "an accurate table of refraction." This was published in *Philosophical Transactions* in 1721 and provided valuable information for the observational astronomer; it can be considered one of Halley's more important papers on practical astronomy.

In 1717 he had discussed the apparent close approach of the moon to the Hyades and Halley now developed this method further, applying it to the determination of planetary positions, using a procedure based on close planetary approaches to those fixed stars whose positions had been accurately determined. This was published in *Philosophical Transactions* toward the end of 1721, being preceded by two other papers, one on "The Variation of the magnetical Compass, observed by Capt. Rogers, Commander of the ship *Duke*, in his passage from Cape St Lucar [Morro Bay?] in California to the Isle of Guam or Guana, one of the Ladrones [south of Hong Kong]" which shows that Halley's voyages had stimulated others to take up where he had left off; and the other giving further details for the "Art of living under Water," including something on the diving helmet and a means of protecting the ears at depth. His last paper for the year described a mock sun which he observed on October 21. On November 27, 1722 Halley observed a partial solar eclipse, but in this year and during 1723, his papers are concerned with longitude determinations at various ports.

By 1724 Halley's lunar observing program was well under way, George Graham's quadrant was delivered, and the only paper in *Philosophical Transactions* for this year was on the "Universal Deluge," being in fact the formal publication of his thoughts on a matter about which he had addressed the Society some thirty years before. Indeed, from 1723 onward, the number of scientific papers that Halley produced shows a sharp decline, but this is not surprising, for most of his energies must have been spent observing at Greenwich. In 1725, he did find time to publish something on the 1723 transit of Mercury from which he deduced not the distance of the sun, but new figures for the average motion of the planet and other details of its orbit; in 1727 he went into print to defend Newton against an attack by Etienne Souciet (1671–1744), a French Roman Catholic priest, on the subject of biblical chronology, and a year later discussed and revised astronomical observations made by a Mr. Joseph Harris at Vera Cruz.

Mention must also be made of the total solar eclipse of May 11, 1724. After his spectacular success over the 1715 eclipse, Halley again prepared a map showing the calculated track of the moon's shadow and, at the same time, ". . . the Passage of the Shadow as it was Observ'd in the last Total Eclipse . . ." At the foot of the map, he commented, "Since the Publication of our Predictions of this Eclipse has had the desired effect, and many curious Persons have been excited thereby to communicate their Observations from most parts of the Kingdom: we thought it might not be unacceptable to represent after the same manner the passage of the Shade, as it really happened; whereby it will appear that our Numbers pretend not to be altogether perfect, yet the correction they need is very small." This map, like the one of nine years before, was sold by John Senex, and was followed by a second map which showed the predicted track for the whole of that part of Europe from which totality could be observed.

Halley's last published papers appeared in 1732 and 1733. The first dealt with the familiar problems of longitude determination at sea and the magnetic observations made on board a ship traveling between Java and St. Helena in 1731–32. The second, a paper on the graphical solution of algebraic equations, appeared in a posthumous edition of Newton's *Arithmetica Universalis*. His final contribution to *Philosophical Transactions* was a brief note on the lunar eclipse of March 15, 1736.

In 1721, the year of his appointment as Astronomer Royal, Halley resigned his Secretaryship of the Royal Society, although from the papers he published over the next fifteen years, it is obvious that he continued his close association with the Society. Indeed, from various records it is clear that he traveled to London to meet friends at Child's coffeehouse before the formal meetings. Often he used to dine in town privately but it is also reported that coffeehouse discussions used frequently to continue so long after meetings were over that Halley and others missed their dinners and, in due course, the habit arose of having dinner out so that conversation could continue until a late hour. According to Sir Joseph Ayloffe, who was elected a Fellow in 1731, an informal kind of dining club for Fellows was formed at this time, but from Flamsteed's correspondence in which he made scathing allusions to gatherings of Halley and others in taverns, as well as from other evidence, it seems likely that a dinner and discussion following Royal Society meetings was the custom before 1731 and, in fact, before Halley became Astronomer Royal. In any event, the Royal Society Club was formally constituted in 1743, the year after Halley's death, yet Halley has been credited as its instigator, and the truth of the matter would seem to be that what was originally an informal arrangement became a more formal kind of meeting. It is not unlikely that Halley had his say about the exact form this should take and, had he lived, would have become one of the members, if not the chairman, of the new group.

It is from Ayloffe whose report, although made as late as 1776, seems to be substantially correct, that we learn that the informal meetings moved from Child's coffeehouse to a house in Dean's Court ". . . between an Ale-house and a Tavern . . . where there was a great Draft of porter . . . ," one of the group buying fish from a nearby fishmonger when the number meeting had gathered together, so that they could have "Fish and Pudding" which, with their beer, cost 2/6d. a head. "Dr. Halley," we are told, "never eat any Thing but Fish, for he had no Teeth." The house in Dean's Court was owned by a man called Reynell who, in due course, became placed in charge of the King's Arms in St. Paul's churchyard, and invited Halley and his companions to transfer their meetings there. This they did, but moved again—we do not know after how long—to the Mitre, which was considerably nearer the Society's rooms in Crane Court. Halley took the chair, and on his death was succeeded by Martin Folkes.

In 1729 George II's consort, Queen Caroline, ". . . thought proper to make a visit at the Royal Observatory, and being greatly satisfied with the polite reception she met with, among other things, took particular notice . . ." that Halley had once served his country as a naval captain. Halley had held his commission from 1698 to 1701, a period of rather more than three years, and technically he therefore qualified for the rank and pay of "post captain" for which a period of not less than three years' command was the official requirement. Queen Caroline did not merely take "particular notice" but, on her return to the King, ". . . was pleased shortly after to obtain of his Majesty . . ." a grant of half pay as post captain to Halley, and this continued until his death.

Halley cannot be considered as having been ill-paid—he held the Savilian chair at Oxford as well as the post of Astronomer Royal —but certainly the stipend at Greenwich was small. Flamsteed had supplemented his income by taking on duties in a nearby parish, and for a time had taken private pupils. Halley may have made much of the fact that his lunar program was very time-consuming and, from what we know of him, may have tactfully suggested to Queen Caroline that his salary was not all he could wish. All the same it seems that his case was certainly put forward by his many friends at court, and perhaps Queen Caroline's visit may have been made with the idea of an increased income in mind. In support of this it may be noted that in 1729 Halley was offered the appointment of "Mathematical Preceptor to the Duke of Cumberland," an honor which he declined ". . . by reason of his great age, and because he deemed the ordinary attendance upon that employ would be inconsistent with the performance of his duty at Greenwich."

On January 30, 1736 Mary Halley, with whom Halley had lived happily and "in great contentment" for over fifty-five years, died. Why she died, whether it was by reason of age alone or because of illness there is no evidence—in fact, we know nothing of their life together. She was buried in the churchyard at Lee, a little more than a mile south of the observatory. Later in the year Halley seems to have had a minor stroke which left him with a slight paralysis of his right hand. He still continued his observing program, however, although his paralysis made it necessary for him to have an assistant.

Gael Morris worked with him, and James Bradley (1692–1762), Savilian professor of astronomy came up to London weekly to help, especially with adjustments of the instruments. Three years later Halley's program was complete and he was certainly pleased with his results, having observed fifteen hundred meridian transits of the moon with precision superior to anything of the kind previously achieved, or so Halley believed. Now he wished to resign in favor of Bradley. His resignation was declined, and he continued to observe until the last few months of his life.

In June 1736, presumably prompted by his stroke, Halley drew up his will, extracts from which are as follows: "In the name of God, I Edmond Halley, Doctor of Laws and Astronomer in the royal Observatory in Greenwich park . . . make and Declare this my last Will and Testament in manner and form following; Imprimis [in the first place] I recommend my Soul to the Mercy of Almighty God, And as to my Body, my Will and Desire is that it may be Interred in the same grave with that of my Dear Wife lately deceased, in the Churchyard of Lee in Kent. Next, since my son Edmond is in actual possession of the best part of the Real Estate of the ffamily and may Inherit the rest after my Decease, . . . besides he being retained in the Service of the Crown as a Surgeon seems to be sufficiently provided for, my Desire is that he may therewith be Contented and accept of Twenty pounds for mourning. As for my personal Estate consisting in the remainder of a Lease of a House in Cannon St., London, now in the occupation of Mrs. Mary Camm or her Assigns, as likewise in Goods, ready Money, Plate, Books, &c., I give them to my . . . two Daughters Margaret and Katherine to be equally divided between them . . . and appoint my said Two Daughters joint Executrices. . . . *Signed:* Edmond Halley."

The Will was witnessed by Ellener Simpson and James Bradley. It will be noticed that Halley unequivocally spells his forename as Edmond. Often he was, and still is, referred to as Edmund, but as extracts from his own correspondence will have made clear, in the seventeenth and early eighteenth centuries, spelling was not consistent and, moreover, he did latinize himself as Edmundus. Yet he would have been extremely careful over his will, and from this alone

—one of the few documents that contains his full signature—one can do no better than follow his example. But if additional evidence is needed, there is also the full signature he made at the end of his third log, which also gives Edmond, while the title page of this section which he wrote in his own hand and is not a fair copy as the first two sections, also spells the name with an "o." It is for these reasons that Edmond has been used throughout this book. As far as his surname is concerned, it would appear likely that Halley was pronounced "Hall'-ey" for Hooke, Evelyn, and the letter from the Earl of Nottingham to the Exchequer authorizing payment for Halley's visit to Vienna all use phonetic forms of spelling, and write it either as "Hawley" or "Hall-ey."

Halley's son died at Gosport, near Portsmouth, on February 7, 1741, one year before his father. He seems to have had no children, and the family's real estate passed not to his wife but to his sister Katherine. During 1741 Halley's health began to fail. The nature of the illness that overtook him is uncertain, but it appears to have been some form of paralysis, perhaps caused by further strokes. Martin Folkes records that he had ". . . a sort of paralitick disorder," and the writer in the *Biographia Britannica* tells us that ". . . his paralytic disorder gradually increasing, and thereby his strength wearing, though gently, yet continually, away, he came at length to be wholly supported by such cordials as were ordered by his Physician." This, it seems, was the first illness that Halley had suffered except for the fever he contracted on his second voyage, but he did not let it interfere, and until a few weeks before his death he continued to observe with the mural quadrant and travel to London for meetings. His doctor was Richard Mead (1673–1754), physician to the King and a noted scholar and collector who entertained at his table nearly every learned man who visited London. A staunch Whig, he fortunately valued his friends for their talents, not for their political persuasions.

Halley's sense of humor never seems to have deserted him. For some of his feverish attacks he was ordered to take water gruel—a kind of thin porridge, in this case probably containing bone-stock for further nourishment—which was laced with "Jesuit's bark" (a tree bark from Peru that contained quinine). When Halley had to take this he referred to it, no doubt with a twinkle in his eye, as his "chocolate," then a fashionable drink. His memory and judgment remained unimpaired till the last, and it was on January 14, 1742 that ". . . being tired . . . he asked for a glass of wine, and having drunk it presently expired as he sat in his chair without a groan, . . . in the 86th year of his age."

As requested in his will, he was interred next to his wife Mary, his burial taking place on January 20. Over the grave, which lay on the east side of the churchyard, his daughters erected a "handsome tomb" of Portland stone, on the top of which the following epitaph was carved:¶ "Under this marble peacefully rests, with his beloved wife, Edmundus Halleius, LL.D., unquestionably the greatest astronomer of his age. But to conceive an adequate knowledge of the excellencies of this great man, the reader must have recourse to his writings; in which almost all the sciences are in the most beautiful and perspicacious manner illustrated and improved. As when living, he was so highly esteemed by his countrymen, gratitude requires that his memory should be respected by posterity. To the memory of the best of parents their affectionate daughters have erected this monument, in the year 1742." Later his son-in-law Henry Price and his daughter Katherine were also buried in the tomb and, in 1836, John Pond, the sixth Astronomer Royal, was also interred there. The tomb fell into disrepair but was restored by the Admiralty in 1854 when the original tombstone was moved, for safety's sake, to the old Observatory at Greenwich where it was let into a wall.

¶ The original is in Latin.

CHAPTER 15

Halley—An Assessment

In the popular mind Edmond Halley is remembered only because a bright comet is named after him. The world at large does not even realize the reason why he is commemorated in this way and has no idea that he was one of the most brilliant and respected scientists of the late seventeenth and early eighteenth centuries.

It has been Halley's misfortune to be eclipsed by a man whose work he himself was mainly responsible for publishing. Yet his very ability to grasp the profound significance of Newton's research entailed a mathematical and astronomical knowledge and insight possessed by few men of any age. He was instrumental in confirming Newton's genius by being the first to apply the theories set out in the *Principia,* and he performed this service for science not as the crown of his achievements, but when he was less than a third of the way through his own productive life. In his own day his cometary predictions could not be confirmed, and this side of his work, while it attracted certain attention, was not considered to be his most important. It was his original research and scholarship that brought him an eminence which he retained until the end of his life and which was acknowledged abroad when in 1729 he was elected a Foreign Member of the Académie des Sciences.

In the physical sciences Halley began a number of lines of research which succeeding generations were to widen into separate disciplines. In geophysics alone he laid many of the foundations of physical oceanography, developed the whole subject of geomagnetism, and made an important contribution to meteorology. In navigation he devised new methods of charting and showed the way to one method of solving the problem of longitude. In pure mathe-

matics his papers on the solution of equations were important, and
his studies in Greek geometry remained a standard reference for
generations. In all fields of astronomy his achievements were valuable, and in many cases stimulated whole new lines of research.
Add to this his contributions to optics, to the improvement of
scientific instruments and his solutions to a host of minor questions
in physics, together with his practical studies in diving, and he appears as Hooke's successor in ingenuity, and possibly his peer.
Administratively, he lifted the Royal Society from a slough that
could well have been its death, and as a man he rose above the
petty jealousies that his combination of money and talents engendered.

The influence of Halley's astronomical work stretched over a
long period. It was not until the first half of the nineteenth century
when John Herschel (1792–1871), son of the famous astronomer
William Herschel (1738–1822), traveled to the Cape of Good Hope
and there, near Table Mountain, examined the southern heavens, that
a new catalogue of the southern stars was prepared. This was an
important task, and if Halley had not already mapped this large
area of the sky, Herschel's catalogue might not have been of so high
a standard. Later on, Herschel's work was followed by the establishment of a number of large observatories in the Southern Hemisphere.

Halley's discovery that stars possess proper motions was not
pursued until the late eighteenth century, when William Herschel
and the German astronomer Tobias Mayer (1732–62) made new
measures and used them to determine how the sun, itself a star,
was moving in space. Even so, Halley's contention that all stars, ir-
respective of brightness or any other characteristics, had their own
proper motion in space was not proved until the nineteenth century
when the Italian Giuseppe Piazzi (1746–1826), using more refined
instruments than were available in Halley's day, was able to proffer
definite observational proof. Piazzi's work established Halley's hypothesis, and from then on, studies of the proper motions of stars
progressed much more quickly, helped by the increasing accuracy
which astronomical measurements were attaining. Thus it was that
Jacobus Kapteyn (1851–1922) in Germany in 1904 was able to follow

Halley's discovery with another which arose from his analysis of the directions of the various motions. Kapteyn showed that there seemed to be two general streams of motion among the stars, and this has later been confirmed and shown to be due to the rotation of the star-island or galaxy of which our sun is a member. In both these aspects of astronomy Halley was at least a hundred years ahead of others, and the work that he carried out directly stimulated later research.

Halley's earliest scientific paper was concerned with planetary motion and one of his last with facts about the orbit of Mercury. He emphasized, even in his earliest paper, the need for continuous observations of the planets and that merely noting their positions when they were in conjunction with a bright star or with the moon was not sufficient. This technique of continuous observation, first adopted by Tycho Brahe some seventy years before Halley's time, was followed everywhere after Halley's death, and some of the anomalies of planetary motion that he found were pursued in the late eighteenth and early nineteenth centuries on the Continent and particularly in France and Germany, where they were analyzed on the basis of Newton's gravitation using Leibniz's development of the calculus. His studies in lunar theory and lunar observing were taken up at Greenwich by Bradley and Maskelyne and in Germany by Mayer.

But Halley's astronomical foresight is best shown in his work on nebulae, variable stars, and cosmology. We have already seen that he considered the nebulae to be large, extended patches of some "lucid medium . . . that shines with its own proper lustre." It was not until a century after Halley's paper in *Philosophical Transactions* that William Herschel made the next real attack on the problem. Many of the objects had been catalogued in the intervening years by the French astronomers Charles Messier (1730–1817) and Nicolas Lacaille (1713–62), but it was Herschel who, examining a number of these objects with a telescope which was quite immense compared with anything available in Halley's day, was able to support Halley's hypothesis. The third Earl of Rosse (1800–67), however, in the mid-nineteenth century, using an instrument even larger than Herschel's, found a spiral structure in some of the nebulae which made it seem that the nebulae were groups of stars after all. It was not until later in the century, indeed almost at its close, that the problem was solved by William Huggins (1824–1910) who, using a spectroscope, obtained evidence that proved Halley correct in respect to certain nebulae, for Huggins showed that there were at least two kinds: the spirals, which we now know to be galaxies lying outside our own, and those that were diffuse, which, as Halley had conjectured, were very large and covered vast volumes of space. It was Huggins too who found that Halley's "lucid medium" was a very tenuous gas.

When he suggested that some stars varied the intensity of their light, Halley was propounding a new concept. It is clear from his paper that he was convinced of this, yet it was not until the late eighteenth century that William Herschel turned the belief into concrete fact and the whole subject of variable stars was set upon a sound observational footing. Yet perhaps the most surprising example of Halley's foresight was his paper on cosmology, in which he argued persuasively for an infinite universe. This was an amazing paper because it was the first scientific attempt to apply the new physical principles of universal gravitation to the whole concourse of stars which goes to make up the visible universe. No further attempt at analysis was made for thirty years, but in 1750 Thomas Wright (1711–86) published his *New Hypothesis of the Universe* in which he proposed that the stars were arranged in a thick layer in the center part of which lay the sun but, like Halley, Wright believed that this layer of stars extended infinitely into space. In the twentieth century the scientific approach to cosmology which Halley began has once more been taken up by astronomers and mathematicians, and various solutions have been offered. Now the general belief is that space can no longer be considered as of a nature amenable to Euclidean geometry, and use is made of the late nineteenth-century conceptions of special "non-Euclidean" types of space, so that the universe appears in one sense to be finite and at the same time unbounded. Yet even now there is a point of similarity between Halley's ideas and those of today, for Halley suggested that there could be no center of the universe, otherwise all matter would gravitate toward it; and now cosmologists, however much they may be divided in their opinion of which general hypothesis is correct, are agreed that there is no specific center of the cosmos.

Halley's studies of comets were published in 1705 in his *Synopsis of the Astronomy of Comets*. The great contribution he made here superficially appears to be the successful prediction of the return in 1758 of the comet of 1682. While it must be admitted, however, that until 1758 Halley's hypothesis remained unconfirmed and that it was the success of his prediction which so excited astronomers and the public at large, it was because of this lack of confirmation in the years soon after his death that little emphasis is laid on his cometary researches in contemporary obituary notices. Yet the success of his prediction was only the outward show of a much more profound insight. His work underlined the fact that some comets are members of the solar system and so formed the basis of the scientific study of comets as it is pursued today. He also provided the stimulus for another development which came late in the nineteenth century. We have seen that Halley observed meteors and made some attempts to determine their height above the earth's surface. With this guidance and his unequivocal proof that comets moved in orbits governed, like those of the planets, by gravitational laws, Halley set the stage for the great synthesis that demonstrated a relationship between comets and meteors. It became realized that the paths taken by swarms of meteors were essentially the same kind as those taken by comets; coupled with the fact that some comets disintegrated, either completely or in part, as they orbited the sun, it was shown that meteor swarms were the debris of this disintegration.

Finally, while on the subject of Halley's astronomical research, the great contribution he made toward finding accurately the distance of the sun must not be forgotten. Slightly modified, his method, of observing transits of Venus served astronomy well for over fifty years. The German astronomer Johann Encke (1791–1865) in the mid-nineteenth century analyzed the eighteenth-century transit observations and obtained a value of the sun's distance correct to within almost 2 percent of the present figure. Thus it can rightly be claimed that Halley brought to astronomy a highly successful means for determining its most important constant.

Halley's approach to the physical characteristics of the earth was something unique in his day and, like his astronomical work, had far-reaching repercussions, the echoes of which have not died away even now. It commenced very simply with his noting that the period of swing of a second's pendulum increased as the equator was approached, a result which later led Newton to realize that this meant that the gravitation of the earth was not constant over its entire surface—a consequence of the fact that the earth is rotating and is not perfectly spherical in shape. In passing, it may be worth noting that specially designed pendulums known as "gravimeters" are now used widely by geophysicists for gravity surveys for determining more accurately the figure of the earth.

Halley's fundamental achievements in physical geography are connected with his work on the trade winds and monsoons, and the voyages he undertook for determining the magnetic variation. His theory of the trade winds is not now accepted, but the kind of map in which he displayed his results showing the direction of the winds and their magnitude in a graphical way still continues, in a modified form, to be used for indicating meteorological data on charts of various kinds.

Halley's hypothesis of the earth's magnetism, like his theory of the trade winds, is no longer accepted, yet the subject is one of great intractability and the point is not so much that his theory was in error as that it stimulated thinking and certainly contributed usefully to the discussion of a problem which even now cannot be said to be in a final form. It led him to undertake his voyages and to produce his Atlantic Chart and World Map on which his lines of equal variation—the so-called "Halleyan lines"—have provided the modern geophysicist with a simple yet effective means of indicating magnetic information. It may also be remarked that even in the later nineteenth century, his World Chart was still considered to be of such importance that George Airy (1801–92), seventh Astronomer Royal, arranged for it to be reissued, and since that time geophysicists have collected old magnetic observations, beginning with Halley's, to obtain an understanding of how the earth's magnetic field varies over long periods and thus provide important raw material for their theoretical research.

The above is a brief sketch of the debt we owe Halley, who

for sixty-six years played an active part in a variety of fields of physical science. As far as the man himself is concerned, even though so little personalia survives, it is possible to feel great sympathy for one who was able to retain the friendship of two such awkward personalities as Hooke and Newton, even while they were bitterly opposed to each other. Of all his contemporaries only Bentley and Flamsteed retained their antipathy: Bentley was an avaricious bigot and Flamsteed loathed Halley more for his friendship with Newton and Hooke than for his own personality. As Clerk to the Royal Society Halley came into contact with many eminent men in the political as well as scientific spheres, but it must have been due to his own tact and geniality that he was able to retain their respect and so find friends at court during the reigns of six somewhat diverse monarchs. "For my part," Halley is supposed to have told Hearne, "I am for the King in possession. If I am protected, I am content. I am sure we pay dear enough for our Protection, & why should we not have the Benefit of it?"

Hearne claims that Halley professed to be a Tory but was a Whig at heart. More of his politics we do not know since his contemporaries were more interested in the man and his work. As to Halley's physical appearance, something can be gained from the portraits of him which confirm that he was a man "of middle stature, inclining to tallness, of a thin habit of body, and a fair complection." He "always spoke as well as acted with an uncommon degree of sprightliness and vivacity," we are told by the author of the *Biographia Britannica* article and by Martin Folkes, who knew him well, who also claimed that he "possessed . . . the qualifications necessary to obtain him the love of his equals," for "he loved them; naturally of an ardent and glowing temper, he appeared animated in their presence with a generous warmth, which the pleasure of seeing them seemed to inspire; he was open an punctual in his dealings, candid in his judgement, uniform and blamless in his manners, sweet and affable . . ." The *Biographia Britannica* article also gives evidence to substantiate its claim that "The reputation of others gave him no uneasiness, a restless jealousy and anxious emulation were strangers to his breast. He was equally ignorant of those extravagant prejudices in favour of one nation . . ." and to these adds "a vein of gaiety and good humour" which nothing impaired.

However much these contemporary eulogies may be thought to exaggerate Halley's personality, it is clear that those who knew him felt a great sense of personal loss at his death. The scientific world was certainly deprived of a man whose contributions have left it permanently in his debt.

Text References

CHAPTER 1   *Early Years*

1   "the Halleys, of Derbyshire": Aubrey, 282;
    "a poor kinsman": Baily, 63;
    "as a soapboiler": Aubrey, 282;
    "a salter": MacPike, *Hevelius* . . . , 33;
    "rents to a value of one thousand pounds a year": *Biog. Brit.*, iv, 2503
    note R.

2   "his own word that he was born on October 29, 1656": Aubrey, 282.

3   "At 9 years old": Aubrey, 282.

4   "resolved to give his son": *Biog. Brit.*, iv, 2494.

5   "body of citizens": Thornbury, I, 272 f.;
    "from my tenderest youth": Halley, *Catalogue*, preface, sig. iij.

6   "He not only excelled": à Wood, col. 981.

7   "good skill": *Biog. Brit.*, iv, 2494;
    "my study was so intense": Halley, *Catalogue*, preface, sig. iij.;
    "book now in the library of the Earl of Macclesfield at Shirburn Castle"
    See pp. 60 verso, 61, 132, 134 and 163. Shirburn Castle MS. 115 G. 14.

8   "I soon realized": Halley, *Catalogue*, preface, sig. iij.;
    "a curious apparatus": *Biog. Brit.*, iv, 2494 note *c*.

CHAPTER 2   *The Astronomical Background*

13 Copernicus meant the title to be *De Revolutionibus Coelestium*: Wolf,
    13.

14 "an indiscreet intellectual vagabond": Thorndike, vi, 423.

23 "a small observatory": Royal Warrant, June 22, 1675.

CHAPTER 3   *Oxford and St. Helena*

24 Halley decided to write to Flamsteed, MacPike, *Corr.*, 37.

27 Observations on the Spots in the Sun . . . , *Philosophical Transactions*,
    xi (1676), 687 f.; occultation of Mars, ibid., 274;
    A Direct and Geometrical Method . . . , ibid., 683 f.

28 "at the instigation of Henry Oldenburg," Rigaud, i, 226 f. and 241.

29 "an ingenious man from Oxford," RAS, April 1675;
    "an ingenious youth," RAS, June 1675.

31 "this would render useless," Halley, *Catalogue*, preface, sig. iij.

33 "great promoters of these studies," *Biog. Brit.*, iv, 2495;
"that Mr Edmond Hally a Student," MacPike, *Corr.*, 179;
"be treated in their passage" and "that you accomodate them," ibid., 179.

37 "I did not go to bed," Halley, *Catalogue*, preface, sig. iij.;
Halley to Sir Jonas Moore, MacPike, *Corr.*, 39 f.

38 "I can say in truth," Halley, *Catalogue*, preface, sig. iij.;
"Halley from St Helena," Hooke, *Diary*, 360.

42 "Having received a good account," MacPike, *Hevelius* . . . , 43.

CHAPTER 4 *The Visit to Hevelius*

46 Cutler Lecture in 1674, Hooke, *Animadversions.*

47 "Let each allow the other," R. S. Letter, Hevelius to Flamsteed, January ?, 1676.

48 "It was ordered that Mr Hevelius," R. S. Journal, January 25, 1676;
"does hope that you will allow," MacPike, *Hevelius* . . . , 82;
he enclosed a letter, *Biog. Brit.*, iv, 2497.

50 The letter dated June 7, MacPike, *Corr.*, 42 f.

51 Hevelius persuaded him to write, Original in Samuel Ward Collection, New York Public Library, but also transcribed by Hevelius and printed in his *Annus Climactericus* . . . Gedani, 1685, 101 f.

52 "a very pleasant guest," Hevelius to Dethelf Cluver, 1681, now in *Bibliothèque Nationale,* Paris [Fonds Latin, n. 10349, xiv, 14];
"As to Mr. Halley," *Biog. Brit.*, iv, 2499 footnote K;
"the High-born and Most Excellent Gentleman," *De Incendio Heveliano*, see MacPike, *Hevelius* . . . , 103 f.

54 "The Controversy between Mr Hevelius," MacPike, *Corr.*, 57 f.

55 "As to Mr Hevelius . . . ", ibid., 64 f.;
"Words fail me to express . . . ," ibid., 45 f.

56 Zacharias van Uffenbach, MacPike, *Hevelius* . . . , 87.

CHAPTER 5 *The Grand Tour, Marriage, and Domestic Crises*

57 "As to the advice you give me . . . ," MacPike, *Corr.*, 47 f.

58 "At Jonathans . . . ," ibid., 183.

59 "having a mind to make the Tour . . . ," ibid., 4;
"eminently distinguished . . . ," *Biog. Brit.*, iv, 2499.

61 "let me have the peruseing . . . ," MacPike, *Corr.*, 49.

63 "Observations made at Ballasore . . . ," *Phil. Coll.*, no. 5, 1681, 124;
"being received with the greatest respect . . . ," *Biog. Brit.*, iv, 2500;
"a charming man . . . ," Arago, iii, 309;
Eugene MacPike suggests, MacPike, *Hevelius* . . . , 45.

64 "He hath contracted . . . ," Aubrey, i, 283;
"a young lady equally amiable . . . ," *Biog. Brit.*, iv, 2500;
"suffering persons to . . . ," MacPike, *Hevelius* . . . , 45 note 3;
"neither the domestic cares . . . ," MacPike, *Corr.*, 4;
"the attendance on these . . . ," *Biog. Brit.*, iv, 2500.

65 observations made on the planet Saturn, *Philosophical Transactions*, xiii (1683), 82 f.;
    "A Theory of the Variation of the magnetical Compass," ibid., 208 f.

67 The jury's verdict, MacPike, *Corr.*, 177.

68 *Biographia Britannica, Biog. Brit.*, iv, 2503 note R.

CHAPTER 6   *The Royal Society and the* Principia

69 Davenport's letter, *Philosophical Transactions*, xiv (1684), 677 f.

73 noted in the Society's records. R. S. Council, December 10, 1684.

75 "ever been esteemed . . . ," MacPike, *Corr.*, 6;
    to sit "uncovered [wigless] . . . ," MacPike, *Hevelius* . . . , 53;
    "I invite you to a communication . . . ," MacPike, *Corr.*, 57 f.;
    "The Royal Society are so far sensible . . . ," ibid., 61 f.

76 "a mark of their respect . . . ," ibid., 66;
    "Your letter contains in it . . . ," ibid., 56 f.

77 "The sweet earth found at Hogsdon . . . ," ibid., 70 f.

78 Hooke's and Halley's results, *Philosophical Transactions*, xvi (1686–87), 85 f.;
    "the first of which was meteorological," ibid., 104 f.

79 "An Historical Account of the Trade Winds . . . ," ibid., 153 f.

80 "A discourse concerning Gravity . . . ," ibid., 3 f.

81 "Mr Halley should have fifty . . . ," R. S. Council, July 1687.

82 "Your Incomparable treatise . . . ," *Corr. I. Newton*, ii, 431 f.

83 In a later letter, ibid., 435 f.

84 "I am heartily sorry . . . ," ibid., 441 f.

85 "was in some respects misrepresented . . . ," ibid., 444 f.

86 "his Honoured Friend . . . ," ibid., 464;
    "I am very sensible of ye great trouble . . . ," ibid., 454;
    "divine Treatise," ibid., 473;
    "In the publication of this work . . . ," *Principia*, trans. Cajori, xviii;
    "It may be justly said . . . ," *Philosophical Transactions*, xvi (1687), 291 f.

87 "You know there is a new edition . . . ," MacPike, *Corr.*, 203 f.;
    "being sencible of the little leisure . . . ," *Corr. I. Newton*, 483 and *Philosophical Transactions*, xix (1695–97), 445 f.

88 "But for him, in all human probability . . . ," De Morgan, xii, 12.

CHAPTER 7   *Science and Sea-Diving*

90 two successive issues of *Philosophical Transactions*, *Philosophical Transactions*, xvi (1686–87), 335 f. and 387 f.;
    evaporation of sea water, ibid., xxix (1714–16), 454 f.;
    evidence for variations in latitude, ibid., 403 f.

91 In December 1694, ibid., xxxiii (1724–25), 118 f.

92 papers on magnetism, MacPike, *Corr.*, 136 f.

93 "there being then great want of proper Ephemerides . . . ," *Philosophical Transactions*, xvi (1686), 35;

a leading part in the production, *Biog. Brit.*, iv, 2507 note BB.

94   "the Daughters are both living . . . ," MacPike, *Corr.*, 5;
"the Degree of Heat . . . ," MacPike, *Corr.*, 137 f.;
"Expansion of Liquors by Heat," ibid., 138;
"A New Thermometer . . . ," ibid., 138 f.

95   "In 1688 he reported on a type of fern," ibid., 211;
"the cliffs of Harwich," ibid., 213;
"it would be scarce possible to find the Longitude . . . ," ibid., 232.

96   "Ordered that Mr Perry . . . ," R. S. Council, May 30, 1688;
"that the Treasurer do pay . . . ," R. S. Council, October 22, 1690;
"Few tears were shed . . . ," Burnet, i, 620.

97   There is a story, *Biog. Brit.*, iv, 2507 note BB;
"In March we find him," MacPike, *Corr.*, 214;
"In July," ibid., 215 and 216.

98   "In October," ibid., 216;
"in his opinion crystals," *Philosophical Transactions*, xvii (1691), 540 f.;
"And so during 1689," MacPike, *Corr.*, 214 f.

99   "some queries, which he conceived to containe the principall difficulties . . . ," ibid., 218.

100 "An Account of the Circulation of the watry Vapours . . . ," *Philosophical Transactions*, xvii (1691–93), 468 f.;
"A Discourse tending to prove . . . ," ibid., 495 f.

101 *Historia Naturalis,* ibid., 535 f.;
Halley's last paper for 1691, ibid., 556 f.;
Halley's unpublished papers, MacPike, *Corr.*, 221 f.

102 "deep sea diving," ibid., 214 and 224 f.

103 Halley's first experiments, ibid., 88;
"In August he was able to report," ibid., 224.

104 "for the men below to sitt on . . . ," ibid., 151.

105 "I can unlade a shipp . . . ," ibid., 153;
"transmission of sounds under water," ibid., 153 f.;
"Newton was later to make use," Newton, *Opticks,* Bk. I, Pt. II (page 183 in paperback reprint, Dover Books, Inc., New York, 1952);
"a double or triple flannel . . . ," MacPike, *Corr.*, 154 f.;
"For Blowing Up the Decks of Ships under Water . . . ," ibid., 156;
"the newspapers of the day," see, for instance, Houghton.

CHAPTER 8   *The Distance of the Sun*

108 "In his paper of 1691 . . . ," *Philosophical Transactions,* xvii (1691), 511 f.;
"Twenty-five years later he published," ibid., xxix (1714–16), 454 f.;
"is by far the noblest astronomy affords . . . ," ibid., xvii (1691), 511 f.

109 "very accurately obtained . . . ," ibid., 511 f.

112 "his comments were published," Whiston.

113 "our younger astronomers," *Philosophical Transactions,* xxix (1714–16), 454 f.;
"to observe the transit . . . ," R. S. Council, June 26, 1760.

CHAPTER 9 *Flamsteed and Halley*

118 "This business [the question of diving] requiring my assistance . . . ," MacPike, *Corr.*, 88.

119 "according to the antiquarian Thomas Hearne," *Collecteana*, ii, 399.

120 "Mr. Halley was then thought of . . . ," Whiston, *Memoirs*, 108; "because it is Friday," *Biog. Brit.*, iv, 2509 footnote to note FF; "if it had not been for the rise now and then . . . ," Whiston, *Memoirs*, 299.

121 "utter want of principle . . . ," Rud, preface, iv; "He was covetous," More, 557.

122 "Stephen Rigaud made a careful analysis," Rigaud, *Defence;* "rumors were current and there is an account," MacPike, *Corr.*, 264 note 10; "We judge him to be . . . ," Rigaud, *Defence*, 17; "some tables of high tides," *Philosophical Transactions*, xiii (1683), 10 f.; "evolved a set of rules," ibid., xiv (1684), 458 f. and 821 f.

123 Molyneux supplied him, ibid., xvi (1686–87), 232 f. and 428 f.

124 "The only information I wrote . . . ," *Biog. Brit.*, iv, 2509 footnote to note FF.; "drafted three times by Flamsteed," R.G.O., MSS. item 35, 10; "corrupt ye youth of ye University . . . ," Baily, 132.

126 "Flamsteed and Halley fallen out," Hooke, *Diary*, 209; "much troubled" with Hooke, Dreyer, xlv, 291; "I used him for some years . . . ," ibid., 294; "David Gregory inserted a note," Rigaud, *Defence*, 20; "art of filching from other people . . . ," R.G.O., MSS. lxii, E.

128 "Geomagnetism, and especially the Earth's main field . . . ," *Occ. Notes*, no. 9, June 1941, 123; "not ashamed to borrow . . . ," Dreyer, xlv, 293.

129 "An Instrument for Measuring . . . ," MacPike, *Corr.*, 160; a new design of quadrant, ibid., 161 f.; "A Method of Enabling a Ship . . . ," ibid., 164 f.; "Hooke in his manuscript diary," ibid., 186.

130 "A Description of an Instrument . . . ," ibid., 162 f.

131 "This was the question," ibid., 229.

132 "a vindication of his Observations . . . ," ibid., 229.

CHAPTER 10 *Comets and Other Subjects*

133 "When he was thirty-six," *Philosophical Transactions*, xvii (1691–93), 596 f. and 654 f.

134 "they appeared to him . . . ," *Biog. Brit.*, iv, 2511.

136 "charters of the Amicable Society were drawn up," Amicable Soc.

137 "was one on thermometry," *Philosophical Transactions*, xvii (1691–93), 650 f.; "the heating effect of the sun," ibid., 690 f.; "the tenth-century astronomer Albategnius," ibid., 931 f.

138   "a couple of pages of various 'Queries,' " ibid., 998 f.;
Halley's second optical paper, ibid., 960 f.

139   "a million or two of acres," Houghton, January 20, 1693, no. 25.

140   "industrious bee," *Biog. Brit.*, iv, 2507;
in a paper published in the next year, *Philosophical Transactions*, xviii
(1694), 183 f.

141   involved in the deluge, MacPike, *Corr.*, 234 f.;
the solution of equations, ibid., 234 f.;
battles and conquests, ibid., 238.

142   "the ancient city state of Palmyra," *Philosophical Transactions*, xix (1695–
97), 160 f.

147   "having done the Comet of 1683 . . . ," MacPike, *Corr.*, 91 f.

148   "I . . . would wish that Mr Flamsteed . . . ," ibid., 94;
"I must entreat you to consider . . . ," ibid., 92;
"I have with some difficulty mastered . . . ," ibid., 95.

149   "to acknowledge that this . . . ," Halley, posthumous tables.

150   "During 1705 they also appeared," *Philosophical Transactions*, xxiv
(1704–5), 182 f.;
"Whiston's book for students," Whiston, *Philosophy*.

CHAPTER 11   *The Mint and Visit of the Czar*

152   "spruce beer prepared by Hevelius," MacPike, *Corr.*, 236;
"molluscs petrified in marble," ibid., 238;
"a passage in Buchanan's history," ibid., 237;
". . . the itinerary of Antonius . . . ," ibid., 238.

153   ". . . in a course of some years . . . ," Burnet, ii, 140.

154   "I had hoped . . . ," MacPike, *Corr.*, 97.

155   ". . . such information as I conceive . . . ," ibid., 98.

156   "built severall years since," ibid., 100;
"The results of the Snowdon expedition," *Philosophical Transactions*, xix
(1695–97), 582 f.;
"an account of an extraordinary Hail," ibid., 570 f.

157   "an eclipse of the moon," ibid., 784;
"description of the tidal theory," ibid., 445 f.;
"I hoped to have waited . . . ," MacPike, *Corr.*, 102 f.

158   "that Lewis may appear face to face . . . ," *Corr. I. Newton*, iv, 254.

159   "the mathematical principles of engineering," ibid., iv, 229 and 230.

160   "This Great Prince . . . ," MacPike, *Corr.*, 7;
"W. G. Hiscocks has suggested," Hiscocks, 200;
"the comments of Evelyn himself," Evelyn, 182.

CHAPTER 12   *Voyages*

163   "Captn. Edmd. Halley . . . ," MacPike, *Corr.*, 243.

164   "he set sail," Log 1698/99, fol. 2 verso;
"we weighed at peep of day," ibid., fol. 2 verso;
". . . Leaky and our pumps brought up . . . ," ibid., fol. 2 verso.

165 "Our people were somewhat doubtfull . . . ," MacPike, *Corr.*, 105;
"past through a Streak of Water . . . ," Log 1698/99, fol. 2 verso;
"I found there two English Marchãt shipps . . . ," MacPike, *Corr.*, 106;
"This Morning between two and three . . . ," Log 1698/99, fol. 3 verso.

166 "having narrowly escaped a Sunk Rock," ibid., fol. 3 verso;
"Halley mapped it," ibid., fol. 4;
"to invite me on Shore . . . ," ibid., fol. 4;
"but great hight of the Planet . . . ," ibid., fol. 4 verso;
"my Officers shewing themselves . . . ," ibid., fol. 5.

167 ". . . not without reflecting language . . . ," ibid., fol. 5 verso;
"which is much bigger than Barbadoes," ibid., fol. 6;
"Water proving excellent," ibid., fol. 6 verso;
"I this day arrived . . . ," MacPike, *Corr.*, 137 f.

168 "there are some Persons in *England* . . . ," Harrison, preface.

169 "I fully proved . . . ," MacPike, *Corr.*, 109;
"A Boatswaine with one Arm . . . ," ibid., 110.

170 "to answer the expectations of those . . . ," ibid., 112;
"Yesterday betweene 3 and 4 . . . ," Log 1699/1700, fol. 11 verso;
"Portugese there with some few Blacks Servants . . . ," ibid., fol. 12 verso.

171 ". . . After Midnight . . . ," ibid., fol. 19;
"which had been kept from the Air . . . ," ibid., fol. 19 verso;
". . . a greate Fogg," ibid., fol. 20.

172 "being all flatt on the Top . . . ," ibid., fol. 21.

173 "recover the warm Sunn," ibid., fol. 22;
"pretty clear Sunn Shine," ibid., fol. 23 verso;
"dry comfortable Air," ibid., fol. 23 verso;
"in these Climates," ibid., fol. 24;
"Terrible high sea," ibid., fol. 24 verso.

174 "in this whole course," MacPike, *Corr.*, 113;
"and put Some Goats and Hoggs . . . ," Log 1699/1700, fol. 27 verso;
"calls himselfe English Consull," ibid., fol. 28 verso.

175 "went up into the Country . . . ," ibid., fol. 30 verso;
"a severe pestilentiall dissease," MacPike, *Corr.*, 114;
"our Decks and upperwarks," Log 1699/1700, fol. 31 verso;
"had we not fell in with some French Fishermen," ibid., fol. 33.

176 "and being come near the English Fishboats," ibid., fol. 33 verso;
"We Deliver'd our Gunns," ibid., fol. 36.

179 "severall of the Diveing birds," ibid., fol. 20.

182 "and the crew was paid off," Log 1701, fol. 47 verso;
"presents to severall Portugese Governors," MacPike, *Corr.*, 123;
"Martin Folkes's suggestion," *Biog. Brit.*, iv, 2512 note *gggg*.

CHAPTER 13 *Recognition*

183 "he discussed rainbows," *Philosophical Transactions*, xxii (1700–1),
714 f.;
"phenomena of mock suns," ibid., xxiii (1702–3), 11;
"paper on Hooke's barometer," ibid., xxii (1700–1), 791 f.;
"the Queen thinking fitt to employ . . . ," *Biog. Brit.*, iv, 2512.

184 ". . . by the hands of Count Mansfelt . . . ," MacPike, *Corr.*, 249 note 3;
". . . likewise received with great respect . . . ," *Biog. Brit.*, iv, 2512;
"he was presented the same evening . . . ," ibid., 2512.

185 "out of the secret service," MacPike, *Corr.*, 250;
"Dr. Wallis is dead," Cudworth, 76;
"Mr. Hally made his Inaugural Speech . . . ," MacPike, *Corr.*, 251.

186 "I return you many thanks . . . ," ibid., 215.

187 "In 1696 in an unprinted paper," ibid., 166 f.

188 "was neither sufficient to discourage . . . ," *Biog. Brit.*, iv, 2513 note LL.

189 "the Apollonios appeared in three separate volumes," Halley, Apollonios.

192 "as a sacrifice to heavenly truth," Baily, 101;
"letter sent to him by Halley," MacPike, *Corr.*, 127 f.

195 "avowed Champion in this quarrell," MacPike, *Corr.*, 128;
"I am commanded by the president . . . ," ibid., 129.

CHAPTER 14   *Astronomer Royal*

196 "An Account of several extraordinary Meteors . . . ," *Philosophical Transactions*, xxix (1714–16), 159 f.;
"on observations of the comet of 1680," ibid., 70;
"comments published on the Continent," ibid., 165 f.;
"reporting his observations of the April eclipse," ibid., 245 f. and 314 f.

197 "'novae' (new stars)," ibid., 345 f.

198 "An Account of several Nebulae . . . ," ibid., 390 f.

199 "some daylight observations of Venus," ibid., 466 f.;
"the appearance of aurorae," ibid., 406 f. and 430 f.

200 "living under Water," ibid., xxxi (1721), 177 f.;
"small 'telescopicall' comet," ibid., xxx (1717–19), 721 f.;
"an 'Advertisement' to astronomers," ibid., 692 f.

202 "showed that such motions did exist," ibid., 736 f.;
"an 'extraordinary' meteor," ibid., 978 f.;
"Dr. Halley was . . . ," MacPike, *Corr.*, 11 f.;
"to apply himself with the utmost care . . . ," *Biog. Brit.*, iv, 2515 note *ppp*.

203 "well known by his Exquisit Care . . . ," MacPike, *Corr.*, 12.

204 "he scarce lost a meridian view . . . ," *Biog. Brit.*, iv, 2515;
they were not published until 1749, Halley, posthumous tables;
a method of using the moon to determine longitude, *Philosophical Transactions*, xxxvii (1731–32), 185 f.;
"undervalued those habits of minute attention . . . ," Grant, 480.

205 the measurement of heights above sea level, *Philosophical Transactions*, xxxi (1720–21), 116 f.

206 a critical assessment of observations, ibid., 1 f.;
methods of observing with a transit instrument, ibid., 113 f.;
"Of the Infinity of the sphere . . . ," ibid., 22 f. and 24 f.

208 "an accurate table of refraction," ibid., 169 f.;
"now developed this method further," ibid., 209 f.;
"The Variation of the magnetical Compass . . . ," ibid., 173 f.;

"Art of living under Water," ibid., 177 f.;
"a mock sun," ibid., 211 f.;
"a partial solar eclipse," ibid., xxxii (1722–23), 197;
"longitude determinations at various ports," ibid., 2 f., 235 f., and 237 f.;
"the 'Universal Deluge,'" ibid., xxxiii (1724–25), 118 f.

209 "on the 1723 transit of Mercury," ibid., 228 f.;
"to defend Newton," ibid., xxxiv (1726–27), 205 f., and xxxv (1727–28), 296 f.;
"revised astronomical observations," ibid., xxxv (1727–28), 388 f.;
"problems of longitude determination," ibid., xxxvii (1731–32), 331 f.;
"a brief note on the lunar eclipse of 1736," ibid., xl (1737–38), 14.

210 "an informal kind of dining club," MacPike, *Corr.*, 252.

211 "thought proper to make a visit . . . ," *Biog. Brit.*, iv, 2515;
". . . was pleased shortly after . . . ," ibid., 2516;
"Mathematical Preceptor . . . ," ibid., 2516.

212 "In the name of God . . . ," MacPike, *Corr.*, 255.

213 ". . . a sort of paralitick disorder," ibid., 12;
". . . his paralytic disorder gradually increasing . . . ," *Biog. Brit.*, iv, 2516.

214 "as his 'chocolate,'" ibid., 2516 note *bbbb*.
". . . being tired . . . ," ibid., 2516.

CHAPTER 15 *Halley—An Assessment*

217 "lucid medium," *Philosophical Transactions*, xxix (1714–16), 390 f.

218 "some stars varied the intensity of their light," ibid., 354 f.;
"his paper on cosmology," ibid., xxxi (1720–21), 22 f.

220 "theory of the trade winds," ibid., xiv (1684), 153 f.

221 "For my part," MacPike, *Corr.*, 269;
"of middle stature, inclining to tallness," *Biog. Brit.*, iv, 2517;
"always spoke as well . . . ," ibid., 2517;
"possessed . . . the qualifications necessary . . . ," ibid., 2517;
"The reputation of others . . . ," ibid., 2518.

222 "a vein of gaiety . . . ," ibid., 2519.

Bibliographical Sources
Referred to in the Text

Amicable Soc.	*The Charters of the Corporation of the Amicable Society, for a Perpetual Assurance Office, together with the By-Laws Thereunto Belonging*, London, 1790.
Arago	François Arago, *Oeuvres*, Paris, 1856.
Aubrey	John Aubrey, *Brief Lives*, ed. A. Clark, Oxford, 1898.
Baily	Francis Baily, *An Account of the Revd. John Flamsteed*, London, 1835.
Biog. Brit.	*Biographia Britannica*, London, 1757.
Bruno	Giordano Bruno, *Cena de la ceneri*, edition by G. Aquilecchia, Florence, 1955.
Burnet	Gilbert Burnet, *Bishop Burnet's History of His Own Time*, London, 1724.
Collecteana	*Collecteana*, 2nd series, ed. Montagu Burrows, Oxford, 1890.
Corr. I. Newton	*Correspondence of Isaac Newton*, ed. W. H. Turnbull and J. F. Scott, London, 1960 to present time.
Cudworth	William Cudworth, *Life and Correspondence of Abraham Sharp*, London, 1889.
Dreyer	J. L. E. Dreyer, *Observatory*, London, 1877 to present time.
Evelyn	John Evelyn, *Sylva*, London, 1706.
Grant	Robert Grant, *History of Physical Astronomy*, London, 1852(?).
Halley, Apollonios	*Apollonii Pergæi de Sectione Rationis Libri Duo ex Arabico MS Latine versi. Accedunt Ejusdem de Sectione Spatii Libri Duo restituti . . . Opera & Studio Edmundi Halley*, Oxford, 1706; *Apollonii Pergæi Conicorum Libri Octo et Sereni Antissensis de Sectione Cylindri & Coni Libri Duo . . . editit Edmundus Halleius*, Oxford, 1710; *and Apollonii Conicorum, libri III, posteriores, ex Sermone Arabico in Latinum conversi; cum Pappi Lemmantibus Graece et Latine. Subjicitur lib. VIII. ab Halleio restitutus. Oxford, 1710.*

Halley, Catalogue   *Edmond Halley, Catalogue des Estoilles Australes ou Supplement du Catalogue de Tycho . . .* , trans. Augustin Royer, Paris, 1679.

Halley,
  posth. tables   *Astronomical Tables with Precepts both in English and Latin for computing the places of the Sun, Moon, etc.,* London, 1752 (to which a Synopsis of Cometary Astronomy was appended).

Harrison   Lieutenant Harrison, *Idea Longitudinis,* London, 1696.

Hiscocks   W. G. Hiscocks, *John Evelyn and His Family Circle,* London, 1935.

Hooke,
  Animadversions   *Animadversions on the First part of the Machina Coelestis of the Honourable, Learned and deservedly Famous Astronomer Johannes Hevelius,* London, 1674.

Hooke, Diary   *The Diary of Robert Hooke,* ed. W. H. Robinson and W. A. Adams, London, 1935.

Houghton   J. Houghton, *A Collection for the Improvement of Husbandry and Trade,* London, 1692–98.

Log 1698/99   *A Journall of a Voyage in his Majes:[ties] Pink the Paramore entered for the Discovery of the Variation of the Magneticall Compass by Edmund Halley Comand[r],* British Museum ADD. MS. 30368, fol. 1–9.

Log 1699/1700   *A Journall of a Voyage in his Ma:[ties] Pink y[e] Paramore intended for The Discovery of y[e] Variation of the Compass kept by Edmund Halley, Commander anno 1699 & 1700.,* British Museum, ADD. MS. 30368, fol. 10–36.

Log 1701   *A Journall of a Voiage in his Mat:[ies] Pink the Paramore: for discovery of the Course of the Tides in the Channell of England. By Edmund Halley Commander Anno 1701.* British Museum, ADD. MS. 30368, fol. 38–47.

MacPike, *Corr.*   E. F. MacPike, *Correspondence and Papers of Edmond Halley,* Oxford, 1932.

MacPike,
  Hevelius   E. F. MacPike, *Hevelius, Flamsteed and Halley,* London, 1937.

Mem. Acad.   *Mémoires de l'Academie Royale des Sciences (Histoire), Anné 1742,* Paris, 1744–45.

More   Louis T. More, *Isaac Newton,* New York, 1934.

De Morgan   Augustus De Morgan, *Cabinet Portrait Gallery of British Worthies,* London, 1847.

Newton, *Opticks*   Isaac Newton, *Opticks,* London, 1704.

Phil. Coll.   *Philosophical Collections,* London, 1679–82.

Principia,
  trans Cajori.   *Newton's Principia,* Motte's translation revised, by Professor F. Cajori, Berkeley, 1947.

R.A.S.   Archives of the Royal Astronomical Society, London: correspondence Flamsteed to Townley.

Rigaud   S. J. Rigaud, *Correspondence of Scientific Men,* Oxford, 1841.

Rigaud, *Defence*   S. J. Rigaud, *A Defence of Halley against the Charge of Religious Infidelity,* Oxford (Ashmolean Society), 1844.

R.G.O.	Royal Greenwich Observatory, Herstmonceux.
R. S. Council	Royal Society of London, Council Minutes.
R. S. Journal	Royal Society of London, Journal Book.
R. S. Letter	Royal Society of London, Letter Books.
Royal Warrant, June 22, 1675	Royal Warrant for the foundation of the Royal Observatory (Now at R.G.O., MSS. 40, p. 117).
Rud	Edward Rud's *Diary, 1709–1720,* edited Luard, London, 1860.
Shirburn Castle	Shirburn Castle MS. 115, G. 14.
Thornbury	Walter Thornbury, *Old and New London,* London (no date).
Thorndike	Lynn Thorndike, *A History of Magic and Experimental Science,* New York, 1941.
Whiston	William Whiston, *The Transits of Venus and Mercury over the Sun at their Ascending and Descending Nodes for Two Centuries and a Half,* London, 1723.
Whiston, *Memoirs*	William Whiston, *Memoirs of the Life and Writings of Mr William Whiston, etc.,* London, 1753.
Whiston, *Philosophy*	William Whiston, *Sir Isaac Newton's Mathematick Philosophy more easily demonstrated, with Dr Halley's account of Comets illustrated: for the use of students,* London, 1716.
Wolf	A. Wolf, *A History of Science, Technology and Philosophy in the 16th and 17th Centuries,* London, 1935.
à Wood	Anthony à Wood, *Athenae Oxoniensis,* Oxford, 1721.

Chronological Résumé
of Halley's Life

Date	Age*	Event
1656	. .	Halley born October 29.
1671 or 1673	15 or 17	Captain of St. Paul's School.
1672	16	Observation of variation of magnetic compass.
1673	17	Entry as commoner to Queen's College, Oxford.
1675	19	Observation of lunar eclipse from his father's house on Winchester Street.
1676	20	Observations at Oxford of sunspot and planetary phenomena. Paper on planetary orbits. Suggests improved geometrical method for determining occurrence of solar eclipses. Departure for St. Helena.
1677	21	Observation of transit of Mercury. Discovers star cluster in Centaurus and charts southern sky.
1678	22	Return to England and presentation of planisphere to Charles II. Catalogue of southern stars presented to Royal Society. Elected Fellow of the Royal Society. Granted M.A. degree.
1679	23	Visit to Hevelius at Danzig. Recommendation of transits of Venus for determining distance of the sun.
1680	24	Tour of the Continent. Observation of the great comet of 1680.
1681	25	In Italy most of this year. Publication of paper on longitude of Ballasore, India.
1682	26	Return to England. Marriage to Mary Tooke and move to house in Islington.

* The figures given in this column strictly run only from October 29 of the year in question.

Date	*Age**	*Event*
1683	27	Regular observations of the moon commenced.
		Publication of paper on correction to the theory of the motion of Saturn's satellite V (Rhea).
		Publication of first paper on terrestrial magnetism.
1684	28	Studies on tides at Tonkin published.
		Visits to Newton at Cambridge.
		Communication of Newton's first eleven propositions on gravity to the Royal Society.
		Death of Halley's father and of his brother Humphrey.
		Moved house to Golden Lion Court, Aldersgate Street, London.
1685	29	Appointment as Clerk to the Royal Society and Editor of the *Philosophical Transactions*. Relinquishes Fellowship of Society.
1686	30	Provides finance for printing the *Principia*.
		Publication of papers on gravity and fall of artillery projectiles, of observations of an occultation of Jupiter, on barometer and determination of heights above sea level.
		Publication of paper on trade winds and monsoons.
		Beginning of Flamsteed's disagreement with Halley.
1687	31	Publication of the *Principia*.
		Publication of mathematical papers, on change of latitude of places on earth, and on evaporation of sea water. Also an ephemeris for 1688.
1688	32	Birth of daughters Katherine and Margaret.
1691	35	Publication of additional work on use of transits of Venus for determining distance of sun.
		Publication of papers on circulation of water vapor in the atmosphere, on Julius Caesar's landing in Britain, on infinite quantities, on thickness of gold plating, and on Pliny's *Historia Naturalis*.
		Refused Savilian chair of astronomy at Oxford.
1692	36	Publication of more fully developed theory of terrestrial magnetism.
1693	37	Relinquishes editorship of *Philosophical Transactions*.
		Publication of mortality tables.
		Publication of papers on heat of fluids, heating effect of sun, the transparency of bodies, and also on the progressive acceleration of the moon's motion.
		Publication of method of algebraic computation of focal length of thick lenses.
1694	38	Publication of papers on roots of algebraic equations, conversion of Cassini's tables of Jupiter satellite, and on experiments on evaporation and discussion of the age of the earth.
		Presentation to the Royal Society—but not publication—of theory of the cause of the biblical flood.
1695	39	Work on cometary orbits.
		Papers published on apparent motion of sun, on logarithms,

Date	Age*	Event
		on gunnery, on areas under curves (integration), and on the ancient city of Palmyra.
1696	40	Paper published on trigonometry. Halley moves to Chester as Deputy Comptroller of the Mint there. First of Halley's reports on scientific and other curiosities at Chester.
1697	41	Expedition to Mount Snowdon and further reports to the Royal Society from Chester.
1698	42	Last report on scientific matters from Chester. Return to London from Chester, and birth of son Edmond. Visits to Czar Peter at Deptford. Departure on first Atlantic voyage.
1699	43	Return to England and court-martial of his first lieutenant. Resignation as Clerk to the Royal Society. Departure on second Atlantic voyage.
1700	44	Return to England from second Atlantic voyage. Re-elected Fellow of the Royal Society. Publication of paper on the rainbow.
1701	45	Probable date of publication of Atlantic Chart. Paper published on Hooke's barometer. Charting of English Channel.
1702	46	Probable date of publication of World Chart. Paper published on mock suns. Visits to Trieste, Boccari, Vienna, Osnaburg, Hanover, and Holland.
1703	47	Return to England.
1704	48	Appointment as Savilian Professor of Geometry, Oxford. Work begun on translations of early geometers.
1705	49	Publication of A Synopsis of Cometary Astronomy.
1706	50	Publication of translation of Sectio Rationis of Apollonios.
1708	52	Publication of Miscellanea Curiosa.
1710	54	Degree D.C.L. conferred by Oxford. Publication of translations of the Conicorum of Apollonios and Sectio Cylindri et Sectio Coni by Serenus.
1712	56	Editing of Flamsteed's observations and publication as the Historia Coelestis.
1713	57	Elected Honorary Secretary of the Royal Society in place of Hans Sloane.
1714	58	Papers published on meteors and on magnetic variation and the World Chart. Paper on comet of 1680 published; probably also by Halley.
1715	59	Papers published on stellar astronomy (novae and nebulae), and on the salinity of the oceans and the derivation of the age of the earth. Publication of a chart of a forthcoming solar eclipse (April) and later of a description of the phenomenon.

Date	Age*	Event
1716	60	Publication of planetary and lunar observations and method of finding longitude.
		Publication of precise methods for determining sun's distance from transits of Venus.
		Publication of papers on daylight observations of Venus and on diving.
		Publication of a description of and theory about the aurora.
1717	61	Publication of observations of a telescopic comet and method of determining the moon's orbit from observations of its close approach to the Hyades.
		Paper on the motions of the fixed stars.
1719	63	Report on a very bright meteor, of a total lunar eclipse observed at the Cape of Good Hope and Halley's determination of longitude from the evidence. Further observations and comments on the aurora.
1720	64	Appointment as second Astronomer Royal in succession to Flamsteed.
		Papers on observing techniques, Cassini's claim to have measured a stellar distance, on barometric determination of heights and on roots of algebraic equations.
		Possible date of publication of new edition of World Chart.
		Papers published on cosmology (infinity of universe and number of stars).
1721	65	Resignation as Honorary Secretary of the Royal Society.
		Papers published on refraction in atmosphere, magnetic variation, determination of planetary positions, on a mock sun, and on diving.
		Erection of transit instrument at Greenwich.
1722	66	New chart for total solar eclipse due in November together with a chart showing success of previous prediction in 1715. Observation of eclipse.
		Paper published on longitude of Buenos Aires.
1723	67	Papers published on longitude of Port Royal in Jamaica and of "Carthagena in America"; also on observations of a lunar eclipse.
1724	68	Publication of paper on the cause of the biblical flood (originally read before the Royal Society in 1694).
1725	69	New eight-foot quadrant by Graham installed at Greenwich.
		Paper published on motion of Mercury and its orbit determined from observations of its transit in 1723.
1727	71	Publishes a defense of Newton's biblical chronology.
1728	72	Paper analyzing observational results at Vera Cruz with a view to obtaining the longitude.
1729	73	Visit of Queen Caroline to Greenwich Observatory. Grant to Halley of half pay as Post Captain.
		Election as Foreign Member of the Académie des Sciences, Paris.
1731	75	Publication of method of using longitude determinations for finding longitude at sea.

Date	Age*	Event
1732	76	Publication of paper on latitude and magnetic variation from Java to St. Helena.
1736	80	Death of Halley's wife, Mary. Slight paralysis of right hand. Halley draws up his will.
1737	81	Paper published on lunar eclipse of 1736.
1740	84	Completion of eighteen-year observing program at Greenwich on moon's position.
1741	85	Death of Halley's son, Edmond.
1742	86	Halley dies.
1749	..	Publication of Halley's astronomical tables, edited by John Bevis.
1752	..	Publication of the above in English translation.
1758	..	Publication of Halley's translation and collation of Menelaus's *Sphaerica* using Hebrew and Arabic manuscripts.

Appearances of Halley's Comet

239 B.C.*	A.D. 912	
162 B.C.	989	
86 B.C.	1066	Depicted on Bayeux tapestry commem-
11 B.C.		orating Battle of Hastings.
	1145	
A.D. 66	1222	
141	1301	
218	1378	
295	1456	
374	1531	
451	1607)	Two appearances identified as
530	1682)	two appearances of the same comet
607		by Halley.
684	1759	This was the return predicted by Halley.
760	1835	
837	1910	Coincided with death of King Edward VII.

* No earlier appearances have been computed, since there is little or no observational material to confirm any calculations made.

Sources of Original Material and Other Information

A number of sources of original material are given under *References*, grouped according to chapter. Of these the most frequently quoted are the two works of E. F. MacPike, who edited Halley's papers and correspondence and also wrote a short volume on Hevelius, Flamsteed, and Halley in which he analyzed something of their mutual relationships. MacPike was assisted by a number of scholars, among whom were the late Mr. Henry Robinson, sometime Librarian of the Royal Society; after discussions with Mr. Robinson it seemed to me that the most convenient references to quote, where relevant, were those from MacPike, since his work is more likely to be readily available than the primary sources which MacPike himself mentions. The other references to original material concern those which were either unknown to MacPike and his colleagues or were not included fully in his work.

For a modern analysis of Halley's scientific work, the reader may refer to Angus Armitage's *Edmond Halley*, London, 1966, although further details of some items are given here. As far as Halley's personal life is concerned the main sources are the *éloge* of de Mairan and a biographical note by Martin Folkes (both reprinted in MacPike's book on Halley's correspondence) and the article in the *Biographia Britannica*, second edition. MacPike also reproduces the verses Halley wrote as a preface to the first edition of the *Principia* and supplies a translation. The verse which he appended to the World Chart are given in a paper on Halley as a physical geographer by Professor Sydney Chapman in *Occasional Notes of the Royal Astronomical Society* for June 1941, with a translation prepared by Mrs. Chapman. This paper also gives large fold-out reproductions of the Atlantic Chart, the World Chart, and the chart of trade winds and monsoons that originally appeared in *Philosophical Transactions*. A further survey of Halley's work as a geophysicist has been prepared by the author with some additional references; it has appeared in the *Geophysical Journal*, vol. 15 for June 1968.

———◄●►►———

Biographical Publications

A list of biographical articles, etc., are given by E. F. MacPike in his *Correspondence and Papers of Edmond Halley*, Oxford, 1932, pp. 279 f. Since that date other material has been published, and the more significant items are given below:

A. Armitage, *Edmond Halley*, London, 1966.

A. Armitage and Colin A. Ronan, *Edmond Halley, 1656–1742. Memoirs of the British Astronomical Association*, 37, no. 3.

E. C. Bullard, *Edmond Halley, Endeavour*, October 1956.

S. Chapman, *Edmond Halley as Physical Geographer, and the Story of his Charts, Occasional Notes of the Royal Astronomical Society*, June 9, 1941, pp. 122 f.

H. Dingle, *Edmond Halley: His Times and Ours*, Halley Lecture, Oxford, 1956 reprinted in the *Observatory*, 76 (1956), pp. 117 f.

E. F. MacPike, *Hevelius, Flamsteed and Halley*, London, 1937.

C. A. Ronan, *Edmond Halley and Early Geophysics, Geophysical Journal*, 15 (1968), pp. 241 f.

In addition to the above a collection of publications, charts, instruments, and portraits was prepared by Sir Edward Bullard, F.R.S., and the author in 1956 for the Halley Tercentenary celebrations held by the Royal Society and the British Astronomical Association. A catalogue of the exhibits is in the libraries of both organizations.

Index

Abingdon, Earl of, 197
Account of the Cause of the Change of the Variation of the Magnetickal Needle . . . , An (Halley), 127
Acta Eruditorum, 193, 194
Adams, Mr., 67–68
Airy, George, 220
Albatagnius (al-Battani), 137–38
Aldrich, Henry, 187
Algebra, 21, 24, 28, 89, 138–39, 209
Almagest (Ptolemy), 11
Almanack (Feild), 14
Analyst or a Discourse Addressed to an Infidel Mathematician, The (Bentley), 121
Animals, Halley's observations on, 178–79
Anne, Queen, 180, 183, 190, 191
Annuity tables, 134–35, 136
Annus Climactericus (Hevelius), 52, 54, 55, 56
Antonius, 153
Apollonios, 10 n, 187–89
Arago, François, 63
Archaeology, 141–42, 155
Arcturus, 201
Argo, 41
Arianism, 120
Aristarchos of Samos, 10 n
Aristotle, 10–11, 12, 20
Ashe, George, 75
Aston, Francis, 74
Astrology, 25 n, 57, 144
Astronomiae Cometicae Synopsis (Halley), 150
Astronomy, 5, 6–8, 10–23, 24 ff., 93, 106–17 (*see also* Comets; Moon;

Planetary motion; Stars; Sun; specific individuals, theories); importance of Halley's work in, 216–19
Atlantic Chart, 177–82, 220
Atlantic Ocean (*see also* Navigation); Halley's Chart of, 177–82, 220; and winds, 79
Atlas Maritimus et Commercialis, 180
Atoms, 19–20, 98
Aubrey, John, 1, 3, 57, 64
Aurorae, 199–200, 202
Ayloffe, Sir Joseph, 210
Azout, Adrian, 65–66

Bacon, Francis, 80
Barometers, 78–79, 183
Barrow, Isaac, 71, 187
Benbow, Admiral, 159, 165
Bentley, Richard, 86–87, 120–21, 221
Bernard, Edward, 29, 118, 186, 188
Bernoulli, Jacob, 99
Bible, the, 16; account of flood (deluge) in, 90, 92, 119, 121, 140, 141
Bills of mortality, 133–35
Biographia Britannica, 4, 8, 38, 120, 123, 134, 184, 188, 189, 213, 221
Biology, 76–77, 98, 99
Birch, Thomas, 4 n
Birds, Halley's observations of, 178–79
Blaeu, Willem, 40
Bond, Henry, 65–66
Borelli, G. A., 83, 187
Borri, Cristoforo, 178 n
Botany, 76–77, 95, 98
Bouchar, Charles, 24
Bowles (Mint clerk), 157–58

Boyle, Robert, 33
Bradley, James, 113–14, 212
Brahe, Tycho, 30, 197; and comets, 144, 145; and observation techniques, 15–17, 22, 46, 47, 50; star catalogue, 22, 25–26, 30, 197
Breslau mortality tables, 134
Brewster, David, 89
British Museum, 74, 164
Bruno, Giordano, 13–14
Bryant, Humphrey, 176
Bubonic plague, 3–4, 175
Burchett, Josiah, 164, 167, 169, 173, 175, 181
Burnet, Bishop, 96
Byers, John, 68

Caesar, Julius, 100–1
Calculus, 73, 129, 146; Newton-Leibniz controversy over invention of, 193–95
Calendars, 13, 15
Cambridge University, 118, 120
Capellus, M., 52
Caroline (queen consort of George II), 211
Caspian Sea, 140
Cassini, Giovanni Domenico (Jacques Dominique), 23, 26, 28, 30, 34, 107, 145; Halley at Paris Observatory with, 59–60, 61, 63
Cassini, Jacques, 58, 206
Cassini-de-Thury, C. F., 115
Castle of Knowledge (Recorde), 14
Caswell, John, 56
Catalogue des Etoiles Australes, 41
Catalogue of the Southern Stars (Halley), 5, 7, 8, 24, 37, 39–42, 48
Catalogues of stars, 5, 7, 8, 21 ff., 37, 39–42, 48 ff., 190–93, 201
Celestial sphere, 34
Centaurus (constellation), 39, 198
Chapman, Sydney, 128
Chappe, Jean-Baptiste, 115
Charles I, 2
Charles II, 4, 52–53, 60, 87, 96, 97, 133; establishes Greenwich Observatory, 23, 52; and St. Helena expedition, 32–33, 40, 41–42
Charlett, Keill's letter on Halley to, 87
Chéseaux, P. L. de, 207
Child's (coffeehouse), 210
Christianity, 12–14. See also Bible;

Church; Religion; specific denominations
Christ's Hospital, 58
Chronometers, 205
Church, the, 118–22. See also Christianity; Religion
Clark (Chester Mint master), 157–59
Clerke, Mr., 33–34, 35–38
Clocks, 35, 38, 97, 114
Coelostat, 131
Coinage, 153–59
Colbert, 45, 59
Colet, Dean, 4–5
Colors, 71, 72, 105, 183
Comets, 59–61, 142–46; appearances of Halley's Comet, 150, 240; Brahe and, 16, 144, 145; Descartes and, 21; early views of, 143–44; Halley and, 59–61, 90, 142–46, 150, 196, 200, 219, 240; kinds of paths, 145–46; orbits, 142–46; and political events, 150; predicting, 148–51, 219
Commercium Epistolicum, 194–95
Compasses, magnetic, variations in, 6, 65–66, 90, 92–93, 127–28, 162–82
Compleat Opticks (Smith), 203
Conduitt, John, 121
Cones, properties of, 99
Conics (Apollonios), 187, 188–89
Conjunction, planetary, 16
Constellations, 25, 39, 41, 197, 201. See also Stars; specific constellations
Coordinate geometry, 21
Copernicus, Nicolas (Copernican theory), 10–14, 17, 19, 144, 206, 207
Corona, the, 197
Cosmology, 10–23, 90–92, 206–7, 217, 218–19
Cotes, Roger, 79, 121
Cromelholme, Samuel, 5–6
Croone, William, 49, 51
Cruft, William, 34
Crystal spheres, 13, 15, 16, 19
Cutler, Sir John, 46 n
Cutler Lectures, 46
Cygnus, 197

Dahl, Michael, 127–28
Dalrymple, Alexander, 164 n
Danzig, Halley's visit to Hevelius in, 43–56
Davenport, Francis, 69
Davis, John, 35

Dee (river), 155, 156
Dee, John, 14–15
Deferents, 11–12
Delisle, Joseph, 113, 114–15
De Magnete (Gilbert), 65
De Moivre, Abraham, 136
De Morgan, Augustus, 88, 89
De Motu Corporum (Newton), 73
De Revolutionibus . . . (Copernicus), 10–14
Descartes, René, 19–21, 41; extended substance theory of, 19–21
Diana Peak, St. Helena, 35–36
Digges, Leonard, 15
Digges, Thomas, 15, 20
"Direct and Geometrical Method of finding the Aphelia, Eccentricities, and Proportions of the Primary Planets . . ." (Halley), 27–28
Distance (parallux) determination, 38, 106–17, 219
Diving, sea, 102–5
Dixon, Jeremiah, 114
Doctrine of the Spheres (Flamsteed), 29
Dublin tides, 123–24

Earth, 95, 215, 219–20; age, 140; as center of universe, 10–22; distance of sun from, 106–17; magnetism, 6, 65–66, 92–93, 127–28, 199–200, 220; motion, 10–22, 220
East India Company, 31–34, 35, 36, 37, 113, 159
Eclipses, 7, 25, 137–38; lunar, 25, 43, 99, 137–38, 209; solar, 28, 43, 44, 137–38, 196–97, 209
Ecliptic, sun's, 38, 40
Edward VII, 150
Elizabeth I, 14, 31
Elliptical orbits, 17–18, 27–28
Encke, Johann, 219
English Channel, charting of, 181–82, 185
Ephemerides, 93
Epicycles, 11–12
Equations, solution of, 209, 216
Erasmus, Desiderius, 4
Ether (space), 131–32, 198
Euclid, 187, 218
Evaporation, water, 90, 94–95, 99, 100, 140
Evelyn, John, 3, 159, 160

Fatio de Duillier, Nicolas, 193–94
Feild, John, 14
Field, Gregory, 37
Fire (fiery particles), 20
Flamsteed, John, 1, 23, 24–27, 29, 30, 42, 50, 58, 61, 197, 204, 210; as Astronomer Royal, 125–26, 127, 152, 190–95; and comets, 147, 148; death of, 202; described, 126, 152, 192; and Halley's St. Helena expedition, 32, 34, 39, 49 ff.; and Hevelius, 46–52; and Newton, 190–91; quarrels with Halley, 122–23, 185, 191–93, 195, 210; quarrels with Royal Society, 190–95
Flood (deluge), biblical, 90–92, 119, 121, 140, 141
Fluents, 73
Fluxions, 73, 193
Folkes, Martin, 59, 64, 75, 94, 159, 185, 221; succeeds Halley to chair of Royal Society Club, 210

Gale, Thomas, 6, 122
Galileo Galilei, 7, 18–19; and tides, 69; and winds, 80
Gallet, Jean Charles, 38
Gazet, 66–68
Genesis, Book of, 91–92, 140
Geocentric theory, 10–22
Geometry, 21, 24, 28, 186–89
Geophysics, 95, 127, 215, 219–20
George, Prince (consort of Queen Anne), 180, 190, 191
George II, King, 211
Gilbert, William, 65
Gold, thickness of, 98
Graham, George, 203
Graunt, John, 133–34
Gravitation, 219, 220; and comets, 145–49, 151; and cosmology, 90–92, 207, 218; Newton and, 71, 80, 83, 87, 145–49, 151
Greeks, astronomers, 10–11, 12, 17, 18; mathematicians, 29, 186–89; philosophers, 13
Greenwich Observatory, 190; Flamsteed at, 125–26, 127, 152, 195–96; Halley at, 202–14; start of, 23, 32
Gregorian calendar, 13
Gregory, David, 122, 126, 139, 186–87, 188
Gresham College, 140

Grey, Ralph, 175
Gunnery, 80–81, 101, 129

Hadley, John, 35
Halifax, Charles Montagu, Earl of, 154, 158
Halley, Anne Robinson (mother), 3, 9
Halley, Catherine (daughter), 94, 212, 214
Halley, Edmond, assessment of his importance, 89, 215–22 (*see also* specific areas of research and investigation); Astronomer Royal post given to, 202–14; birth and early years, 1–9; broad interests and abilities of, 62, 81, 89 ff., 95 ff., 101–5, 127–28, 137 ff., 152 ff., 215–22 (*see also* specific areas of research, titles of published works); chronology of his life, 235–39; and the Church (religion), 90–92, 118–22; Clerk of Royal Society post to, 74–75 ff.; contemporaries' opinion of, 89; Dahl portrait of, 127–28; death and burial of, 213; death of his father, 66–68; death of his son, 213; death of his wife, 211; descriptions of, 3, 5, 25–26, 99, 132, 185, 210, 213–14, 221–22; edits *Philosophical Transactions*, 75 ff.; education, 4–8, 10, 24 ff. (*see also* specific schools); elected to Académie des Sciences, 215; elected to Council of Royal Society, 185; elected Fellow of Royal Society, 42; family of, 1–9, 64, 65, 93–94, 161, 211 (*see also* specific members); first recorded scientific observation, 6; genius of, 89; last days, 211–13; marriage, 64; politics of, 232; practical nature of his investigations, 81, 105, 183–85; receives Master of Arts degree from Queen's College, 42; receives Oxford chair of geometry, 185–89; receives Oxford degree, 41–42; recognition of, 89, 139, 183–85, 196 ff., 215; refused chair at Oxford, 118–22, 124, 129; relations with specific individuals (*see by name, e.g.* Charles II; Flamsteed, John; Halley, Edmond, Sr. (father); Hevelius, Johannes; Newton, Sir Isaac); resigns Secretaryship of

Royal Society, 209–10; Secretary of Royal Society post to, 195; sense of humor of, 213–14, 222; spelling of his name, 212–13; takes Grand Tour, 58–64; voyages, 161–82
Halley, Edmond, Sr. (father), 1–2, 3–4; death of first wife and remarriage, 9, 63–64; encouragement and aid to son, 4, 8, 31, 35, 64; mystery of death of, 66–68
Halley, Edmond III (son), 212, 213
Halley, Humphrey (brother), 2
Halley, Humphrey (grandfather), 1
Halley, Katherine (sister), 2, 94
Halley, Margaret (daughter), 94, 212, 214
Halley, Mary Tooke (wife), 64, 65, 93; death of, 211, 214
Halley Bay, 181
Halleyan lines, 177–78
Halley's Comet, 150, 240
Halos, 183
Hanover, Elector of (later George I of England), 184
Harding, Fisher, 162
Hardwicke (English consul), 174
Harold II, King, 150
Harris, Joseph, 209
Harrison, John, 205
Harrison, Lieutenant, 168–70
Hastings, Battle of, 152
Hearne, Thomas, 119, 185, 221
Heat, 79, 80, 90, 94–95, 99. *See also* Thermometers
Heliocentric theory, 10–22
Henshaw, Thomas, 52
Hercules (constellation), 196, 198
Hermetists, 14
Herschel, John, 216
Herschel, William, 216, 217, 218
Hevelius, Catherina Elisabetha, 45, 55–56
Hevelius, Johannes, 30, 34, 39, 42, 43–56, 76, 148, 152; death of, 55–56; Halley's visit to, 43–56; observatory destroyed, 55–56; open sights controversy, 45–56; star catalogue of, 48–56
Hill, Abraham, 103, 118, 119
Hipparchos, 11, 21–22
Hiscocks, W. G., 159
Historia Coelestis (Halley), 191–92

Historia Coelestis Britannica (Flamsteed), 192
Historia Naturalis (Pliny the Elder), 101, 144
Historia Piscium (Willughby), 81
History (historic events), Halley's research on, 100–1, 150, 152–53
History of St. Paul's School, A (McDonnell), 6 n
Hobbes, Thomas, 133
Hooke, Robert, 3, 38, 58, 64, 71, 72, 73, 78, 80, 89, 129, 161, 221; barometer, 183; controversy with Newton, 81, 82–86; and Flamsteed-Halley quarrel, 126; Halley compared to, 216; Halley's letters to, 60–63; *Micrographia*, 98; and telescopic sights, 46–47, 51, 52, 54, 130–31
Horoscopes, 57
Horrox, Jeremiah, 109
Hoskins, Sir John, 60, 85, 163
Houghton, James, 139–40
Houtman, Frederick de, 40
Huggins, William, 218
Huyghens, Christiaan, 138
Hyades, 200, 208

Idea Longitudinis (Harrison), 168
Index librorum prohibitorum, 14
Indian Ocean, and winds, 79
Infinite quantities, Halley on mathematics of, 99, 101
Islington, 64, 126

James II, 87–88, 96, 97
Jeffreys, Judge, 68
John III (Sobieski) of Poland, 45
Jonathan's (London coffeehouse), 58
Julian calendar, 141
Jupiter, 18–19, 78, 141; and comets, 148, 149; occultations, 78, 177; satellites of, 18–19, 22–23, 60–61, 141, 177
Justel, Henri, 60, 134

Kapteyn, Jacobus, 216–17
Keill, John, 87, 194–95
Kepler, Johannes, 16–18, 57; and comets, 145; and planetary motion, 17–18, 27–28, 70–71, 72, 106–8, 111
Kirch, Gottfried, 196
Krüger, Peter, 43, 44, 46

Lacaille, Nicolas, 217
Land area statistics, 139–40
Latitude determination, 163–82; variations in, 90
Lectures and Collections (Hooke), 60 n
Lee, Weyman, 136
Leeuwenhoek, Anton van, 76
Le Gentil, Guillaume, 115–16
Leibniz, G. W. von, 193–95
Leigh, Luke, 1
Lenses, 138–39
Leopold, Emperor, 183–84
Lethiouler, Mr., 34
Lewis (Chester Mint clerk), 157–59
Life insurance statistics, 62, 133–35
Light, 99, 105, 183, 198, 207; and colors, 71, 72, 105, 183; refraction of, 99, 101, 138, 183, 208
Locke, John, 58, 60
London, Great Fire of 1666 in, 2, 3, 5, 98; Halley's social statistics of, 133
London, George, 159
Longitude determination, 95, 152, 198, 202–5, 208, 209, 215; Halley's voyages and, 162–82; Jupiter's satellites and, 60–61; lunar observations and, 22–23, 40–41, 64–66
Louis XIV, 23, 45, 60, 96
Louville, Chevalier de, 197
Lucas, Henry, 71
Lucas, Lord, 181
Lunar eclipses, 25, 43, 99, 137–38, 209

Macclesfield, Earl of, 7, 114, 197
McDonnell, Sir Michael, 6 n
Machin, John, 4 n
Machina Coelestis (Hevelius), 45, 51, 52
MacPike, Eugene, 63, 86 n
Magnetic declination (variation), 6, 65–66, 90, 92–93, 127–28, 162–82
Magnetism (magnetic fields), 6, 65–66, 92–93, 127–28, 199–200, 220. *See also* Magnetic declination
Mansfelt, Count, 184
Maps (mapping), 61–62, 80, 141, 162–82, 196, 209, 220. *See also* Latitude determination; Longitude determination; Navigation; specific charts and maps

Mars, 17; distance, 107–8; occultations, 27

Mary II, Queen, 96, 162

Maskelyne, Nevil, 114, 205, 217

Mason, Charles, 114

Mathematical Principles, (Newton). *See Principia* . . . (Newton)

Mathematics, 6–7, 24, 28, 29, 73, 81 ff., 89, 98, 101. *See also* Algebra; Calculus; Geometry; Trigonometry

Maurice, M., 40

Mayer, Tobias, 138, 216, 217

Mead, Richard, 213

Medicine (medical matters), Halley's correspondence on, 77–78

Menelaus of Alexandria, 189

Mercator, Gerard, 141, 179

Mercator, Nicholas, 28

Mercator projection, 179

Mercers' Company, 5

Mercury (planet), 16, 38, 40; distances and transits, 107–15, 209

Messier, Charles, 217

Meteorology, 78–80, 141

Meteors, 143, 202, 219

Micrographia (Hooke), 98

Middleton, Benjamin, 161–62, 163

Miscellanea Curiosa (Halley), 189

Mock suns (parhelia), 183

Molyneux, William, 54–55, 56, 75, 124, 154; *Dioptrice Nova,* 138

Monsoons, 69, 79

Montagu, Charles, 154, 158

Montmort, Pierre de, 197

Moon, 11, 12, 40–41, 44, 45, 64–65, 66, 198–99, 200, 204, 207–9; determination of position of, 27, 64, 177; eclipses, 25, 43, 99, 137–38, 209; maps of, 61–62; and navigation, 22–23, 40–41, 64–66; occultations, 27, 78, 201; orbit and motion, 11, 16, 19, 40–41, 44, 45, 64–65, 66, 137–38, 152, 200–1, 204; and tides, 69–70, 123–24

Moore, Sir Jonas, 32–33, 37, 40, 42, 58

Moray, Sir Robert, 65

Morris, Gael, 212

Mortality statistics, 133–35

Mortars, firing of, 80–81

Motion, 8, 10–23; cometary (*see* Comets); "fixed" stars, 201–2, 216–17; geocentric vs. heliocentric theories, 10–22; Halley and, 25–28, 39, 70–71, 72, 198–99, 208–9; Kepler, 17–18, 70–71, 72, 106–8, 111; lunar (*see* Moon); Newton and, 71–74, 80–88; planetary (*see* Planetary motion); stellar, 201–2, 216–17; uniform circular concept, 11, 17

Mus's (*or* Muss's, London coffeehouse), 125

Myddleton, Hugh, 141

Natural and Political Reflections . . . made upon the Bills of Mortality (Graunt), 133–34

Navigation, 6–7, 22–23, 33, 40–41, 64–66, 78, 97, 162–82, 202–5. *See also* Latitude determination; Longitude determination; Maps

Nebulae, 38, 198, 217–18; diffuse, 218; spiral, 217–18

Nelson, Robert, 59, 62, 63

New Hypothesis of the Universe (Wright), 218

New River, 141

New System of the Mathematicks (Moore), 58

New Theory of the Earth, A (Whiston), 112

Newton, Sir Isaac, 38, 91, 105, 138, 154, 205, 221; background and description of, 71–74; calculus controversy with Leibniz, 193–95; and the Church, 91, 118–19, 120, 209; and comets, 145–48; elected President of Royal Society, 185–86; and Flamsteed, 190–91; gravitation theories, 71, 80, 83, 87, 145–49, 151; Halley and, 70, 71–74, 80 ff., 89, 122, 129, 154, 158, 159, 195, 209; and Halley-Flamsteed quarrel, 123–24, 126, 127, 128; and light and optics, 71–72, 99, 105, 138; *Opticks,* 71, 99, 105, 138, 194; and planetary motion, 71–74, 80–88; *Principia* . . . , 70, 80 ff., 89, 91, 121, 126, 145, 147, 150, 193–94; at Royal Mint, 154; and tides, 70, 80, 87

Nottingham, Earl of, 183, 185

Novae, 197–98

"Observations made at Ballasore, in India . . ." (Halley), 63

"Observations and Maximes," (Halley), 7

"Observations on the Spots in the Sun . . ." (Halley), 27

Observatories, 15, 23, 44–56, 106–18. *See also* Greenwich Observatory; Paris Observatory; specific areas of investigation; individuals

Occultations, 27, 177; Jupiter, 78; lunar, 27, 78, 201

Oceans. *See* Seas (oceans); specific oceans

Olaff, John, 55

Olbers, H. W. M., 207

Oldenburg, Henry, 28, 31, 32, 43, 47–48, 49, 60, 194; death of, 63

Opposition, planetary, 16

Optics, 71–72, 99, 101, 105, 138

Opticks (Newton), 71, 99, 105, 138, 199

Orbits (*see also under specific objects, e.g.* Comets); elliptical, 17–18, 27–28, 145 ff.; hyperbolic, 145 ff.; and measurement of distances in space, 108 ff.; parabolic, 145 ff.

Osiander, Andreas, 12–13

Oxford University, Halley attends, 6–8, 10, 24–30, 57; Halley given chair of geometry at, 185–89; Halley given D.C.L. by, 189; Halley receives degree from, 41–42; Halley refused chair at, 91, 118–22, 124, 129

Pacific Ocean, and winds, 79

Paget, Mr., 72, 73

Palmyra, 142

Papin, Denis, 74, 105

Pappus, 187, 188–89

Parallax (distance) determination, 38, 106–17, 219

Paramore (ship), 162–82

Parhelia, 183

Paris, Halley's comparison of London's population to, 62

Paris Observatory, 59–62, 63; founding of, 23

Parker, Lord (*afterward* Earl of Macclesfield), 7, 114, 197

Pascal, Blaise, 78

Paul III, Pope, 12

Pendulum clocks, 35, 38, 114

Pepys, Samuel, 1, 31; as President of Royal Society, 86, 96–97

Perkins, and magnetic poles, 128

Perry, William, 95–96

Peter, Czar, 159–60

Petty, William, 133–34

Philosophiae Naturalis Principia Mathematica. See Principia . . . (Newton)

Philosophical Collections, 62–63

Philosophical Transactions, 29, 43, 46, 63, 65, 69–72, 86, 88, 91, 92, 112, 122, 127, 133, 138, 156–57, 189, 196, 197, 200, 204, 208, 209; Halley edits, 75 ff., 136–37; in difficulties, 136–37; six of Halley's papers appear in (1691), 99–105; suspended temporarily, 97

Physical geography, Halley's achievements in, 220

Piazza, Giuseppe, 216

Picard, Jean, 59

Pingré, Alexandre-Gui, 115

Plague, the, 3–4, 175

Planetary motion (observations and theories), 8, 10–23, 106–17, 217; Aristotle, 10–11, 12, 20; Brahe, 14–17; Copernicus, 10–14, 17, 19; Descartes, 19–21; Digges, 15, 20; Galileo, 18–19; Halley, 25–28, 39, 70–71, 72, 198–99, 208–9; Hevelius, 43–56; Kepler, 16–18, 27–28, 70–71, 72, 106–8, 111; Newton, 71–74, 80–88; Ptolemy, 10, 11, 12, 22

Planets, 11 ff. (*see also* Planetary motion; individual planets); distances of, 106–17

Planisphere, 41

Pliny the Elder, 101, 144

Political Arithmetick (Petty), 134

Pollux, 25

Pond, John, 214

Pope, Walter, 58

Population statistics, 62, 133–36

Portsmouth, Duchess of, 23

Pressure, barometric, 78–79; water, 103–5

Price, Henry, 4, 6, 214; marries Halley's daughter, 94

Principia . . . (Newton), 70, 80 ff., 89, 91, 121, 126, 145, 147, 150, 193–94

Principia Philosophiae (Descartes), 19–21

Procyon, 201

Prognostication Everlasting, A (Digges), 15
Protestant Church, 13, 96–97
Ptolemy, 10, 11, 12, 22, 137, 201
Pythagoras, 11
Pythagorean philosophers, 10 n

Quadrants, 15, 24–25, 50, 197, 203, 204; backstaff ("Davis"), 35, 36; improvements in, 35, 36, 129, 130
Queen's College, Oxford, 6–8, 10, 24–30, 32, 122

Rainbows, 183
Ravius, Christopher, 187
Recorde, Robert, 14
Reflecting telescope, 130–31
Refraction of light, 99, 101, 138, 183, 208
Religion, 7, 18, 90–92, 121–22. *See also* Christianity; Church, the
Rhea, 65
Richer, Jean, 40, 107–8, 132
Rigaud, Stephen, 122
Robert III, King of Scotland, 153
Robur Carolinum, 41
Roman Catholic Church, 13–14, 96–97. *See also* Church, the
Romans, ancient, 100–1, 141, 155
Römer, Claus, 59, 141
Rosse, Earl of, 217
Royal Society, 27, 28, 69, 96–97, 113, 142, 154–55, 161, 181, 190–93, 195, 209–10; background and origin of, 74; Club formed, 210; financial difficulties, 81, 96; Halley becomes one of the Secretaries, 195; Halley as Clerk of, 74 ff., 89 ff.; Halley elected to Council of, 185; Halley elected Fellow of, 42, 58; Halley resigns Clerkship, 169; Halley resumes Clerkship, 136, 140, 152; Halley's importance to, 216; Halley's increased interest and activity in, 64, 65; and Halley's St. Helena expedition, 31, 33; and Halley's visit to Hevelius, 49–56; Hevelius elected Fellow of, 45; *Journal Books,* 131, 132, 154–55, 161; moves to new premises, 196–97; Newton and, 72 ff., 80 ff., 185, 186; Newton elected President of, 185, 186; *Philosophical Transactions* (*see Philosophical Transactions*); recommends Halley to Oxford, 122
Rumford, Count, 136

St. Helena, 29–42, 54, 109, 113–15, 125, 132, 173
St. James' Church, London, 64
St. Margaret's Westminster, 2–3
St. Paul's School, 4–6
Saint-Pierre, Le Sieur de, 23
Sarotic periods, 199, 204
Satellites, 18–19, 21, 22–23; Jupiter's, 18–19, 22–23, 60–61, 141, 177; Saturn's, 65
Saturn, 25, 65; and comets, 148, 149; satellites, 65
Savile, Sir Henry, 61, 185
Sayes Court, 159–60
Sea diving, 102–5
Seas (oceans), 22, 98, 184 (*see also* Navigation; Ships); Halley's diving investigations, 102–5; Halley's voyages and charts, 161–82; and water evaporation, 90, 100, 140; and winds, 79–80
Sectio Rationis (Apollonios), 187–88, 189
Sectio Spatii (Apollonios), 189
Secular shift, 127, 128
Selenographia (Hevelius), 45
Senex, John, 112, 196, 209
Sextants, 8, 15, 35, 46, 50, 51
Sharp, Abraham, 128–29, 136, 185, 192
Ships (shipping), 22, 129, 159, 161 ff., 184. *See also* Navigation
Silver, 153–59
Sirius, 201
Sloane, Hans, 74, 154, 156–57
Smith, Robert, 203
Snowdon, Mount, expedition to, 156
Social statistics, 133–36
Solar eclipses, 7, 28, 43, 44, 137–38, 196–97, 209
Solar parallax, 38, 106–17, 219
Solar system, creation theories, 20
"Some Considerations about the cause of the universal Deluge" (Halley), 91–92
Souciet, Etienne, 209
Southern stars, 30–42; Halley's catalogue of, 5, 7, 8, 24, 37, 39–42, 48
Southwell, Sir Robert, 161

Sphaerica (Menelaus of Alexandria), 189

Star catalogues, 5, 7, 8, 21 ff., 37, 39–42, 48 ff., 190–93

Stars, 5, 7, 8, 11, 18, 21 ff., 34–42 ff., 190 ff., 196–98, 201–14, 216–17; motion of "fixed," 201–2, 216–17; nebulae, 38, 198, 217–18; novae, 197–98; number of, 15, 206–7; refraction of light, 198, 208; transits, 203; variable, 197–98, 217, 218; vortex theory, 20–21

Statistical studies, 133–36, 139–41

Stepney, George, 184, 185

Stillingfleet, Edward, Bishop, 119–20, 185

Street, Mr., 25

Sturm, Johann, 76

Sumatra, 40, 113–15

Sun, corona, 197; eclipses (*see* Solar eclipses); ecliptic, 38, 40; heating effect of, 79, 80, 90, 95, 99; heliocentric theory, 10–22; parallax (distance), and transits, 38, 106–17, 219; path and motion, 38, 137–38; and planetary motions, 70–71; size, 111; and winds, 79, 80

Sunspots, 26–27, 44

Sykes, Dr., 188

Synopsis of the Astronomy of Comets, A (Halley), 150, 186, 219

Tarbat, Lord, 153

Telescopes, 8, 24, 25, 30; come into use, 18, 22; Halley's improvements in, 35, 36, 129, 130–31; Hevelius' improvements in, 44; Newton's improvements in, 71–72; open vs. telescopic sights controversy, 44–56

Terrestrial magnetism, 6, 65–66, 92–93, 127–28, 199–200, 220

Thābit b. Quarra, 188

Thames River, 47; tides, 122–24

Theory of the Variation of the Magnetical Compass, A (Halley), 65

Thermometers, 94, 135, 171

Tides, 69–70, 87; tables of, 122–24

Tillotson, Dr., 118

Toothe's (London coffeehouse), 39

Torricelli, E., 78

Towneley, Richard, 29, 126, 127, 128

Trade winds, 79–80

Traité de la Lumière (Huyghens), 138

Transit observations, 108–17, 199, 219; instruments for, 109, 113–14, 203, 206

Trigonometry, 6, 24

Trinity College, Oxford, 121

Uffenbach, Zacharias van, 56

Ulu-Begh, 22

Unity (ship), 34

Universe, concepts of, 10–23, 206–7, 218–19; finite vs. infinite, 206–7

Uraniborg, 15, 39

Vaporization, 90, 94–95, 99, 100, 140

Variable stars, 197–98, 217, 218

Variations (declinations) magnetic, 6, 65–66, 90, 92–93, 127–28, 162–82

Venus (planet), 16, 107–17, 199, 219

Vortex theory, Descartes', 19–21

Waddington, Robert, 114

Wallenstein, Kepler's horoscope for, 57

Waller, Mrs., 136, 137

Wallis, John, 29, 52, 77–78, 185, 186

Ward, Seth, Bishop of Salisbury, 28, 145

Weddell (Chester Mint warden), 157–58

Wells, Professor, 96

Westminster Cathedral, 2

Whiston, William, 112, 114, 120, 150, 151, 154

White, Manley, 170

William III (William of Orange), 96, 97, 153, 177, 178

Williamson, Sir Joseph, 32–33, 40, 41–42

Willughby, *Historia Piscum* by, 81

Winds, 79–80

Winthrop, John, 114

Wood, Anthony à, 6, 93

World Chart, 180, 220

Wren, Sir Christopher, 23, 71, 83, 84, 89

Wright, Thomas, 218

Wright, William, 176, 182

Wyche, Peter, 52